The Food Pharmacy Cookbook

Also by Jean Carper

The Food Pharmacy
The Food Pharmacy Guide to Good Eating

JEAN CARPER

THE FOOD PHARMACY COOKBOOK

With More Than 200 Totally Healthy Recipes

SIMON & SCHUSTER

LONDON·SYDNEY·NEW YORK·TOKYO·SINGAPORE·TORONTO

First published in Great Britain by
Simon & Schuster Ltd in 1991
First published in this edition in 1992
A Paramount Communications Company

Edited by Fiona Eves

Simon & Schuster Ltd
West Garden Place
Kendal Street
London W2 2AQ

Simon & Schuster of Australia Pty Ltd
Sydney

A CIP catalogue record for this book is
available from the British Library
ISBN 0-671-71091-5

Typeset in Times 10.5/13 by Goodfellow & Egan
Printed and bound in Great Britain by
Billing & Sons, Worcester

Contents

List of Recipes

Appetizers, Starters and Snacks

Soups

Salads, Relishes and Chutneys

Vegetables and Legumes

Pizza, Pasta and Grains

Seafood, Poultry and Meat Main Dishes

Beverages

Sauces and Dressings

Acknowledgments

First, I am grateful to the physicians and researchers who have the wisdom, curiosity and skill to pursue the investigations on which this book is based and for their willingness to share their exciting new findings with me. Next, I must thank the testers and tasters of the recipes in this book, the people who so graciously gave recipes and suggestions for improving the recipes. Foremost is Maxime Rapoport, coauthor of four cookbooks with Nina Graybill, including the best-selling *Pasta Salad Cookbook*, who generously shared her impeccable recipe-writing sense as well as many of her own recipes. Other food professionals I depended on for a number of recipes are Kenneth Juran, executive chef, Park Hyatt Hotel in Washington, D.C. and his executive sous chef, Gerard Thompson; Carol Mason, chef and cooking instructor in Washington, D.C.; Steven Raichlen, a national food writer based in Miami; and Howard Solganik, food consultant, newspaper columnist and TV chef in Dayton, Ohio.

Then there are the many tasters who graciously consented to try the dishes I put before them. Many thanks to Pat Altobello, Lisa Berger, Ashley Barnes, Laurel Barnes, Evan Berlack, Phyllis Bonanno, Jim Boring, David Burnham, Suzanne Bywaters, Natella Carper, Robert Carper, Judy Carper, Aaron Carper, Ashley Carper, Michael Carper, Melissa Carper, Lauren Carper, Jennifer Carper, Terry Carper, Patti Carper, Daniel Carper, David Carper, Douglas Carper, Chauncey Ching, Teddie Ching, Rolf Clark, Joan Claybrook, Mary Crisp, Kathleen Drew, Susan Dweck, Jamie Fenwick, John Foldes, Daryl Glenny, Manny Goldstein, Mariana Gosnell, Nina Graybill, Ray Heverling, Jill Hickson, Scott Hickson, George Jacobs, Cynthia Johnson, Clyde and Connie Kauffman, Patricia Krause, Joan Levin, Bill Mead, Jenny Mead, Joanne Omang, Richard Pollock, David Rall, Gloria Rall, Daniel Rapoport, Leora Rosen, Norman Rosenthal, Jerilyn Ross, Jim Rutledge, Ray Shibley, Novera Herbert Spector, Judy Stevens, Ben Stevens, Lynn Stevens, Bart

Stevens, Jane Stevens, Jerry Stilkind, David Taylor, Isabel Taylor, Katie Taylor, Michael Whalen, and Lilyan Wilder.

Some of the above also gave me their favourite recipes for the book, as did many others whose names are mentioned with the recipes. I wish to thank them—and in particular, Nina Graybill, Phyllis Richman, and Lee Koromvokis.

For comments on the entire manuscript, thanks to my friend Thea Flaum.

As always I wish to express my affection and respect for my agent, Raphael Sagalyn, and my editor, Michelle Rapkin. Also my appreciation to Lisa Di Mona of the Sagalyn Literary Agency.

And a special thanks to Lynn Hill of Hill Nutrition Associates for her expert guidance.

Foreword

I do not pretend to be an expert on food, recipes or medicine. But I do know something about powerful trends that transform society and individuals. And Jean Carper is the nation's foremost chronicler of a monumental shift toward the use of food as potent modern-day medicine that vitally affects all our lives.

In her ground-breaking book, *The Food Pharmacy*, she reported on astonishing discoveries by leading scientists of the powers of common food to treat and prevent disease and the biological principles explaining food's medicinal properties. She told how respected professors at prestigious medical schools are prescribing onions to control cholesterol, chilli peppers to fight emphysema, carrots to prevent cancer, cranberries to ward off infections, garlic to thin the blood, beans to regulate diabetes, fish to lower blood pressure, and yoghurt to boost immunity. She gave the complete therapeutic possibilities of fifty-five common foods—from apples to yoghurt—as suggested by folklore and now being confirmed by current scientific studies.

In this book she carries the concept further by offering prescriptive recipes against disease, in the tradition of pharmacopoeias of the past. Thus she merges old traditions with new truths, bringing the use of food to treat and prevent disease into mainstream practice.

Of course using food as medicine is ancient. The pharmacopoeias of ancient Egypt, Babylonia, Greece and China, as well as those of the Middle Ages, were based on food. Only in this century has society become almost exclusively dependent on manufactured pills to cure our miseries. But now that pharmaceutical model is breaking down as a panacea for today's plague of chronic diseases such as cancer, arthritis, and heart disease and the ancient wisdom about food's medicinal powers, newly confirmed by twentieth-century scientific research, is increasingly infiltrating mainstream medicine.

Compelling new scientific evidence is thrusting us into a new age in which food is becoming a very credible medicine.

It's not surprising to see food re-emerge as a therapeutic agent at this time. Nor is it coincidental that the new trend parallels another major health thrust, preventive medicine. The two are made for each other, for food is the perfect preventive medicine. Food as medicine dovetails perfectly with our continual modern-day battle against chronic disease, which is most effectively tackled by prevention, not treatment.

For a civilization wracked with chronic disease, the traditional pharmaceutical model, for the most part, is bankrupt. What pill does one dispense to try to forestall cancer, for example? Or arthritis? Diabetes? Thrombosis? Flooding the populace with potent drugs to try to ward off erratic maladies, of uncertain origin and course, that develop over many years would subject millions to untold hazard and expense without clear-cut knowledge of risk or benefit. Generally prophylactic drugs are too risky and are too expensive and time-consuming to develop for use as scattershot medicine in trying to protect individuals from diseases that may never occur.

But food's medicinal powers mesh perfectly with the new imperative of preventive medicine. For they provide not single large jolts of curative medicine but a regular, steady regimen of low levels of nontoxic therapeutic chemicals over a lifetime. Such minute infusions of natural drugs, many scientists believe, provide cells with a shield of protection against everyday assaults, lessening the body's susceptibility to full-fledged illness in later years of life.

What also makes food a superior preventive medicine—and the antithesis of the current pharmaceutical model—is its potential for fighting many diseases at once. Conventional pharmacology demands one drug to combat a single disease factor. Claiming a drug can alleviate numerous disparate illnesses is a hallmark of quackery. But a single food indeed may trigger far-reaching mechanisms that help ward off seemingly unconnected diseases.

Researchers, for example, believe that fish—or certain constituents of oils in fish called omega-3 fatty acids—affect underlying biological processes that can help thwart cancer growth, high blood pressure, blood clots, psoriasis, rheumatoid arthritis and migraine headaches. Dutch scientists have reported in the *New England Journal of Medicine* that eating only 1oz (30g) of fish a day—2–3 servings a week—could cut your risk of fatal heart attack in half. Additionally, several foods such as garlic, have been found in both animal and human studies to bolster the immune system, showing a potential for battling both a range of acute infections and chronic diseases at once.

Using food as medicine also removes some of the worry generated by modern drugs with their often frightening side effects. Food implicitly has passed a 5,000-year toxicity test, although it sometimes does possess natural toxicants as well as modern man-made ones such as pesticides, which we should do our best to eliminate. Nevertheless, food is rarely harmful even in outrageously high doses and seldom triggers life-threatening druglike reactions except in rare cases of serious allergic reactions. Everybody is already "on" food; it is hardly an unfamiliar new substance.

So why not, as some pioneering doctors suggest, simply find out how to use common food in a more targeted scientific fashion? Dr. David Jenkins, a professor at the University of Toronto and leading expert on diet and blood sugar, envisions the day that foods will be prescribed to combat many specific diseases. He is already utilizing food, not to cure diabetics but to regulate their blood sugar and insulin, in efforts to reduce complications. As quoted in *The Food Pharmacy*, he says, "Actually all we are doing is taking the sort of thinking understood by pharmacists for centuries and applying it to food. I mean food is a [combination therapy] drug we take every day. We should find out its pharmacological effects and direct them to our individual needs and benefits, just as we do drugs."

The economics are right, too. In a nation burdened by the overwhelming expense of chronic diseases, relief cannot come too soon. And it's a bargain to get both instant nourishment and long-term medication in one dose. In the April 15, 1988, issue of the *Journal of the American Medical Association*, two physicians compared the cost-effectiveness of treating high blood cholesterol with food, such as oat bran cereal, with treatment with a pharmaceutical drug. Both, they say, can slash cholesterol by about 20 per cent. But, after calculating the cost of the two medications, the University of Maryland doctors suggested that oat bran "may be preferable as public health policy". Their reason: a lifesaving year's supply of cereal costs $249 compared with $1,412 for the common cholesterol-lowering drug cholestyramine.

Surely some of the impetus to accept food as medicine comes from a new emphasis on natural healthy foods, as well as influences from Far Eastern cultures and new scientific discoveries. But it is also intriguing that low-cost food is making a comeback as medicine at a time when we are increasingly fed up with the extravagance of our health care system.

Thus food, not drugs, is the therapeutic model in a new age of preventive medicine.

In this book Jean Carper tells you how to become a part of that trend by learning to use foods as drugs in the everlasting pursuit of staying well.

John Naisbitt, author of Megatrends
and coauthor with Patricia Aburdene of Megatrends 2000

Introduction

Medicines in Your Food

Food is definitely a drug. Every time you put food in your mouth you experience hidden pharmacological and biological reactions. Indeed, it can be a wonder drug. Food can cause your cholesterol to drop, your blood pressure to fall, your blood sugar to remain steady, your pain to disappear, your blood to resist clots.

Food can act as an anti-inflammatory agent, cancer-blocker, antidepressant, tranquillizer, diuretic, anticoagulant, painkiller, vasodilator or vasoconstrictor, antibiotic, antiviral agent.

More critically, food—because it is the most frequently consumed drug—can keep cells in continual pharmaceutical supply with armies of powerful compounds that resist assaults by malicious invaders intent on precipitating both acute and chronic diseases.

Certain foods can put more killer cells in your blood to ward off infections and cancer. Food can set certain enzymes in action to neutralize cancer-causing agents that otherwise could force their way into cell nuclei, damaging the DNA and setting the stage for cancer development. Certain foods can tell your liver's production of cholesterol to slow down, triggering mechanisms that deplete cholesterol in the bloodstream, lessening chances of dangerous plaque buildup and consequent heart attack. Certain foods can kill bacteria outright in the body or flush them away so they don't induce infections.

Food can help ward off nausea, gas pains, headaches, arthritis, heart attacks and strokes, cancer of many types, haemorrhoids, colds and influenza, diabetes, ulcers, bone diseases, dizziness, depression, gallstones, psoriasis, constipation and virtually any other malady you can think of.

In my book *The Food Pharmacy*, published in 1988, I explored the scientific evidence to date supporting those myriad ways foods can act as medicines. Since then research on food's pharmacological agents has really exploded.

The American National Cancer Institute has developed a vast new $20 million programme to study natural phytochemicals found in microscopic amounts in fruits and vegetables that experts believe inhibit cancer. At the top of the Institute's list are garlic and onions, citrus fruits, the cruciferous family, which includes cabbage and the parsley family, which includes carrots. By 1995 Dr. Herbert Pierson, director of the Institute's programme, plans to have test results from both laboratory and human studies on the cancer-preventive potential of twenty common foods.

As Dr. Pierson says, "The future is prevention, and looking for preventive agents in foods is more cost-effective than looking for new drugs." He agrees that both the government and science now "look at food as a preventive medicine of the future".

Scientists in the academic community have stepped up their research on all facets of food pharmacology. What was once a faintly questionable pursuit has now become not only respectable but prestigious, attracting leading scholars and investigators from around the world. Appearing at international conferences to discuss the merits of eating fish and using fish-oil capsules to stop the spread of breast cancer are professors of medicine at Harvard. Investigating the molecular reasons onions, grapes and broccoli may thwart cancer are professors of medicine at the University of California. Trying to decipher the biochemical and genetic interactions that make legumes a secret weapon against cancer consumes the energies of professors of medicine at New York University. And similar pursuits by men and women of similar stature are going on at Cornell, the University of Minnesota, the University of Florida, the University of Texas, Tufts, Ohio State University, the University of Utah, the Massachusetts Institute of Technology, George Washington University and practically any other major university you can mention.

The U.S. Department of Agriculture has teams of researchers, spread throughout the country, who constantly probe the secrets of the food pharmacy, coming up with startling new discoveries. Some examples: cinnamon stimulates insulin; vitamin E improves immunity and fruit and nuts improve brain functioning and protect ageing bones. From numerous publications I receive, the data bases I consult and the materials sent to me, often by researchers, it appears to me that the amount of research on food's pharmacological properties has surged at least 500 per cent since I first undertook to investigate the subject in 1985.

On the following pages you will find the latest findings on the multiple ways foods can promote your health as well as information on important directions of research and new discoveries of underlying disease-fighting mechanisms that may explain how a specific food or a group of foods exerts its therapeutic benefits.

Additionally, you will find much practical advice on using the food pharmacy. After publication of *The Food Pharmacy* I was peppered with questions on radio and television, from the print media and friends concerning practical ways to exploit food's pharmacological treasures. Is it better to eat foods raw? How can I get so much garlic into my diet? How can I eat more raw onions—one of the best ways to boost good-type HDL cholesterol? Do you have any good recipes for spring greens and kale—two super cancer inhibiting (but unpopular) vegetables?

The Food Pharmacy Cookbook is designed to answer such questions and to meet the need for practical advice and recipes based on eating for pharmacological effects. I have selected more than 200 recipes. They come from the collections of friends and relatives as well as from cooking professionals, including chefs, food consultants, cooking instructors and restaurant and food critics. A few recipes are taken from my favourite cookbooks. Many come from my own recipe files, including some adaptations of recipes I have loved.

With each recipe you'll find not just the conventional prologue—what to expect from the recipe gastronomically—but also what to expect pharmacologically. Since a headnote to a recipe cannot include everything, you will also find throughout the recipe section new food pharmacy facts and advice from both scientists and culinary experts.

All of the recipes are generally low in total fat and consequently calories. If there is added fat, it almost always is highly unsaturated, usually monounsaturated vegetable fats. You will find very little saturated fat in these recipes, for I think the evidence is persuasive beyond a doubt that such dairy and meat fats in overabundance cause general havoc in the body, possibly promoting a wide range of diseases, primarily heart disease. The oil I prefer is olive oil, for good reason. (See Mediterranean Lifesaver: Olive Oil, page 32.) This does not mean you should not use other oils occasionally; my choice, as a close second, is rapeseed oil—called by the more attractive name of canola oil in the U.S. Flaxseed oil also appears to be spectacular but at this time of writing is of limited availability. Soya bean, sesame, and walnut oils are okay sometimes. I tend to shy away from corn, safflower, and sunflower oils, fearing their high concentrations of so-called omega-6 polyunsaturated fatty acids. (See Wonder Medicines from the Sea, page 27.)

Seafood is used liberally in the recipes. Poultry, especially white meat, is also a favourite. Red meat is used more sparingly, for the simple reason that it is usually higher in fat, which not only raises cholesterol but appears to have other deleterious effects on the blood and cells.

You will find a few recipes that call for whole eggs. If you want to use egg substitute, that is up to you. It should make little difference in the recipe's outcome. Be aware, though, that eggs have less cholesterol than previously thought and some egg substitutes have added vegetable oils, often corn oil.

How much salt you use is also an individual decision. The evidence of salt's harm to a general population is equivocal. However, for many people with high blood pressure, excessive salt does not seem advisable and there is considerable evidence that sodium elevates blood pressure in those genetically predisposed to it. Additionally, some new evidence is coming out from animal studies suggesting that salt may be detrimental by precipitating strokes and premature death even when it does not boost blood pressure.

Of course, since pungent foods appear to be so health-promoting, the recipes contain lots of onions, garlic, peppers and spices. Many recipes come from other cultures—Asian, Mediterranean, Middle Eastern— known for their healthy cuisines. More than a few recipes naturally have a Southern States or Mexican flavour. You will also find the frequent use of curry spices, which pep up the breathing apparatus as well as the taste buds. And most of all, you will find a multitude of ways to prepare vegetables and fruits, which are surely the brightest and most numerous stars in the food pharmacy.

PART ONE

Exciting New Discoveries You Need to Know About

On the Frontier with Antioxidants

Imagine that your body is slowly rotting and rusting from being exposed to oxygen. Now imagine that scientists in their labs, aware of this problem, are discovering specific bullets—many in common foods—that are effective ammunition against oxygen's damaging effects and presumably slow down the deterioration.

This is not your imagination. It is actually happening. The investigation of the detrimental health effects of oxygen reactions and the benefits of oxygen antagonists called *antioxidants* is one of the biggest scientific stories currently unfolding. It gets extravagant play in scientific journals; however, news of the discoveries rarely reaches the public. Yet such findings are of enormous consequence in our lives, particularly in choosing what we eat. For our diet, unwittingly or by intention, supplies some of the wherewithal to disarm these oxygen-chemical reactions that ultimately disable and kill us.

Consider the cholesterol problem, for example. Here's a new way some researchers see it. High cholesterol may not be particularly harmful unless it undergoes extensive chemical transformation. That happens when molecules of bad-type LDL cholesterol circulating in the blood collide and chemically react with oxygen free radicals—unstable molecules created by normal metabolic processes or from outside factors like cigarette smoke, radiation or environmental chemicals. This reaction, called *lipid peroxidation*, turns the cholesterol molecules rancid or toxic.

The theory holds that receptors jutting from cell surfaces then snag these toxic cholesterol molecules in misguided efforts to dispose of them, and suck them into cells. Eventually these cells become cholesterol-stuffed and are transformed into "foam cells" that amass against artery walls, building up fat deposits that clog arteries.

Now, what if something intervened in that plaque-depositing process so it didn't happen? What if you could even prevent the oxygen chemically altering the cholesterol molecule in the first place so that the cholesterol did not become toxic?

As scientists understand more about how atherosclerosis occurs—and that is not yet entirely clear—they will be able to devise new intervention strategies to interrupt the process. Lowering cholesterol so there's less of it to become toxic is one way of saving yourself from heart disease and strokes. Another seems to be blocking the chain of events that renders cholesterol dangerous.

A possibility is to call in antioxidants. Certain compounds can help block the oxygen reaction (lipid peroxidation) that makes cholesterol toxic. Surprisingly, one of the most potent antioxidants that may help retard arterial clogging and stiffening known as atherosclerosis turns out to be vitamin C, according to several studies, including a remarkable one by Dr. Balz Frei, a biochemist researching at the University of California at Berkeley.

Essentially, in laboratory tests, Dr. Frei, to his and his colleagues' astonishment, found that vitamin C completely eradicated the oxygen free radicals in blood plasma that attack LDL cholesterol molecules, making them rancid and destructive. "Of all the antioxidants we tested, only ascorbic acid destroyed 100 per cent of the radicals and totally protected the lipids [cholesterol] from oxidative harm," says Dr. Frei. As soon as vitamin C is exhausted, free radical damage to fats in the blood starts immediately, even if other antioxidants, including vitamin E, are present, he says. This makes vitamin C "much more important than anyone ever dreamed," says Dr. Frei.

The way Dr. Frei explains it, the LDL cholesterol globules exist in blood plasma, the water part of the blood, where they are vulnerable to chemical attack by the oxygen free radicals. But if enough vitamin C is present, it traps all the radicals before they can even corrupt the fatty globules. Thus the chemically altered cholesterol is not ushered into the cell membranes where it can carry on its destruction, eventually resulting in clogged arteries and heart attacks and strokes.

Vitamin C works only in the water part of the blood, Dr. Frei points out. Once a fat molecule is corrupted by free radicals and taken into the membrane of fatty cells, it is out of reach of vitamin C antioxidant capabilities. At that point fat-soluble antioxidants, such as Vitamin E, must take over, doing what they can to clean up the mess by continuing to fight off the free radicals. (Dr. Frei's studies, however, show that vitamin E does not offer a perfect defence against free radicals circulating in the lipids or fat. He found that, unlike vitamin C, vitamin E wiped out only 70 per cent of the radicals.)

Thus, clearly, if this antioxidant theory is correct, vitamin C stands at the vanguard, in premier position to zap cardiovascular disease at the very instant of its genesis.

The antioxidant muscle that both vitamin C and vitamin E can exert has been demonstrated dramatically in studies on the arteries of primates by Dr. Anthony J. Verlangieri, director of the Atherosclerosis Research Laboratories at the University of Mississippi. For six years Dr. Verlangieri observed the effects of doses of vitamins C and E on monkeys fed lard and cholesterol to give them heart disease. He found that too little vitamin C and E allowed the linings of arteries to deteriorate and become inflamed and embedded with plaque. In fact he documented that moderately high doses of both vitamins C and E slowed the progression of artery damage (atherosclerosis) and thus heart disease, by an astonishing 50 per cent. Further, the vitamins caused a healing or regression of the arterial damage amounting to about 30 per cent. Thus both antioxidant vitamins separately prevented and reversed heart disease in the test animal closest to humans.

Dr. Frei is convinced that modest doses of vitamin C—easily obtained from food—are crucial in curtailing arterial damage leading to heart attacks and strokes. He says that a mere 160–250 milligrams per day is enough to keep body tissues saturated with maximum pools of vitamin C needed to mount a 100 per cent defence against the artery-destroying free radicals used in his experiments. That is two-and-a-half times the recommended dietary allowance (RDA) for nonsmokers and smokers, respectively. Smokers need the most because their bodies are constantly assaulted by floods of free radicals in cigarette smoke, says Dr. Frei.

Vitamin C is just one example of the potential power of antioxidants in food. Countless other antioxidants exist, usually in plants, and work in quite different ways to vanquish free radicals. Two other premier food antioxidants are vitamin E, concentrated in grains, seeds and vegetable oils and beta-carotene, a member of the carotenoid family found in deep orange fruits and vegetables and green leafy vegetables.

Vitamin E is also crucial in protecting cell membranes, says Dr. Joseph McCord, an antioxidant researcher and a leading authority on the subject at the University of South Alabama. Different antioxidants perform their execution of free radicals in various ways. Vitamin E is particularly useful because it defends the membranes of cells from becoming attacked by out-of-control free radicals. Without such defence free radicals literally tear apart cell membranes; the cell leaks its vital fluids and dies.

One of the most catastrophic events in the body is a chain reaction of oxidizing cell membranes. Dr. McCord explains how this happens. Suppose you inhale ozone from polluted air or cigarette smoke, both of which contain oxygen free radicals. If one free radical oxidizes one lipid (fat) molecule, it sets off a monumental chain reaction in which oxygen reacts with lipids, and so on indefinitely until something squelches it. Says McCord: "From this single oxidation event, a chain reaction might go on for, let's say, 2,000 molecules but if vitamin E happens to intercept one of those chains, the reaction will stop right where it is. So if a membrane has lots of vitamin E, the chain might last for only 200 molecules. Vitamin E is like a little fire extinguisher in a cell's membrane."

Beta-carotene's antioxidant capabilities are altogether different. Beta-carotene is a pigment in dark orange fruits and vegetables and green leafy vegetables and is considered a major reason such fruits and vegetables are consistently linked to lower rates of certain cancers, notably lung cancer. Beta-carotene, among other things, can seek out and quench a particular type of free radical called *singlet oxygen*. Such singlet oxygen molecules are linked to sunlight-sensitive diseases like skin cancer.

Numerous other cousins of beta-carotene in the large carotenoid family are also antioxidants, with exotic names like lycopene and leutin. Lycopene is a red pigment found in strawberries and tomatoes, both linked to lower rates of cancer. Tomatoes are also high in leutin.

Many prominent food antioxidants being studied are of a family of plant compounds called *polyphenols*; these include quercetin, ellagic acid, caffeic acid, and ferulic acid. For example, Dr. Terrance Leighton, a professor of biochemistry and molecular biology at the University of California at Berkeley, has tested quercetin and found it "a very effective antioxidant and one of the most potent anticancer agents ever discovered". Quercetin, says Dr. Leighton, is one of the few food substances that promises to block cancer both at the earliest stage—when a single cell's genetic material is altered—and during the crucial promotional phase, when the single cell proliferates into a tumour, a period that in humans takes ten to twenty years or more.

Quercetin is most highly concentrated in yellow and red onions and shallots, but, oddly, there is none in white onions or in garlic, a close cousin of onions, Dr. Leighton has found. "It's rather amazing how much quercetin onions have, quercetin can account for up to 10 per cent of an onion's dry weight," he says. "There's enough in 2–3 oz (55–85g) of onions to give a pretty substantial dose." Next highest in quercetin are red grapes, then broccoli and yellow Italian (crookneck) squash.

Onion eaters have been found to have lower rates of cancer, notably stomach cancer, than non-onion eaters. Quercetin, in animals, also protects arteries and discourages blood clots. And the compound, according to lab tests, kills bacteria, inhibits viruses, and is an anti-inflammatory and anti-allergenic agent.

U.S. Department of Agriculture researchers are investigating ellagic acid, found primarily in strawberries, blackberries, raspberries, blueberries, cranberries, grapes, apples and various nuts, including Brazil and cashew nuts. Dr. Gary Stoner, director of experimental pathology, at the Medical College of Ohio in Toledo, says ellagic acid helps block four different types of cancer-causing agents, including the mould aflatoxin and nitrosamines, a class of virulent cancer-producing compounds.

A team of researchers at Emory University School of Medicine is exploring the disease-fighting potential of glutathione, another antioxidant concentrated in green leafy vegetables, namely broccoli, parsley and spinach. In laboratory tests glutathione can inactivate at least thirty cancer-causing agents that may damage cells, according to Dr. Dean P. Jones, associate professor of biochemistry at Emory.

Although free radicals have most extensively been investigated for their part in triggering heart disease and cancer, they have also been in some way implicated in about sixty different diseases, including autoimmune diseases like arthritis (free radicals promote inflammation), Parkinson's disease and cataracts.

New knowledge about the immense powers of food antioxidants in fighting disease is only just emerging. Scientists think, however, that these chemicals possess an important secret as to why certain foods—notably fruits and vegetables, legumes, grains and nuts among others—can promote health and ward off disease.

FOODS HIGHEST IN ANTIOXIDANT VITAMIN C
IN MILLIGRAMS PER 3¹/₂OZ (100G)

Red and green peppers	128
Broccoli	113
Brussels sprouts	102
Cauliflower	78
Strawberries	59
Spinach	51
Oranges	50
Cabbage	47
Grapefruit	38
Cantaloupe melon	33

FOODS HIGHEST IN ANTIOXIDANT VITAMIN E
IN MILLIGRAMS PER 3¹/₂OZ (100G)

Vitamin E is fat-soluble and thus concentrated in vegetable oils, nuts and seeds, as well as legumes and brans that are fairly high in oils. Vitamin E does not occur in foods from animal sources.

Nuts and Seeds:

Sunflower seeds	52
Walnuts	22
Almonds	21
Hazelnuts filberts	21
Cashews	11
Peanuts, roasted	11
Brazil nuts	7
Pecans	2

Brans and Legumes:

Wheat germ	28
Soya beans, dried	20
Rice bran	15
Butter beans, dried	8
Wheat bran	8
Corn	6

Oils:

Wheat germ	250
Soya bean	92
Corn	82
Sunflower	63
Safflower	38
Sesame	28
Peanut	24
Coconut	4

The Vegetarian Advantage

> *Recommendation:* Eat fruits and vegetables with abandon—at least five servings a day. Vegetarians definitely have a health advantage. But you don't have to give up meat entirely to reap the disease-fighting rewards of fruits and vegetables. Nonvegetarians, too, can help save themselves from disease and promote a longer healthy life by increasing their consumption of fruits and vegetables.

Nothing looks surer in the food pharmacy than the powers of fruits and vegetables to help ward off disease and prolong life. Evidence is piling up at a fast pace, confirming that fruits and vegetables are full of exotic health-promoting compounds that boost bodily defences against disease in all kinds of ways. Undeniably vegetarians and even meat eaters who eat lots of plant foods have an impressive health advantage.

Amazingly, the first of many studies showing that vegetarians have a health edge was done in the fifth century B.C., some 2,500 years ago. According to the biblical account, Daniel implored the guard of King Nebuchadnezzar, ruler of ancient Babylon, to perform an experiment: "'Submit us to this test for ten days. Give us only vegetables to eat and water to drink; then compare our looks with those of the young men who have lived on the food assigned by the king. . .'"

"The guard listened to what they said and tested them. . . at the end of ten days they looked healthier and were better nourished than all the young men who had lived on the food assigned them by the king. So the guard took away the assignment of food and the wine they were to drink, and gave them only the vegetables." (Daniel 1:11–16.)

This ancient finding is echoed constantly by current research. Advice to eat more fruits and vegetables is insistent from leading physicians, investigators and public bodies. After a massive survey of the medical evidence linking diet and disease, the U.S. National Academy of Sciences/National Research Council in 1989 issued a 747-page report, *Diet and Health*, assessing hundreds of studies. The case for fruits and vegetables was overwhelming, leading the council to a prime recommendation, "Every day eat five or more servings of a combination of vegetables and fruits, especially green and yellow vegetables and citrus fruits."

Unquestionably fruits and vegetables are full of potent chemicals with known and unknown effects on health. Scientific teams throughout the world are probing the vegetable kingdom in search of their unique compounds and combination of compounds that promote health and fight specific diseases. The U.S. National Cancer Institute funds such research and has developed a $20 million five-year programme to analyse the cancer-fighting properties in twenty common foods, including garlic, onions and citrus fruits. Laboratory tests in both human cell cultures and animals have demonstrated powerful abilities of chemicals from these and other fruits and vegetables to put the brakes on cancer.

Numerous dietary studies also show that eating fruits and vegetables may dramatically reduce your chances of contracting an array of health problems, including cancer, heart disease, diabetes, high blood pressure, high blood cholesterol, gallstones, kidney stones, degenerative eye diseases and diverticular disease of the colon. To be sure, vegetarians have the best health odds but research shows you don't have to swear off all meat to derive monumental vegetable benefits. Simply raising your intake of fruits and vegetables, studies show, may help offset some of the damage inflicted by a meat diet.

New Reasons to Eat More Fruits and Vegetables

Vegetarians Live Longer. Since 1958 doctors at Loma Linda University, California have been studying the diet-disease connection in a group of 34,000 Seventh-day Adventists, half of whom are vegetarians and also rarely smoke or drink alcohol. When the researchers account for all such factors, they still find that vegetarians within the group live about three years longer than the nonvegetarians.

More dramatic, the longevity odds soar when compared with those for typical Americans, according to Dr. Jan W. Kuzma, professor of vital statistics at Loma Linda. Dr. Kuzma finds that a thirty-five-year-old male

Seventh-day Adventist, who eats a vegetarian or near-vegetarian diet, can expect to live to eight-two, nine years longer than a typical Californian white male, who is expected to reach age seventy-three. Dr. Kuzma predicts others who eat similar diets (and don't drink or smoke) could also stretch their life spans.

Vegetables Fight Cancer and Heart Disease. Seventh-day Adventists, according to the study, are only 85 per cent as likely to die of cancer and 65–75 per cent as apt to die of coronary heart disease as other Americans. Within the group of Seventh-day Adventists, vegetarians again win out. They have lower rates of all cancers (except brain tumours and lymphomas) and of cardiovascular disease. Researchers have even identified specific plant foods that appear to protect against certain cancers and heart disease.

"Consumption of legumes and dried fruits seems markedly protective in cancer of the pancreas," says Dr. Gary Fraser, professor of epidemiology and medicine, Loma Linda School of Medicine and head of the research project. Beta-carotene seems to help ward off colon cancer, which means carrots and green leafy vegetables such as spinach, says Dr. Fraser. Meat, beef in particular, may be a hazard for colon cancer, he notes. There was some suggestion that eating meat also predisposed to bladder cancer. On lung cancer: "We found strong protection from fruit consumption." The same was true for stomach cancer.

Extremely fascinating is the food link to cardiovascular disease revealed in the study. "When we accounted for every other factor, such as age and sex," Dr. Fraser says, "one food stands out as protective against heart disease—nuts." Those who ate nuts four times a week were about half as likely to have a fatal or nonfatal heart attack as once-a-week nut eaters. The question now, says Dr. Fraser, is what kind of nuts? "Are all nuts equal?"

He speculates the type of fat in nuts might account for the lower risk. Although nuts are high in fat—deriving 70 per cent of their calories from fat—the fat is unique, he says, usually quite high in monounsaturated-type fat, the same type that dominates olive oil, known to benefit blood cholesterol and blood pressure. To find out which nuts most benefit the heart, Dr. Fraser's team plans to feed men different types of nuts and then check their blood pressure, blood fats, blood-clotting mechanisms and other such factors.

Immune Superiority. Vegetarians have a more active immune system, according to a 1989 study at the German Cancer Research Centre in

Heidelberg. When researchers compared the blood of male vegetarians and meat eaters, they found that the white cells of vegetarians were twice as deadly against tumour cells as those of meat eaters. In other words, it took half the vegetarian white blood cells to kill tumour cells. Vegetarians did not have more white blood cells but apparently more ferocious ones. One theory suggests that their white blood cells may harbour more natural killer cells or the NK cells may be more powerful. Vegetarians also had more carotene coursing in their veins, a vegetable substance also found (in high doses) to boost immune functioning. This finding may be one reason vegetarians and heavy vegetable eaters have lower cancer odds.

Fruits Block Meat-Induced Cancer. So powerful are foods of the plant kingdom, it appears, they can even help counteract some of the damage inflicted by a high-meat diet. A dramatic example comes from an American National Cancer Institute study that showed meat eaters who ate lots of fruits and vegetables were less likely to develop pancreatic cancer than meat eaters who skimped on fruits and vegetables.

A research team headed by Roni T. Falk recently linked the diet and lifestyle of people living in a region of southern Louisiana with one of the highest rates of pancreatic cancer in the nation. The area is heavily populated by Cajuns, descendants of French settlers whose diets are high in pork, mainly bacon, ham, sausage, cold meats and unprocessed fresh pork, usually eaten along with rice.

Indeed Cajuns who ate the most pork products and rice were more apt to develop pancreatic cancer. Those who ate a serving of pork once a day were about 70 per cent more likely to have the cancer than those who ate pork less than twice a week. On the other hand, those who ate fruit or fruit juice (bananas, oranges, strawberries, canned fruits, orange juice and apples) twice a day were only 40 per cent as likely to develop the cancer as those eating fruits less than once a day. All well and good.

But what most surprised researchers was the fact that eating fruit seemed to wipe out the risk of eating too much pork. In other words, if you ate both a lot of fruit and a lot of pork you were no more at risk of pancreatic cancer than skimpy pork eaters. Why? Apparently something in the fruit counteracted the danger of eating pork. One possibility is vitamin C, highly concentrated in fruit. Further analysis did find that the amount of vitamin C intake in foods seemed to protect against cancer to the same degree as the fruit.

And there was a dose response—the more fruit consumed, the lower the cancer risk. A possible explanation for this is that vitamin C is known to help prevent formation of nitrosamines, cancer-causing agents that can arise from nitrite put into cured pork products.

In dozens of other studies it has been shown that people who eat the most vegetables and fruits have lower odds of various cancers, in particular lung, colon, stomach, throat, breast and pancreatic cancer. For example, a couple of dozen studies find that people who eat the most foods high in carotenoids, like carrots and spinach, have about half the chances of developing lung cancer—even if they are ex-smokers.

Exactly how the plant kingdom protects against disease is unclear. Scientists are now trying to sort that out. But there is little question that your best bet for a long life and less disease is to eat more fruits and vegetables of all types.

New Fibre Mysteries

> *Recommendation:* If you have a typical Western diet, you need to eat two or three times as much fibre as you are now eating. That means lots more fruits, vegetables, legumes, grains and nuts.

Yes, you should eat food full of fibre.

That's what health experts have been saying over and over until they are hoarse—and they are unquestionably right. But, amazingly, nobody really knows why fibre works or if in fact it does work.

Fibre, seemingly one of the most boring subjects, is actually one of the most exciting and most mysterious. Just when scientists think they have the answer, some new finding throws them off course. Fibre itself comes in maybe a hundred different shapes, sizes and chemical makeups—all of which may have varying physiological effects. Just as mysterious are the many co-travellers in high-fibre foods. In other words, maybe health benefits in high-fibre foods derive not entirely from fibre per se but partly or wholly from other constituents that tag along with fibre.

Gone are the days when the main fibre fact you needed to know was that there are two types: soluble and insoluble. Soluble fibre, as found in apples and oat bran, supposedly lowered cholesterol. Insoluble fibre, found in grains and cereals, supposedly did not, but protected against bowel problems, including colon cancer.

Now it's been discovered that a food high in insoluble fibre like rice bran also lowers cholesterol. High-soluble-fibre starchy foods, like potatoes, may help fight cancer in strange ways. And in one of the most intriguing discoveries, fibre may relieve gastrointestinal disorders by killing off a parasite that until recently virtually nobody even blamed.

We've come a long way from the original contemplations of Denis Burkitt, the British gastroenterologist who sparked the fibre craze in the late 1970s by noting that Africans who ate a high-fibre diet were spared a multitude of Western maladies of the digestive tract.

New Reasons for Eating More High Fibre Foods

Here are some fascinating new reasons for eating more high-fibre foods like grains, cereals, legumes, fruits and vegetables:

The Hidden Parasite. Chronic digestive problems, striking nearly thirty million Americans, are often given the catchall diagnosis of irritable bowel syndrome. It's characterized by flatulence, bloating, pain and alternating diarrhoea and constipation.

Some physicians, including Dr. Burkitt, blame too little fibre in the diet for the symptoms. Now there's a surprising new rationale for that. Dr. Leo Galland, a New York internist, claims, as a result of his studies, that about half of patients with digestive complaints may be actually infected with an intestinal parasite, *Giardia lamblia*, commonly picked up from drinking contaminated water. He says antibiotics kill the parasite and cure the intestinal complaints in 90 per cent of the cases.

But cellulose, an insoluble fibre in corn and wheat bran, can also destroy the parasite, according to a new discovery by physiologist Gordon J. Leitch at Atlanta's Morehouse School of Medicine. The fibre creates mucus in the gut, entrapping the parasite; it is then swept from the small intestine into the large intestine, where it cannot survive. Dr. Leitch found that gerbils fed a low-fibre diet were about twice as likely to get the parasitic infection as those fed a diet high in cellulose fibre. He says fibre in human colons would do the same thing. It's a novel and unexpected but credible new explanation for some of fibre's long-reputed powers to relieve intestinal distress. The food highest in cellulose is corn bran.

All-Bran Breakthrough. A remarkable study in 1989 by Dr. Jerome J. De Cosse, Memorial-Sloan Kettering Cancer Center, found that eating two ordinary servings (1 oz/30 g each) of Kellogg's high-fibre All-Bran cereal a day could shrink precancerous growths in the colon that often erupt into tumours. The fifty-eight patients in the study all had an inherited tendency to develop the small growths, called *polyps*, which are the foundation for tumours. If the polyps are not present, experts believe, colon cancer does not arise.

In the carefully conducted study patients ate either All-Bran or a look-alike low-fibre cereal. The All-Bran eaters took in about 22 g of fibre a day; the low-fibre eaters ate 12 g of fibre, average daily fibre consumption for Americans.

Six months into the four-year study Dr. De Cosse noticed that the polyps of those eating the high-fibre diet were decreasing in size and number. By three years the shrinkage was at its peak.

Most exciting is how quickly the cereal fibre acted to slow down the progress toward this deadly cancer. That suggests it's not too late even after the initial signs of colon cancer appear to switch to a high-fibre diet, although De Cosse noted that starting early in life is preferable. What in the cereal worked? Maybe it was the fibres, says De Cosse, but it could have been other things, including a sugar called *pentose*.

Barley and Rice Bran Surprise. Barley is rich in soluble fibre, similar to that in oat bran; rice bran is high in insoluble fibre, like that in wheat bran, generally thought to have little impact on cholesterol. Nevertheless, both barley bran and rice bran—the outer coat of the kernels—lower blood cholesterol, according to new studies. In a study at the University of California at Davis, eating 3oz (85g) rice bran daily for six weeks drove cholesterol down an average 8 per cent in people with moderately high cholesterol.

At Texas A & M University Dr. Joanne Lupton found that 1 oz (30 g) barley bran a day for a month also pushed cholesterol down an average 8 per cent in men and women with high cholesterol (6.5–7.8).

How could two such different types of fibre push down cholesterol? Experts suspect in both cases that fibre is not the only or most active cholesterol-lowering agent in either barley or rice bran. "We think what suppresses cholesterol is actually a specific chemical in the oil of rice bran," says Dr. Robin Saunders, a U.S. Department of Agriculture authority. University of Wisconsin researchers say the same thing about barley. In fact they have identified specific chemicals in the oil that can lower cholesterol in animals. Interestingly, the barley oil compound is tocotrienol. It is also a formidable antioxidant.

The Phytate Phenomenon. Dr. Lilian Thompson, nutrition researcher at the University of Toronto, spends much time trying to work out just what makes high-fibre, complex-carbohydrate foods so good for you. She has a theory, too—with facts to back it up—that it's not just fibre but also so-called antinutrients that are plentiful in high-fibre foods, especially one called phytic acid or phytate.

Legumes, for example, are well documented to prevent steep rises in blood sugar, which is expecially crucial for diabetics. The credit almost always goes to the soluble fibre in beans. Dr. Thompson says that's a mistake; she contends the active agent is phytate. In an experiment she removed phytate from the beans and left the fibre. The beans no longer had the ability to hold down surges of blood sugar. In fact the phytate-free legumes allowed starch to be digested more quickly thus sending blood glucose levels up sharply. When Dr. Thompson restored the phytate, the beans again kept blood sugar under control. Since the mechanism is thought to be the same for lowering cholesterol, it may be phytate, not soluble fibre in beans, that brings cholesterol down.

Phytates, present in oat bran and wheat bran, may also play a role in high-fibre foods' reputed cancer-fighting capabilities. Phytates are anti-oxidants, squelching cancer-promoting oxygen free radicals. Scientists at the University of Maryland have blocked cancer in animals by giving them phytate.

Agents in wheat bran have also thwarted conversion of compounds to nitrosamines, powerful cancer-causing chemicals. Even the starch in high complex carbohydrate foods, like potatoes, can react in the intestinal tract to form anticancer agents, according to British tests.

With all this new research swirling around, perhaps it is unfair to prize a high-fibre food purely for its fibre, when other agents coincidentally found in high-fibre foods may also have potent pharmacological activity. Even so, it seems abundantly clear that high-fibre foods, for whatever reason, can help rescue you from disease and prolong your life.

Foods That Fight Strokes

Recommendation: If you are at all concerned about strokes, be sure to eat foods that contain more than 3500 milligrams of potassium every day. That could cut your risk of a stroke dramatically.

Amazing as it may seem, experts say that adding any one of the following foods to your daily diet could cut your chances of dying of a stroke by 25–40 per cent:

A quarter of a cantaloupe, half an avocado, a baked potato, a glass of milk, ten dried apricots, 3oz (85g) butter beans, a 5oz (140g) piece of salmon, 3oz (85g) spinach or beetroot tops, 2oz (55g) almonds or peanuts—or a serving of any other food rich in potassium.

Potassium seems to be a prime regulator of high blood pressure, a major cause of strokes. Adding potassium to the diet can lower blood pressure. High intakes of potassium can even help counteract the ability of salt or sodium to raise blood pressure in animals. Especially intriguing, researchers say, potassium seems to help immunize blood vessels against damage from high blood pressure, allowing cells of the blood vessel walls to function normally despite high blood pressure. Potassium even acts to thwart strokes that are unrelated to high blood pressure.

Potassium is widely distributed in roots, fruits, tubers, nuts, grains and seeds—the forage available to our prehistoric ancestors. Early humans thrived on these high-potassium, low-sodium foods. Today we eat less than a quarter of the potassium consumed by prehistoric humans. And we are much worse off for it, says Louis Tobian, Jr., chief of the hypertension section at the University of Minnesota at Minneapolis. He urges practically everybody to "eat more potassium". He is persuaded that potassium helps prevent strokes from blood clots and haemorrhages in people with and without high blood pressure.

In exquisite studies on the brains of animals, Dr. Tobian has documented the hazard of too little potassium. In one experiment he fed rats high amounts of salt to induce high blood pressure. Then he fed some rats a high-potassium diet and others a "normal" potassium diet.

Forty per cent of the rats fed the "normal" potassium diet suffered bleeding in the brain—small strokes. None of the rats on the high-potassium diet had any signs of brain haemorrhage. Tobian's theory is the extra potassium kept artery walls elastic and able to withstand increased pressure, averting arterial rupture and bleeding and thus preventing strokes.

The evidence is impressive that potassium also protects *humans* from strokes. The first major study demonstrating this was among an elderly population in California; it was published in the *New England Journal of Medicine in* 1987. Dr. Kay-Tee Khaw, at the University of Cambridge, and Elizabeth Barrett-Connor, at the University of California at San Diego, studied the diets of 859 men and women over age fifty and their stroke rates over a twelve-year period. Those with the highest potassium diets had no strokes in that time, compared with twenty-four strokes among those eating less potassium. And there seemed to be a dose response. The more potassium, the fewer the strokes.

For example, those eating the least potassium—about 1,950 milligrams per day—were two-and-a-half times more likely to die of a stroke than those eating up to 2,600 milligrams per day—the U.S. average. No one died of a stroke in the 3,500 milligrams or more per day group.

This meant, to the amazement of researchers, that the stroke death rate fell 40 per cent for every daily addition of 400 milligrams of potassium in the diet. (Incidentally, our prehistoric ancestors probably ate between 7,800 and 11,000 milligrams of potassium a day.)

Other studies confirm potassium's stroke-fighting abilities. In a study of 7,591 men of Japanese descent living in Hawaii, high-potassium diets appeared to lower the rate of a fatal stroke from blood clots to the same degree as in the California study. A large-scale Norwegian study found about a 25 per cent reduction in deadly strokes, primarily "bleeding" strokes from brain haemorrhage, in the highest consumers of potassium.

Japanese researchers tracking the diets of two groups with decidedly differing intakes of potassium and sodium over a twenty-five-year period found that the population with the highest-potassium/lowest-sodium diets were much less susceptible to strokes. Some of the farmers in the study ate eight to ten apples a day, providing from 1,280 to 1,600 milligrams of potassium—a factor the researchers credited in preventing strokes.

It's probable that fruits and vegetables may harbour other compounds that could fight stroke and high blood pressure. One is vitamin C. A large-scale study in Finland documented "marked high blood pressure" among those with the lowest blood levels of vitamin C and selenium, a trace mineral concentrated in some vegetables for example, garlic and Brazil nuts, as well as seafood.

Interestingly, a series of studies in Japan also showed that heavy seafood eaters were much less likely to die of strokes. Residents of fishing villages who eat about 9oz (255g) of seafood daily have a 25–40 per cent lower risk of a stroke than farmers who eat only 3oz (85g) of fish a day. In Japan most strokes come from haemorrhages, in the U.S. from blood clots. Researchers theorize that the omega-3 fatty acids in seafood may modify blood factors, helping protect against strokes. Seafood is also high in potassium.

A new study by Japanese scientists at Tohoku University School of Medicine found that drinking green tea may reduce vulnerability to strokes. Their four-year study of 5,910 women over age forty found that those who drank at least five cups of green tea per day were only half as likely to have a stroke as those who drank less tea. Interestingly, the tea did not seem to reduce blood pressure, considered a common cause.

Green tea, like many vegetables and fruits, contains compounds called *phenols*. Tannin is a phenol commonly found in tea. Numerous studies have found that such phenols operate as antioxidants, helping protect cells from a variety of assaults, including possibly those leading to strokes.

Some researchers have speculated that eating more fruits and vegetables simply replace fat in the diet, especially saturated meat fat, that could promote high blood pressure. But Dr. Frank M. Sacks, Harvard Medical School, who studied vegetarian populations in New England, says otherwise. He believes that the low blood pressure of vegetarians is "so striking" that it is most likely accounted for by active agents in fruits and vegetables that lower blood pressure.

It would be surprising if there were not several unidentified agents in foods that help protect against high blood pressure and its frequent consequence, strokes. Until these agents are determined, here are some foods high in potassium, so far the best-proved antagonist of strokes. Each serving has at least 400 milligrams of potassium, providing that daily margin of safety between no stroke and a fatal stroke as shown in Dr. Khaw's California study. Most are also low-calorie and give the most potassium for the fewest calories.

HIGH-POTASSIUM (ANTI-STROKE) FOODS

Food	Serving	Potassium (mg)
Blackstrap molasses	3oz (85g)	2,400
Potato, baked	1 medium	844
Cantaloupe melon	½ fruit	825
Avocado, Florida	½ fruit	742
Beetroot tops, cooked	2½oz (70g)	654
Peaches, dried	5 halves	645
Prunes, dried	10 halves	626
Tomato juice	8fl oz (225ml)	536
Snapper	3½oz (100g)	522
Butter beans, dried, cooked	3oz (85g)	517
Tomatoes	8oz (225g)	495
Salmon	3½oz (100g)	490
Yoghurt, low-fat	8oz (225g)	487
Apricots, dried	10 halves	482
Swiss chard, cooked	2½oz (70g)	466
Pumpkin seeds	2oz (55g)	458
Banana	1 fruit	451
Soya beans, dried, cooked	2oz (55g)	428
Almonds	2oz (55g)	426
Acorn squash	4oz (115g)	419
Herring	3½oz (100g)	419
Milk, skimmed	8fl oz (225ml)	418
Sweet potato, cooked	4oz (115g)	410
Mackerel	3½oz (100g)	406
Peanuts	2oz (55g)	400
Spinach, cooked	3oz (85g)	396

The Therapeutic Powers of Spices, Herbs and Seasonings.

The phrase "the spice of life" is not a misnomer. Since early civilization our most potent medicines have been spices and herbs and there is increasing proof of their pharmacological effects. Here's what modern science knows about the health benefits of some common spices and herbs.

Ginger

The best studied of all spices is ginger. It has a formidable reputation in folklore as a "medicine for the stomach" and has long been proclaimed an antinausea agent, especially for preventing seasickness. And that it does. Several years ago scientists tested the theory in simulated circumstances and ginger worked—even better than the common antinausea drug Dramamine.

But would it work in the actual tumult of ocean waves? In 1988 researchers at Odense University in Denmark came back with the answer. They accompanied eighty green navel cadets sailing on the high seas. One day out of port the investigators gave one gram of root ginger (a scant half teaspoon ground) to one group of the rookie sailors and a placebo to another group. Then they checked for symptoms of seasickness every hour for four hours.

Sure enough, root ginger reduced the severity of seasickness by suppressing vomiting, cold sweating, nausea, and vertigo. The most pronounced effect was control of vomiting—dampening it by 72 per cent. Overall they pronounced ginger 38 per cent protective against the symptoms of seasickness. The Danish scientists note that the pharmacological component in ginger that combats motion sickness is totally unknown. However, they say it takes effect within twenty-five minute and lasts for at least four hours.

Curbing motion sickness is not ginger's only pharmacological asset. In animal tests ginger lowers blood cholesterol; in test tubes it is an antibiotic, very effective against salmonella, the bacteria that frequently contaminate eggs and chickens. Could that account for the Chinese wisdom behind Ginger Chicken? With its many assets perhaps it is a recipe cross-channel ferries should adopt.

Ginger is a strong antioxidant, which perhaps gives it some anticancer properties. In certain medical circles ginger is best recognized as a blood thinner or anticoagulant, even in doses present in commercial jars of ginger marmalade—an easy daily "dose".

Japanese scientists recently found that ginger (as well as Japanese ginseng) has antiulcer effects in animals, inhibiting stomach ulceration by more than 90 per cent.

Ginger may even help patients with rheumatoid arthritis. It's been used in folk medicine to treat a variety of rheumatic disorders. Recently Dr. Krishna C. Srivastava, also at Denmark's Odense University, found that patients with rheumatoid arthritis got significant relief from rheumatic pain by eating ginger for three months. The dose was $1/6$ oz (5g) per day of fresh root ginger or $1/2$–$1 1/2$g (about a teaspoonful) of ground ginger daily. The ginger eaters also said they could move around better and had less swelling and suffered less from morning stiffness. Dr. Srivastava found no side effects from the ginger.

Cinnamon

Dr. Richard Anderson, U.S. Department of Agriculture, is an expert on the metabolism of sugar. He suspected that certain foods might stimulate the activity of insulin and help the body process sugar more efficiently—with less insulin. That could be especially important to Type II (adult-onset) diabetics. Eating such foods might reduce their need for insulin, he hypothesized.

When he measured insulin activity in test tubes in the presence of many foods, most had slight or no effect. But three spices and one herb actually tripled insulin activity: cinnamon, cloves, turmeric, and bay leaves. Cinnamon was the most powerful. Dr. Anderson says eating cinnamon, even in small amounts sprinkled on toast, can boost insulin activity. Thus there is pharmacological wisdom behind using cinnamon and cloves in sweets like apple pie.

Rosemary

This leaf has been shown to be a potent antioxidant by Japanese scientists. They have isolated at least four compounds in rosemary that act as antioxidants. In fact two of the rosemary compounds were about four times more active than (and the two others equal to) BHT and BHA, antioxidants used in the food industry to prevent rancidity.

Thyme

In the Middle Ages thyme was used as a stimulant and an antispasmodic and was inhaled as a remedy for melancholia and epilepsy.

Today thyme is used in folk medicine to fight cold symptoms, especially as a cough medicine and expectorant. According to modern scientific tests, the herb decidedly relieves coughing. It also contains in its oil a potent antibiotic called *thymol*, which was detected by a German scientist in 1725. Largely because of the thymol, thyme acts as an expectorant that breaks up phlegm in the respiratory tract so that it can be coughed up. Thyme additionally, tests show, can help relieve muscle spasms, as medieval herbalists claimed.

Turmeric

As well as exhibiting insulin activity stimulating properties like cinnamon (see page 24), yellow-coloured turmeric, a primary ingredient in curry powders, appears to have anticancer properties. American scientists recently noted that turmeric contains a compound called *curcumin* that is anticarcinogenic.

Indian scientists at the Cancer Research Institute, Tata Memorial Centre, Bombay, also found that turmeric neutralized certain compounds that are mutagenic—that is, they disrupt the genetic material of cells, which is the first step toward the initiation of cancer. Turmeric worked against dangerous mutagenic agents in cigarette smoke, which led the Indian scientists to speculate that the Indian people who smoke a lot and are exposed to carcinogens in the environment may be somewhat protected from cancer because they eat so much curried food that includes up to a gram or more of turmeric per day.

Anise

Used since ancient days as a liquorice-type flavouring, anise, was touted as a carminative—to relieve flatulence. Modern research shows anise does have such capabilities—which gives credibility to the longtime European practice of using anise liqueurs to settle upset stomachs.

Basil

Herbalists have long recommended tea brewed from this sweet, popular, spicy green leaf to relieve nausea, flatulence and dysentery. Basil does relieve intestinal gas and inhibits organisms that can cause dysentery.

Fenugreek

Now commonly used in Middle Eastern spice and curry mixtures, fenugreek seeds are an ancient medicinal herb, prescribed in ancient Egypt and India as a cure-all but in particular for tuberculosis, bronchitis and sore throats. The seed is a carminative, relieving flatulence. It is used in the Middle East as a treatment for diabetes and there is increasing evidence showing that fenugreek seeds are effective in lowering blood sugar, as well as blood cholesterol.

Peppermint

Definitely this mint is an aid to digestion, mainly because of its volatile oil, containing various forms of menthol. These compounds stimulate bile flow, promoting digestion. Peppermint stimulates the appetite; it also acts on the sphincter muscle, leading to both belching and heartburn in susceptible persons.

Sage

Adding a little sage to your meals may help ward off flatulence and even might lower a fever. Additionally, sage and several other spices are known antioxidants that may help protect cells from numerous assaults associated with as many as sixty different diseases. In recent tests spices showing the greatest antioxidant activity against lipid peroxidation were, in order, oils of caraway, sage, cumin, rosemary, thyme and clove.

Soy Sauce

There is something about soy sauce that may help ward off cancer. That's what researchers at the Food Research Institute at the University of Wisconsin in Madison suggest. They found that animals given soy sauce and then subjected to potent cancer-causing chemicals had fewer tumours than mice deprived of soy sauce.

"We actually went into this to confirm some work by Japanese scientists showing that soy sauce is a mutagen that predisposes cells to turn cancerous. We found just the opposite," says Dr. Michael Pariza, director of the institute. Surprised, the researchers repeated the studies twice, each time witnessing an even greater cancer-fighting effect.

In a study completed in February 1989 they found "a tremendous reduction with one particular batch of soy sauce". The mice not given soy sauce had three-and-a-half times more cancers of the forestomach than mice protected by soy sauce. "There is definitely something in soy sauce that's combating the tumours," says Dr. Pariza. "But we have no idea what it is—whether it's in the fermentation or the soya bean itself."

A large-scale study in Japan several years ago did show that daily eaters of soup made from fermented soya bean paste, known as *miso*, had lower rates of stomach cancer.

Wonder Medicines from the Sea

Recommendation: Eat seafood, especially fatty fishes like salmon, mackerel, sardines and tuna, at least twice a week and more often if you can. So far no other single food has been shown to have such broad influence on health and disease.

"Eat more seafood!" is the clarion call from scientists around the world. And for good reason. Eating fish, especially deep-sea, cold-water fish high in omega-3 fatty acids, is one of your best bets for escaping numerous modern maladies, including heart disease, cancer, arthritis, psoriasis, high blood pressure and strokes. Fish and fish oil may even slow down the spread of already existing cancer. Here's why.

Once upon a time, eons ago, our cells existed in physiological normality, explains Alexander Leaf, chairman of the Department of Preventive Medicine at Harvard Medical School. Then came agriculture and modern technology. And our cells, overwhelmed by modern fat and starved for the quieting oils of the sea, went into major malfunction.

Because of this recent "fat imbalance," our cells are continually besieged by biochemical assaults, giving rise to a rampage of chronic diseases. Infusing our cells with the oil in seafood may restore that biochemical balance of old and help rid us of our modern plague. In other words eating more fish may help prevent and relieve the symptoms of an array of diverse diseases.

What makes seafood so pharmacologically attractive is its unique type of fat or oil made up of long chains of molecules called *omega-3 fatty acids* These omega-3s, it is thought, help suppress the activity of bodily messengers called *prostaglandins* and leukotrienes that promote all kinds of havoc, including blood clots and inflammation. The omega-3s also have direct effects on the immune system.

Rather quickly after you eat seafood, the omega-3s enter the membranes of your cells, rendering them less stiff and more pliable—more "normal," in evolutionary terms. By regulating the activities of prostaglandins and leukotrienes, fish oil decreases blood platelet stickiness, boosts clot-dissolving mechanisms and hampers inflammatory damage to artery walls, discouraging blood clot formation, the primary cause of heart attacks and strokes. Fish oil is an anti-inflammatory agent and probably an anticancer agent and animal studies show it can stave off heart arrhythmias (irregular heartbeats) that are the most immediate trigger of deadly heart attacks.

New Reasons to Eat More Seafood

The evidence for the benefits of omega-3 and seafood is piling up. Here are the new, compelling reasons to eat more seafood.

Combats Heart Disease. Most dramatic is the connection between eating seafood and having less heart disease. Several population surveys (epidemiological studies) have shown that certain groups of people who eat lots of fish have lower rates of heart disease. But the most conclusive evidence of fish's powers to fight heart disease comes from a major study done by Dr. Michael Burr at the Medical Research Council epidemiology unit in South Wales.

Dr. Burr and colleagues studied 2,033 men under age 70, all of whom had had at least one heart attack. One group of the men was asked to eat fatty fish like salmon, sardines and mackerel, twice a week or take fish oil capsules. Another group was instructed to cut down on consumption of saturated fat, such as butter, cheese and cream, and to substitute polyunsaturated fats, such as margarine. A third group was to boost fibre intake by eating more bran cereal and wholemeal bread. For comparison, a fourth group was given no dietary advice at all.

After two years, researchers found that the group on a fish diet had 29 per cent fewer deaths from heart attack. In other words, just eating about 10½oz (300g) of oily fish a week cut the chances of death among heart disease patients by an amazing one-third. Dr. Burr credits the omega-3 type oils. Interestingly, the study found no lifesaving effect from following a low-fat or high fibre diet.

Similarly, a recent study of 6,000 middle-aged American men found that those who ate the amount of omega-3 in a single 1oz (30g) bite of mackerel or a 3oz (85g) portion of bass every day had a 36 per cent lower chance of dying of heart disease over a six-year follow up period.

Additionally, three major studies at this time of writing have shown arteries did not close up as rapidly after angioplasty—a procedure to dilate clogged arteries—in patients fed fish oil. In one study the rate of re-blockage was cut in half in men taking fish oil and eating a low-fat diet.

Thwarts Cancer Spread. There's evidence that fish eaters have lower rates of cancer, notably breast cancer. Incredibly eating more oily fish and taking fish oil capsules may actually help halt the spread of cancer in those who already have the disease, says Dr. George Blackburn, associate professor of surgery at Harvard Medical School. Fish oil does suppress the promotion of cancer in animals. Also, Rashida Karmali, associate professor of nutrition of Rutgers University, found that fairly low doses of fish oil suppressed increased biological activity signifying developing cancer in women at highest risk of breast cancer.

Consequently Dr. Blackburn has launched a major two-year test to see if fish oil can curb the cancer spread, or metastasis, in a large group of women with breast cancer. The women in one group are instructed to eat more seafood and take low-dose supplements of fish oil for two years after breast cancer surgery. Dr. Blackburn believes the oil from fish will strengthen their immune systems, helping to destroy wandering cancer cells that may escape during surgery, as well as creating other changes hostile to cancer-cell growth. He suspects fish oil may also thwart the metastasis of cancer in those with lung, pancreatic and colon cancers.

Relieves Inflammatory Diseases. Unquestionably authorities term fish oil an anti-inflammatory agent. In some patients with rheumatoid arthritis symptoms of joint swelling, tenderness and fatigue have diminished after taking fish oil equal to that in a daily serving of 7oz (200g) of salmon.

Psoriasis, an inflammatory skin disease, also improves in some people given varying doses of fish oil, according to reports. In one study dermatologists at the Royal Hallamshire Hospital in Sheffield gave 28 patients with chronic psoriasis either 1.8g of EPA type fish oil per day or an olive oil placebo. They all continued their usual treatments and diets.

After eight weeks, the patients on fish oil had significantly less itching and redness. The researchers concluded that a person could get the same amount of therapeutic fish oil from eating a daily 5.3oz (150g) of oily fish, such as mackerel.

Fish oil has also improved the blood flow in the hands of some patients with Raynaud's disease. It has lessened the pain and frequency of migraine headaches, lowered blood pressure and helped victims of bronchial asthma breathe better.

Contrary to popular belief, fish oil does not consistently lower blood cholesterol. It does generally reduce triglycerides, another type of blood fat linked to heart disease. Most authorities believe that fish's ability to fend off heart disease has very little to do with an impact on cholesterol. More important is fish oil's ability to "thin" blood, preventing clots.

A Delicate Balance. As research marches on, scientists have come to the crucial realization that simply dumping more omega-3 into your cells does not always suppress disease processes. What is critical is the "correct balance" of different types of fatty acids in cells. That's because omega-3 must fight for control over the cells with another type of fatty acid known as omega-6. This omega-6 type fat is concentrated in land-based foods, like corn, safflower and sunflower oils. Animals like beef cattle fed plant foods also have have lots of omega-6 in their fat.

Once inside a cell, the omega-6 and omega-3 molecules seem to battle for biochemical supremacy and control over cell activities. Because Western diets usually contain about fifteen times more omega-6 than omega-3, the land-based omega-6s almost always win by virtue of sheer numbers. Thus omega-6s rule many cellular activities of westerners most of the time.

This is exceedingly detrimental, says the experts, because too much omega-6 tends to incite cellular destruction, leading to numerous disease symptoms. The omega-6 tends to trigger overproduction of overactive prostaglandins and leukotrienes that carry out destructive deeds, promoting events like inflammation and inappropriate blood clotting. Conversely, omega-3s put the brakes on such rampages caused by omega-6s. If cells are short on omega-3, the omega-6s are free to carry out destructive disease-promoting missions with less restraint.

Thus it's important both to cut back on foods with omega-6 and to eat more seafood with omega-3, says Dr. William Lands, professor of biological chemistry at the University of Illinois at Chicago and a pioneer in fish oil research. If you don't, you simply cancel out fish's benefits. For example, Dr. Jay Whelan, a researcher at Cornell University, says that if you eat a big slab of salmon along with salad doused in corn oil, you wipe out some of the benefits of the fish. (For foods highest in omega-3s, see page 268; for oils highest in omega-6s, see page 37.)

Nobody knows for sure how much omega-3 you must eat to keep fatty acids in the proper balance needed to counter the hazardous effects of omega-6. Dr. Blackburn of Harvard thinks the best balance is equal amounts of each. That means that if you eat 30 per cent of your calories in fat, as U.S. health authorities recommend, 5 per cent should be from land-based omega-6 and 5 per cent from marine-type omega-3. The other 20 per cent comes from a combination of saturated animal-type fat and mono-unsaturated fats, the type concentrated in olive oil.

To meet that quota a person consuming 2,000 calories a day should eat about 5oz (140g) of fish every day. If this sounds like a lot, it is still far less than many populations eat, including the Japanese, who typically consume 9oz (255g) of seafood a day. Generally, to help stave off heart disease, authorities recommend at least two serv 's of fish a week. You may need more, depending on the rest of your diet and current state of your health.

To what extent fish and its oil can cure and treat disease is yet unknown. Certainly it appears potent against heart disease. In the British study only small amounts of fish (twice a week) reduced death risk by one third in the amazingly short period of two years.

But most experts think the more profound benefits of eating omega-3s lie in *prevention*, rather than *cure*. Several experts, including Drs. Leaf and Lands, think regular amounts of fish oil in the diet over the years are likely to thwart the constant assaults that turn into full-blown disease. That's one reason experts urge people to eat fish regularly. It promises the best dietary insurance against a variety of chronic diseases.

Nonseafood Omega-3

You can also get some omega-3 from plant foods—notably English walnuts, flaxseed and a green leafy plant called *purslane* contain considerable amounts of omega-3 fatty acids. Soya beans also contain omega-3.

Scientists at Cornell, however, find that the short-chain omega-3 in plants is less powerful than the long-chain marine-type omega-3 in suppressing destructive prostaglandin and leukotriene activity in the body. Nevertheless, recent studies at the U.S. Department of Agriculture showed that the body can convert some of the plant-type omega-3 into the long-chain seafood-type omega-3. "Think of it this way, the body can naturally make its own fish oil... from soya bean oil," said Edward A. Emken, USDA chemist. In Dr. Emken's tests about 20–25 per cent of the soya bean omega-3 was converted to seafood-type omega-3.

Mediterranean Lifesaver: Olive Oil

> *Recommendation:* Do as many experts do—substitute olive oil for other fats, especially if you're concerned about heart disease. But that doesn't mean exclusively. Other excellent-health choices are rapeseed and flaxseed oil. Go easy on corn, safflower and sunflower oils. It is important, however, to restrict all fats, including oils.

It's scant surprise to people who live around the Mediterranean Sea that olive oil is emerging as one of the superstars in fighting disease. After all, numerous studies find that Italians, Greeks and in particular citizens of Crete, who are said to drink olive oil, have lower death rates from heart disease (about half that of Americans) and cancer. Yet, oddly, they eat as much fat as we do—about 40 per cent of calories in fat. The big difference: their fat calories come primarily from olive oil, 77 per cent of which is monounsaturated fat.

A decided advantage of monounsaturated-type fat is that it can lower blood cholesterol without lowering the beneficial HDL-type cholesterol. Polyunsaturated fats like corn and safflower oils are unfortunately indiscriminate; they typically lower both good HDL and bad LDL cholesterol. Since Dr. Scott Grundy, a leading cholesterol researcher at the University of Texas Health Science Center at Dallas, made that crucial discovery a few years ago, olive oil has displayed ever more of its fascinating pharmacological tricks.

New Reasons to Eat Olive Oil

Down Goes Blood Pressure. Several studies now confirm early clues that olive oil can lower both systolic (higher number) and diastolic blood pressure. Dr. Stephen Fortmann, Stanford Medical School, analysed the intake of monounsaturated fats and the blood pressure readings of a group of seventy-six men aged thirty to fifty-five. He discovered that systolic blood pressure fell by three quarters of a point and diastolic by half a point for every gram of monounsaturated fat the men ate. That would mean that three tablespoons of olive oil a day might depress systolic pressure by 9.4 points and diastolic by 6.3 points.

Helping clinch the case is a major analysis of the diets of nearly 5,000 Italians in nine communities, published in the *Journal of the American Medical Association*. As anticipated, those who ate the most olive oil had lower cholesterol. But the big news from the study was that their blood pressure was also lower by three or four points, with the main reduction in systolic blood pressure. Enthusiastic male olive oil eaters, but not women, also showed lower diastolic readings.

Olive oil can even lower blood pressure in people eating a high-fat diet—40 per cent of calories from fat. That's what Dutch researchers discovered when they put twenty-three subjects with normal blood pressure on a high-fat diet, most of it coming from olive oil. Their blood pressure fell 2.7 systolic and 4.4 diastolic points. It dropped similarly in those on a low-fat, high-carbohydrate diet.

Blood pressure went up in subjects eating lots of saturated animal fats, as is typical. In the Italian study, for example, eating butter pushed-up blood pressure.

Olive Oil Zaps Cholesterol. In reducing cholesterol, a high-fat olive-oil diet outstripped the usual low-fat diet in another study by researchers at the University of Nijmegen in the Netherlands. For thirty-six days half of a group of forty-eight healthy individuals ate a high-fibre, low-fat diet (22 per cent of calories from fat). The other half ate a high-fat diet (41 per cent of calories from fat), most of it from olive oil. The cholesterol of the low-fat dieters dropped an average seventeen points. But the cholesterol fell twenty points in the olive-oil eaters. Also crucial, the desirable HDL cholesterol, thought to ward off heart disease, sank in the low-fat dieters but not in the olive-oil group.

Blood Sugar Regulator. The large-scale Italian survey also showed that those eating the most olive oil had significantly lower blood glucose. This confirms what Dr. Grundy found in a small study of ten patients with Type II (adult-onset) diabetes. For twenty-eight days they ate a high-carbohydrate, low-fat diet, then switched for twenty-eight days to a diet high in fat (50 per cent of calories from fat), most of it from olive oil's monounsaturated fats. On the high-olive-oil-type-fat diet the patients had lower LDL (bad-type) blood cholesterol, higher good-type HDL cholesterol—and lower blood sugar levels, which meant all the diabetic patients required less insulin.

An Antioxidant Surprise. One of the most exciting new findings about olive oil is that it has potent antioxidant activity that appears to inhibit that awful process called lipid peroxidation that makes LDL cholesterol in the blood so dangerous. Such oxidation of fats is believed to be the first step in triggering a chain of events causing buildup of plaque on artery walls, subsequent arterial clogging and heart attacks. Thus olive oil's remarkable antioxidant powers may help explain its abilities to ward off heart disease.

Pioneering research by Dr. Daniel Steinberg and co-workers at the University of California in San Diego shows that LDL cholesterol from animals fed monounsaturated oil is "remarkably resistant" to becoming oxidized. In fact only one third to one quarter as much LDL cholesterol from rabbits fed monounsaturated oil became oxidized as LDL from rabbits fed regular safflower oil, low in monounsaturated fat.

Other research reveals at least two antioxidants in olive oil—oleic and palmitoleic fatty acids. The discovery, made by scientists at London's United Medical School, identified oleic acid as olive oil's most potent antioxidant. Nearly all olive oil's monounsaturated fat is oleic acid. Sure enough, when researchers at the Medical Centre of Athens, Greece, recently analysed the blood of seventy-six boys in Crete, who consume lots of olive oil, they detected extremely high levels of oleic acid circulating in their arteries. Crete is known for its extremely low rate of heart disease. The bottom line is highly monounsaturated fats like olive oil appear to help block LDL cholesterol from becoming capable of destroying arteries.

Olive oil's antioxidant capabilities could also be expected to inhibit development of cancer and numerous other diseases, even ageing, promoted by destructive oxygen free radicals. Other oils high in antioxidant oleic acid are rapeseed, groundnut, walnut and avocado. (This is good news for avocado lovers. Most of the fat in an avocado is monounsaturated, and 95 per cent of that is made up of antioxidant oleic acid.)

Research on animals turns up even more surprising clues about how olive oil may thwart heart disease. In both rabbits and rats olive oil's protection was not limited to changes in blood and blood cholesterol. Independently the oil induced beneficial changes in the aorta, the heart's main arterial trunk. In rats, for example, olive oil stimulated production in the aorta of a hormone-like substance called *prostacyclin*, one of the "good guys" in squelching disease at the cellular level. Increased prostacyclin lowers blood pressure.

A Final Good Word About Olive Oil. "There's only one fat that's safe to eat—olive oil," contends Dr. Harry Demopolous. But then, you might expect him to say that since he's of Greek heritage and grew up eating olive oil. But he has also spent thirty years studying the ravaging effects of oxygen free radicals and their ability to turn oils rancid. When you eat rancid oils, he says, you infuse your body with destructive free radicals that create chain reactions, breeding more free radicals to attack your cells. Of all the oils, olive oil, because it is so concentrated in monounsaturated fatty acids, is least likely to turn rancid and destructive, he says. On the other hand, most likely to become rancid are oils high in polyunsaturated fatty acids, like corn, safflower and sunflower.

Still, all this does not mean you should overdose on olive oil. Like other oils, it is 100 per cent fat and thus has the same number of calories as other fats, 120 per tablespoon. So overdoing it can add unwanted pounds just as other fats do, leading to other health problems. Best advice is to substitute olive oil for both saturated animals fats, such as lard and butter and other vegetable oils like corn, safflower and soya bean. And to eat less of all of them.

The Health Scoop in Other Oils

New knowledge about the chemistry of oils and their impact at the cellular level is making judgements about the health consequences of all oils exceedingly complex. Oil's constituents, once they enter cell membranes, exercise unimagined powers over cell functions, discouraging or encouraging disease processes.

New research tries to tease out not just the physiological effects of single types of fatty acids in oils but also their interactions within cells. Such a "balance of power" among fatty acids in cells—the chains of molecules that make up fat or oil—appears to be a big determinant of whether you are healthy or ill.

Cheers for Rapeseed and Flaxseed Oils. As a result of such research, new oils, notabley rapeseed oil, rice bran oil and the mighty flaxseed oil—are coming on strong, backed by substantial scientific claims for their health-promoting properties. For example, little-known flaxseed oil is popular with cancer researchers because in addition to other health-boosting qualities it contains anticancer agents, lignans. Other health experts praise flax oil, pressed from flaxseed, because it is nearly 60 per cent omega-3 fatty acids, similar to the amazing oily stuff in seafood that scientists think helps protect cells from a multitude of diseases. Flaxseed, at this time of writing, may be found in some health food stores. However rapeseed oil is readily available in health food stores and in supermarkets—a popular brand is Golden Fields.

Questions About Groundnut and Soya Oils. Both soya bean oil and groundnut oil seem poised in scientific limbo, with some good points, some bad ones. Soya bean oil has some omega-3-type oil, which is a plus, but lots of omega-6s, which is a minus. Groundnut oil is high in favoured monounsaturated fat but is still controversial. Dr. Grundy doesn't like it because studies found it detrimental to the arteries of monkeys. But other experts, including one who did some of the negative studies, pronounce it okay, pointing out it does not seem to trigger high heart disease among Orientals who use it frequently.

Doubts About Corn, Safflower and Sunflower Oils. The spotlight of scientific acclaim is definitely dimming on such highly polyunsaturated oils as corn, safflower and sunflower. As one expert says, "I think we oversold these oils." The shine is off corn oil, especially because in animals it lowers immunity and enhances cancer. Corn oil's most obvious fault is its high concentration of omega-6 fatty acids and absence of omega-3s. Ditto sunflower and safflower oils.

Such a skewed ratio in favour of omega-6 alarms many authorities. Omega-6, they say, incites cellular activities leading to lowered immunity, inflammation, blood clots, deadly heart arrhythmias, cancer and other disasters, whereas omega-3s cool down disease processes. When omega-6s so out number omega-3s within cells, theory goes, the destructive omega-6s have free rein to go on their cellular rampages.

Some authorities believe that, unfortunately, our cells are ruled and doomed by too much omega-6 and that most of it comes from an over-consumption of corn oil and similar oils.

TYPES OF FATTY ACIDS IN OILS
(IN PERCENTAGES)

Oil	Saturated	Mono-unsaturated	Polyunsaturated Omega-6	Omega-3
Flax	9	18	16	57
Pumpkin seed	9	34	42	15
Rapeseed	6	62	22	10
Soya	15	24	54	7
Walnut	16	28	51	5
Olive (Extra virgin)	14	77	8	1
Groundnut	18	49	33	
Corn	13	25	61	1
Safflower	10	13	77	
Sesame	13	46	41	
Sunflower	11	20	69	

Source: U.S. Department of Agriculture

Yoghurt: An Ancient Medicine Looks Better than Ever

Recommendation: Eat yoghurt regularly, especially if you are prone to upset stomach, infectious diarrhoea, ulcers, vaginal yeast infections or an "allergy" to milk (lactose intolerance).

The active bacteria in yoghurt can often help correct what is wrong in the stomach and colon, may boost immunity and may have other beneficial long-term effects even perhaps reducing the risk of colon cancer.

Yoghurt, one of the world's universal health foods, is more than just tangy, thickened milk. It has a venerable reputation, from biblical days, for settling the stomach and preventing and curing gastrointestinal maladies. Modern research decidedly proves that yoghurt contains several natural antibiotics that can kill infection-causing bacteria, including salmonella (the cause of salmonella food poisoning) and *E. coli* bacteria, often responsible for traveller's diarrhoea. And solid studies show that the acidophilus-type culture used to make some yoghurts can help block the activation of cancer-causing agents in the human colon.

Yoghurt's Therapeutic Secret. Yoghurt is teeming with quadrillions of living bacteria. It is the quantity and type of bacterial cultures and strains in yoghurt that create both its distinctive tangy taste and powers against disease. In the U.K. the manufacturers Code of Practice says they should make yoghurt by adding two cultures: *Lactobacillus bulgaricus and Streptococcus thermopolis*; plus any others of their choice. Companies may add acidophilus culture, one of the most health-promoting.

The bacteria convert milk into yoghurt by the process of fermentation. When subjected to a warm temperature, the microbes multiply rapidly, causing the milk protein to coagulate and thicken. The organisms even continue to multiply in the warm environment of the stomach and intestines. During fermentation the bacteria create numerous chemical by-products, such as lactic acid, that also fight disease.

New Reasons to Eat Yoghurt

Ulcer Fighter. As modern science discovers strange new causes of age-old diseases, foods, like yoghurt, emerge with unexpected powers to cure and prevent such maladies. For example, who a few years ago would have dreamed that stomach and duodenal ulcers may be partly or entirely due to an infection that promotes stomach acid damage—and that if you cure the basic infection, you are more likely to get rid of the ulcer? Yet that's what physicians are finding. They are also finding that yoghurt kills the particular bacterium, now called *Helicobacter pylori* (formerly named *Campylobacter pylori*), incriminated in both ulcers and gastritis, an inflammation of the stomach lining.

According to new studies, 95 per cent of people with duodenal ulcers are infected with *H. pylori*. So are almost three-quarters of sufferers with stomach ulcers and about half of those with gastritis. Some doctors now prescribe antibiotics to destroy the bacteria, promote healing and prevent recurrence of the ulcer.

"Yoghurt is an antibiotic that can do the same thing," says Dr. Jean Michel Antoine, an adviser on nutrition and toxicology at the BSN Groupe in Paris. When he and colleagues put the *H. pylori* bacteria in test tubes with yoghurt, all the bacteria died in thirty minutes. The question is this. Does yoghurt stay in the stomach long enough to zap the ulcer-promoting bacteria? "Yes," says Dr. Antoine. "Experiments show when you eat 1lb (450g) of yoghurt, about half ordinarily stays in the stomach for forty minutes. Since *H. pylori* pathogens are killed in thirty minutes, that's long enough for the yoghurt to destroy the bacteria," he says. The assassin is probably the *L. bulgaricus* culture in yoghurt, he adds.

This new research confirms animal studies of several years ago, showing that mice that ate yoghurt were less likely to develop ulcers.

Cure for Vaginitis. Another folk remedy scores points. For many years yoghurt has been used as a folk treatment for vaginitis, a recurring candida or "yeast" infection but the medical community was skeptical. Now a controlled study done by Dr. Eileen Hilton, an infectious disease specialist at Long Island Jewish Medical Center in New York, shows that eating yoghurt does indeed ward off the vaginal infections.

In fact, eating 8oz (225g) of yoghurt a day reduced the incidence of vaginitis threefold in a group of women susceptible to the infection. Whereas the women ordinarily had three vaginitis episodes in a six-month period, they had only one or none when eating natural yoghurt. Dr. Hilton called the results "dramatic". She says studies carried out in Europe show the same thing.

However, the therapeutic culture in yoghurt that fights vaginitis is *Lactobacillus acidophilus*—a culture that is not required in yoghurts made in the U.K. Some companies do add it. Some large manufacturers and many smaller yoghurt manufacturers also include *L. acidophilus*, which they may or may not note on the label. Take a good look at the small print. Some yoghurts may say *Lactobacillus acidophilus* or just *acidophilus*. Another wording that means *acidophilus* culture is "mild". This is an indication that the culture used does not produce an acid yoghurt. Many brands, including supermarket own brands, use *acidophilus* culture. Avoid any yoghurt that has the word "pasteurized", this means it has been heat treated after the addition of the cultures and they will no longer be active. The milk used will have been pasteurized before the cultures are added anyway. Some pots may say "live" or "active" but if you aren't sure whether yoghurt contains the *L. acidophilus* culture try making your own yoghurt using an acidophilus culture available at health food stores, Dr. Hilton suggests.

Immunity Booster. Exciting new human studies in Italy confirm animal and test-tube studies showing that yoghurt can boost immune functioning, meaning that yoghurt may have broader powers than first suspected in broadly combating disease. Dr. Claudio DeSimone, an immunologist at the University of Rome, has found that eating yoghurt boosted blood levels of gamma interferon in a group of volunteers.

Dr. DeSimone first determined that the group had similar levels of gamma interferon, a component of the immune system that rallies killer cells to fight off infections and possible cancer. Half of the group then ate about 2½lb (1.1kg) of yoghurt every day for four weeks. Half ate no yoghurt. At the end of the test yoghurt eaters had about two-and-a-half times more disease-fighting gamma interferon in their blood.

Although DeSimone used large amounts of yoghurt in his study, experts say smaller amounts of yoghurt would be expected to stimulate immune functioning to a lesser degree. DeSimone credits *L. bulgaricus* in yoghurt for the medical job. This particular culture should be in all U.K. yoghurts and is commonly used around the world to make yoghurt.

Lactose Intolerance. A large percentage of the world's population cannot drink milk or use dairy products because they lack the lactase enzyme needed to properly digest milk sugars, or lactose; thus drinking milk inflicts diarrhoea, bloating, flatulence, nausea and abdominal pain, a condition known as *lactose intolerance*. But such people can almost always eat yoghurt with no ill effects—a fact pinned down by new research.

Studies at the University of Minnesota by Dr. Dennis Savaino demonstrate that yoghurt reduces problems of lactose malabsorption by 50–100 per cent in most lactose-intolerant people. Once again the active agent is *L. bulgaricus* bacteria that reportedly chew up the offending lactose in the milk. In Dr. Savaino's tests neither buttermilk nor acidophilus milk, both lacking *L. bulgaricus*, was safe to drink for people with lactose intolerance. Nor were all yoghurts on the market. Some dairy manufacturers repasteurize yoghurt before packaging thus destroying the protective *L. bulgaricus* and other "good" cultures. This is often the case with frozen yoghurt desserts. It is not freezing which destroys the cultures.

New research also suggests that yoghurt may help fight dental caries and enhance absorption of calcium in the diet.

Without doubt, modern science is making this age-old medicine look better than at any time in its long history.

Hooray for the Hot Stuff!

Recommendation: Eat some garlic and onion every day. The bulbs contain chemicals that may help ward off numerous ills, including cardiovascular disease, diabetes, infections and cancer. Also eat more peppers, especially the fiery-hot ones, if you are vulnerable to lung or respiratory problems. All three of these foods are highly recommended for smokers and ex-smokers.

Listen to your ancestors. Listen to modern science. If there is a single bit of dietary advice that can boost your defence against disease easily, quickly and safely, it is to eat more onions, garlic and peppers!

The ancient reputation of these pungent foods as disease combatants is formidable and gaining credibility daily in scientific circles throughout the world. By finding ways to put garlic, onions and peppers into your diet, you supply your body with regular infusions of known and unknown compounds that protect cells from regular assaults that can result in numerous diseases, such as infections, cardiovascular disease and cancer.

Since the beginning of civilization humankind has used garlic, onions and peppers as natural medicines. Their inclusion in the diet has been advocated for many many reasons over many years. The scientific validity behind that practice is becoming clear.

In tests on humans garlic has been found to: lower cholesterol; raise good-type HDL cholesterol; lower blood pressure; produce more NK (natural killer) cells in the blood, cells that help fight off infections and tumours; inhibit blood platelet stickiness, reducing the risk of blood clots; destroy infection-causing bacteria and viruses; cure encephalitis and reduce the risk of certain cancers.

Onions, too, can dramatically boost good-type HDL cholesterol (when raw), lower total cholesterol even in people eating high-fat foods, rev up the blood-clot-dissolving activity, help control blood sugar, kill infection-causing bacteria, act as a decongestant and reduce cancer odds.

Peppers seem to be God's gift to the lungs. In ancient Chinese traditional medicine hot peppers were the drug of choice for many respiratory problems. They contain capsaicin, the stuff that provides their "bite" and also helps lungs function better, according to Dr. Irwin Ziment, professor of medicine and pulmonary expert at the University of California in Los Angeles.

New Reasons to Eat Onions, Garlic and Peppers

Anticancer Bulbs. American National Cancer Institute researchers have found that people in Shandong province of China, which is known for its high stomach cancer rate, have less cancer the more garlic and onions they eat. Chinese who eat at least a daily total of 3oz (85g) of garlic, onions, spring onions and leeks are only 40 per cent as likely to develop stomach cancer as those who eat only 1oz (30g) of the allium vegetables daily. In other words, those who skimped on eating garlic and onions were two-and-a-half times more vulnerable to stomach cancer. One small to medium raw onion or thirty cloves of garlic would be about 3oz (85g) in weight.

This is the first well-controlled study documenting the bulbs' anticancer powers in humans. It confirms studies showing that onion and garlic extracts suppress formation and spread of tumours in animals, according to William Blott, Ph. D., epidemiologist and biostatistician at the American National Cancer Institute.

Garlic Improves the Blood. New research is closing in on garlic's mechanisms for favourably modifying the blood, particularly blood-clotting factors that help stave off blood clots—the immediate cause of most heart attacks and strokes.

At Tulane University Dr. Krishna Agrawal, professor of pharmacology, has traced the biochemical pathway by which allicin—one of the odoriferous compounds in raw garlic—stops blood platelets from clumping together to help form blood clots. Infinitesimal amounts of allicin from both raw garlic and synthetic allicin halted a specific enzyme from instructing platelets to stick together. Aspirin also "thins" the blood but by working on a different enzyme. Like aspirin, garlic's allicin would be expected to be anti-inflammatory, says Dr. Agrawal, confirming folklore practices using garlic to curb inflammation and pain. Since the amounts of allicin needed to block platelet aggregation are so small, Dr. Agrawal says eating raw garlic probably has beneficial effects on the blood. But if you cook garlic, the allicin is destroyed.

However, other research by Drs. Amar Makheja and John M. Bailey, at George Washington University School of Medicine, has identified another onion-garlic chemical called *adenosine* as the primary blocker of platelet clumping in allium vegetables. They found that 46 per cent of such antiplatelet activity was due to adenosine. The good news here is that adenosine is not destroyed by cooking. Thus cooked garlic and onions, as well as raw ones, can help "thin" the blood, warding off clots, they say.

German researchers at the University of Heidelberg have found that garlic acts to ward off clots in another way. They gave dried garlic to twenty patients with high cholesterol and other blood fats. After four weeks of garlic eating the patients' blood levels of fibrinogen—an important protein that forms the basis for blood clots - went down. The famous Framingham (Massachusetts) Heart Study has noted that high fibrinogen is a prominent risk factor for heart disease—as dangerous as high blood pressure and high cholesterol. The German tests also found that garlic pushed down blood cholesterol levels by 10 per cent and reduced both systolic and diastolic blood pressure.

New Onion Power. Dr. Victor Gurewich, professor of medicine at Tufts University School of Medicine, advises all his patients with coronary heart disease or high cholesterol to eat more onions. He has found raw onions boost good HDL-type cholesterol by an average of 30 per cent. Even cooked, he finds onions help thin the blood and rev up the fibrinolytic system that wards off blood clots.

Now researchers at the University of California at Berkeley have identified a compound in onions that may be partly responsible for those benefits—plus more. It's quercetin, a powerful antioxidant and anticancer agent. Yellow and red onions and shallots have higher concentrations of quercetin than any other food. White onions, however, have none.

Not only does quercetin possess all the powers of an antioxidant, says researcher Dr. Terrance Leighton, but it has another critical role. It can shut off the growth control switch that allows cancer cells to go berserk and start wildly reproducing. Dr. Leighton explains that a principal way cancer cells escape ordinary control and grow abnormally is by activating a substance called *protein kinase C*. Quercetin blocks this activation so squelching release of protein kinase C.

Thus, with quercetin in your system, your cells are much less likely to be turned on to cancer. Incidentally, eating a high-animal-fat diet helps switch on the devastating protein kinase C switch. Dr. Leighton speculates this may be one reason people eating lots of animal fat tend toward certain cancers, especially of the colon. The cancer promoting activity of fatty meat may be blunted by the presence of quercetin from vegetables, primarily onions, he theorizes. Cooking does not destroy the quercetin so cooked onions are just as good in this respect as raw ones.

Bronchitis Preventive. UCLA's Dr. Ziment advises his patients with chronic bronchitis and emphysema to eat pungent foods, including garlic, onion and hot peppers, at least three times a week to help keep airway passages open and clear. In surveys among Hispanic populations he has also discovered that eating lots of hot, spicy foods lowers the chances of developing these smoking-related lung diseases. Dr. Ziment attributes the therapeutic benefit to capsaicin in the hot foods, the compound that gives peppers their fire.

There's new evidence giving Dr. Ziment's advice added validity. In British tests people with mild cases of asthma were able to breathe better after inhaling capsaicin; it dilated their air passages. Similarly, Austrian researchers cured all symptoms of a particular sinus problem (vasomotor rhinitis), including sinus headaches, by applying capsaicin to the inside lining of the nasal passages.

In a strange twist Joel Schwartz, a senior scientist at the Environmental Protection Agency, has discovered another compound in peppers that also seems to fight off lung disease—plain old vitamin C. His analysis of the diets of 9,000 adults found that those who eat foods containing 300 milligrams of vitamin C daily are only 70 per cent as likely to have a case of chronic bronchitis as those who eat foods providing 100 milligrams of C per day. Thus this vitamin, which is a potent antioxidant, may be one more reason peppers help protect lungs, particularly from the ravages of cigarette smoke.

Surprisingly few people know that peppers of all kinds, including ordinary mild green and red sweet peppers, are super sources of vitamin C, outranking the most common source, oranges. In fact one red pepper contains 140 milligrams of vitamin C compared with 70 milligrams in one orange; a green pepper contains 95 milligrams of vitamin C. Hot chilli peppers contain the same high concentrations of vitamin C. A 1½oz (45g) chilli pepper has about 110 milligrams of vitamin C. (For foods high in antioxidant vitamin C, see page 7.)

A Burning Question. Some people shun peppers, fearing they damage the stomach. But recent tests reveal that eating hot chilli peppers will not cause ulcers or otherwise harm normal stomachs. Researchers at Baylor College of Medicine in Houston, by taking photos of stomach cells flooded with hot peppers, have disproved the suspicion that spicy foods irritate or inflict damage on the lining of ordinary stomachs.

The researchers asked twelve healthy volunteers to eat four different test meals and then examined their stomachs via videoendoscopy—a procedure that takes close-up pictures of the interior stomach surface. None of the subjects ordinarily ate spicy foods. Meal number one was a bland steak, potatoes and peas dinner; two was the same dinner plus three aspirin tablets; three was a Mexican meal with 1oz (30g) of jalapeño peppers; and four was a pizza with 1¼oz (35g) of pepperoni sausage.

There was no evidence of harm (cell erosion or bleeding) after any of the meals except those containing aspirin.

Just to be sure, the investigators ground up 1oz (30g) of fresh jalapeño pepper in a food processor and dumped it directly into stomachs through a tube. Still no damage.

The conclusion: eating highly spiced meals does not cause visible stomach or duodenal damage to the lining in normal individuals.

If peppers bother you, you shouldn't eat them. However, even if you have an ulcer, such peppers need not be banned from your diet. Research in India a few years ago found that eating chillies did not hinder the healing of duodenal ulcers. One group of ulcer patients was given a normal hospital diet without peppers. Another group additionally got three grams of red chilli powder daily—the average amount consumed in the Indian diet. At the end of four weeks the healing rate in the two groups was identical. And the pepper eaters showed no damage to the stomach lining.

Do your health a favour and remember to eat garlic, onions and peppers regularly. Have them raw or cooked; chop them, mince them, put them in casseroles or on hamburgers; use them as a flavouring, as a side dish, as a vegetable, or as a condiment.

PART TWO

New Food Pharmacy
Facts, Cook's Advice,
Doctor's Advice,
Recommendations
and Recipes

Food Pharmacy Bottom-Line Recommendations

Here are the most important food pharmacy recommendations for better health and a longer life.

- Eat more fruits and vegetables. The evidence is overwhelming that people who eat more fruits and vegetables enjoy better health—have lower rates of cancer, heart attacks and strokes as well as certain other chronic diseases. Strive for at least five servings every day.

- Use fresh fruits and vegetables when possible, they contain more active pharmacological agents. Freezing does not seem to destroy the beneficial agents significantly but canning may.

- Eat vegetables raw as well as cooked to be sure you are getting maximum benefit. Some pharmacological agents are diminished or destroyed by heat. The best way to preserve pharmacological agents in cooked food is to use a microwave oven.

- Eat some garlic and onion every day. The bulbs may help prevent numerous problems, including cardiovascular disease and cancer. Use fresh garlic and onions. Garlic and onion powder or salt lack the active ingredients needed for a therapeutic effect.

- Eat more beans. Probably no other food is as underrated as the lowly legume; that includes all kinds of haricot beans, black beans, pinto beans, broad beans, butter beans, chickpeas, soya beans, split peas and lentils. All pack a powerful therapeutic and disease-preventive punch. Eat some soya bean products, including tofu (soya bean curd).

- Be sure to eat yoghurt that contains live cultures, preferably yoghurt that includes acidophilus cultures. Be aware that if you heat yoghurt you destroy the cultures along with much of the therapeutic benefit.

- Eat seafood at least twice a week or more, especially the fattier fishes like salmon, tuna, mackerel, sardines and herring. It's okay to include some shellfish. Mussels, clams and oysters are particularly high in beneficial omega-3 fatty acids. Scallops are rock-bottom low in fat. Although shellfish has a reputation for being high in cholesterol, most types, except squid, have only moderate amounts. Tests show that eating shellfish generally benefits blood cholesterol. Shrimp or prawns appear to be neutral— neither lowering nor raising cholesterol.

• Grill, bake, steam, barbecue or poach fish, using little or no fat. Frying seafood, especially deep-frying, increases seafood's fat content about twelve times, according to research. Such fat can flood the cells with undesirable types of polyunsaturated fatty acids, undoing some of the benefits of eating seafood in the first place.

• Eat less meat, but if you do eat meat, be doubly sure to eat lots of fruits and vegetables for studies indicate that these are apt to help soften some hazards of eating meat, notably cancer. Try to think of meat as Asians do, not as a main course but as just one more ingredient in a main dish that incorporates vegetables, legumes and grains.

• Eat less fat. Probably no other item in your diet has more pharmacological impact on the functioning of your cells than fat. The health of your cells depends on the amount and type of fat and the proper ratio of each. Generally considered worst are saturated dairy and animal fats. The best are omega-3 fish fat and monounsaturated fat found in olives, avocados and almonds. Also excellent are rapeseed oil and flaxseed oil. When possible, use *extra-virgin* olive oil.

• Trim meat of all visible fat. Remove skin from poultry. Substitute low-fat or yoghurt for soured cream. Use a very-low-fat skimmed milk instead of whole milk. Go easy on butter and high-fat cheese and also on margarine, as well as corn, soya bean, and safflower oils, all containing high amounts of omega-6 fatty acids that are increasingly suspect as disease contributors. Trimming the fat off meat and poultry to be barbecued also makes it safer because it is less likely to drip fat and create smoke that rises and deposits cancer-causing agents on the surface of the food.

• Eat only moderate amounts of cholesterol. Old evidence stated that eating cholesterol, as in egg yolks, actually raised blood cholesterol levels in only 30–50 per cent of individuals. So some people may have thought they didn't have to worry. However, new evidence suggests that those who eat the most cholesterol trim several years off their life spans, regardless of any effect on blood cholesterol.

• Whether or not you have high cholesterol, restrict your intake of egg yolks, (not white) even though each yolk has about 213 milligrams of cholesterol, 22 per cent less than previously thought. The European Atherosclerosis Society advises not more than four yolks a week.

• If you are a smoker, or have been a smoker in the last ten years, be sure to eat foods rich in antioxidants. They may help block the development of smoking-related diseases such as lung and throat cancer and chronic bronchitis. Such foods include carrots (beta-carotene), green leafy vegetables (folic acid, various carotenoids, quercetin, indoles, glutathione, vitamin C) and oranges (vitamin C). Broccoli is an all-around antioxidant superstar. However, no diet can fight damage from continued smoking.

• If you have polyps (small growths) of the colon which increase your risk of colon cancer, eat more high-fibre wheat cereals, such as a serving of All-Bran once or twice a day and vegetables, notably cruciferous vegetables (cabbage, broccoli, Brussels sprouts, kale, cauliflower).

• If you have a history of strokes in your family, be sure to eat lots of high-potassium foods, which have been shown to dramatically lower stroke risk. (For such foods, see page 21.)

• If you are worried about lung and breathing problems, eat more pungent, hot foods, such as onions, garlic and fiery chilli peppers. Hot peppers are highly recommended for smokers or ex-smokers and people with emphysema, chronic bronchitis, sinus problems, bronchial asthma or congestion due to a cold.

• If you drink alcohol, limit it to two drinks a day and make it wine or beer. Both wine and beer in low doses have medicinal properties that may help ward off cardiovascular disease and promote longevity. More than two drinks a day can shorten life.

• Drink small amounts of caffeine if it makes you feel better. Studies show that moderate amounts of caffeine and coffee drinking do not seem to encourage heart disease or other chronic diseases. Low doses (a cup or two a day) can elevate mood and increase mental concentration and performance but caffeine is highly individual in its effects. If it makes you jittery or produces other adverse effects, avoid it. Caffeine is addictive.

• Use restraint in eating sodium. The old theory was that sodium's only danger was raising blood pressure and thus only certain people prone to high blood pressure and in whom salt acts as a booster need worry. New theory, according to animal studies is that sodium may harm arteries, leading to death, in ways independent of raising blood pressure. Also, research shows that high-salt diets cause the body to lose more calcium, which could be quite detrimental to the bones of older women.

• Use common sense. Don't eat large amounts of only a few fruits, vegetables, grains, legumes or seafood while avoiding others. Various plant foods have varying pharmacological benefit and science is not yet advanced enough to know where a new natural drug of critical importance may turn up. Also, overdosing on anything can be hazardous and all plants contain toxins and carcinogens as well as antitoxins and anticarcinogens.

• At present it's wisest to choose from a wide range of such foods, although admittedly it also makes sense to eat those for which there is substantial evidence of specific benefit. As Dr. James Duke, expert on medicinal plants at the U.S. Department of Agriculture, says, "Variety in your diet may not only be the spice of life; it may be the guardian of life."

• Do not substitute food remedies for current medications without consulting with your physician. Often food and medicine can work together for increased benefit, resulting in lower doses of a medication. But such an experiment needs monitoring by a physician for benefits as well as adverse effects.

A Word About the Recipes

Obviously the recipes have been chosen for their specific therapeutic and disease-preventive potential. Additionally, all have been analysed nutritionally by Hill Nutrition Associates to determine their calorie, fat, cholesterol, sodium, vitamin and mineral contents.

Low in Fat. Because fat is detrimental to good health in many ways, the recipes are consistently low in fat. When the fat content is relatively high, it comes from monounsaturated fat, as in olive oil, nuts and seeds, or omega-3-type fat in seafood. You will find very little saturated fat, from meat and dairy products, in the recipes.

How to Make Low-Fat Recipes Even Lower in Fat. Even so, if you wish, you can further reduce fat in the recipes. Many recipes in the book follow the tradition of sautéing or stir-frying onions, garlic and other vegetables in small amounts of oil, usually a tablespoonful. Often you can get by with a teaspoon or two of oil or sometimes none in a nonstick pan. Also, you can reduce the fat needed for sautéing to virtually zero if you skip the oil and simply blanch the onion, garlic and other vegetables in a small amount of water, defatted chicken or vegetable stock, wine, tomato juice or other nonfat liquids. Microwaving is an excellent way to soften vegetables without any added fat. Simply put the vegetables in a dish with a small amount of nonfat liquid, cover and microwave. After the vegetables are softened, continue with the recipe.

Low in Cholesterol. The recipes are also low in cholesterol. When some is present, it is almost always from sources that are highly beneficial in other ways, such as seafood. In recipes that call for eggs—of which there are very few in this book—you can use egg substitutes. Be aware that egg substitutes sometimes have three times the amount of sodium as a whole egg. You can also cut back on the egg yolk. If a recipe calls for two eggs, use one whole egg and two egg whites.

Low in Sodium. The ingredients used in the recipes are almost always very low in sodium. Noted exceptions are canned anchovies, sardines and mackerel, which however, are full of beneficial omega-3 oil. What generally raises the sodium content of recipes is added salt. Because of the great variations in salt preference and tolerance and to give you the widest options, in this book no specific amount of salt is called for except in rare cases. The recipes nearly always call for "salt to taste". This means that added salt has not been calculated in the nutritional analysis of the recipes; only the amount of natural sodium in ingredients has been counted. Thus adding salt raises the sodium count; one teaspoon of salt contains about 2,000 milligrams of sodium.

When chicken stock is an ingredient, you can make your own, adding as little or as much salt as you like. The recipes just call for chicken stock, but the sodium count is based on stock containing 66 milligrams of sodium per $1/2$ pint (285ml). Those who find this unpalatable can substitute stock with more sodium but be aware that most readily available commercial stock cubes are very high sodium indeed.

Since standard canned tomato juice can be fairly high in sodium, the tomato juice used in the recipes is "low sodium," containing about 15 milligrams of sodium per $1/4$ pint (140ml). Be aware that if you substitute normal tomato juice the sodium count can be about 550 milligrams per $1/4$ pint (140ml). Of course, if you want an in-between salty taste you can use low-sodium tomato juice and add a little extra salt. Canned tomatoes can be sieved for a very low-sodium alternative.

When butter or margerine is an ingredient, the analysis figures assume that it is lightly salted. If you use unsalted butter or margarine, the sodium count will go down slightly.

Pepper. Unless otherwise designated, pepper called for in the recipes is black. Here, too, the amount is generally left up to your taste buds. Freshly ground black pepper straight from a pepper mill is preferable because it is coarsely ground and has more flavour and punch. Thus freshly ground pepper is called for in the recipes. Of course you can substitute ready-to-use finely ground black pepper if you wish. Or you can also buy ready-to-use pepper that is coarsely ground. But if you don't already have one, a pepper mill is a good, inexpensive investment.

A Tomato Tip. When a recipe calls for fresh tomatoes that are to be cooked and the only ones around are the hard, tough, tasteless variety, you are better off substituting canned whole tomatoes. The usual canned plum tomatoes are especially good for cooking as their flavour has the sweetness and intensity of a ripe tomato all year round. Simply chop the canned tomato and substitute if for the amount of fresh tomato in the recipe. I've done that when making many of the recipes in this book and the results are terrific. Of course canned tomatoes cannot substitute in recipes requiring fresh tomatoes to be used raw.

How to Read the Nutrient Analysis. When an ingredient is listed as optional, it is not included in the analysis. In all cases the first ingredient or measure is the one included in the analysis when a choice of ingredients and amounts is given. If a recipe states that it serves "4–6," the nutrient analysis is for four, not six; the more conservative first serving size is used. If you divide a recipe into more servings, the calorie, fat, cholesterol and sodium counts will be lower.

Appetizers, Starters and Snacks

Quick Mexican Bean Dip

About 1 pint (570ml)

This is a quick and simple cholesterol-reducing dip with no added fat. It's great for a party. You whip it up in a blender in thirty seconds. And, of course, you can easily double or triple the recipe to serve a crowd. If you want more seasoning, add a couple of tablespoons of chilli sauce or Mexican salsa, a finely chopped jalapeño pepper or a tablespoon of chopped coriander.

2 x 15oz (425g) cans pinto beans, 1 can drained
1¹/₂ teaspoons ground cumin or to taste
¹/₄ teaspoon chilli powder or to taste
¹/₄–³/₄ teaspoon Tabasco sauce or to taste
2 teaspoons lemon juice
Salt to taste

Place the drained can of beans in a food processor or blender. Add the other can of beans with their liquid. Add the cumin, chilli powder, Tabasco sauce, lemon juice and salt. Blend at high speed until it becomes smooth and creamy.

Serve with fresh vegetables, tortillas or crackers.

Note For a thicker dip, drain both cans of beans before processing.

Per tablespoon:

Calories	16
Total fat	.03g
Saturated fat	0
Cholesterol	0
Sodium	80mg

FOOD PHARMACY FACT
No Beans About It

Eating dried beans—legumes—can depress blood cholesterol whether you are on a low-fat or high-fat diet. Dr. James Anderson at the University of Kentucky College of Medicine found that eating 7oz (200g) of cooked beans, such as navy or pinto beans or even canned baked beans, every day decreased blood cholesterol an average of 19 per cent. And the beans worked on people eating a moderately high-fat diet—36 per cent of calories from fat. Dr. David Jenkins at the University of Toronto found that a daily regimen of beans (kidney beans, pinto beans, chickpeas or red or green lentils) depressed cholesterol an average of 7 per cent in men with high cholesterol who were already on a low-fat diet.

Guacamole

Serves 2

The secret to good guacamole is an extra-ripe avocado. After that I prefer this very simple version. Avocado, contrary to what you have heard, will not kill you with all its fat. In fact the fat is mostly the same good type as found in olive oil. However, the avocado is high-fat and fairly high in calories—so it should be regarded as a treat, not an everyday staple.

    1 small to medium avocado, peeled, stoned and cut into chunks
    1 teaspoon lemon juice (more if needed to preserve
        the avocado's colour)
    1 garlic clove, crushed
    1 tablespoon finely chopped onion
    1 heaped tablespoon coarsely chopped tomato
    5 drops Tabasco sauce or to taste
    Salt and freshly ground pepper to taste

In a bowl, mash the avocado coarsely. Add the remaining ingredients and mix but do not purée.

Serve with vegetables and/or tortilla chips (recipe follows).

    Per serving:
        Calories   147
        Total fat   13 g
        Saturated fat   2 g
        Cholesterol   0
        Sodium   16 mg

Low-fat Tortilla Chips

Lightly brush both sides of a corn tortilla with olive oil. Cut into quarters. Put on a baking sheet in the oven at 190°C/375°F/Gas 5 for 12–15 minutes or until crisp.

IN DEFENCE OF THE AVOCADO

The avocado is often maligned because it is high in fat. But the fact is most of the fat in an avocado is good fat. Fully 70 per cent of the fat in a California avocado and 60 per cent in a Florida avocado is monounsaturated; that's the same type that predominates in olive oil and is credited with olive oil's artery-protecting, heart-disease-fighting properties.

Moreover, the monounsaturated fat in avocado is 95 per cent oleic acid and that's good news because oleic acid, researchers recently discovered, is an antioxidant. That means it can help destroy vicious disease-causing oxygen free radicals. Oleic acid is the stuff that makes up virtually all of olive oil's monounsaturated fat, which is so widely heralded by scientists for its anti-artery-clogging, cholesterol-lowering abilities. If oleic acid makes olive oil the lifesaver it is, then the avocado qualifies too. Additionally, avocado contains lots of stroke-fighting potassium.

THE WONDROUS MEDITERRANEAN DIET

For a quarter of a century scientists have been marvelling over something they call "the Mediterranean diet". They think it is a prime reason that people of southern Italy and Greece, countries bordering the Mediterranean Sea and the Mediterranean island of Crete, have some of the lowest rates of heart disease in the world. If only other Europeans and Americans, they say, would eat more like Mediterranean peoples, heart disease rates would drop. And what does that mean? According to Gene Spiller, director of the Health Research and Studies Center, Los Altos, California and author of a book *The Mediterranean Diets in Health and Disease*, it means more fruit, vegetables, seafood and monounsaturated fats, such as olive oil. It means less fatty meat and cheese.

Surprisingly, people practising this diet do not necessarily eat a Spartan, fatless diet. In fact, in Crete the population eats more than 40 per cent of its calories in fat, but the fat calories come almost entirely from olive oil and nuts—the monounsaturated-type fat — and seafood with its omega-3s. Thus all fat is not always bad— indeed it may even be protective—if it's the Mediterranean type. If the rest of the diet too is "Mediterranean"—rich in fruits and vegetables—the benefits may be wondrous indeed.

Tzatziki

About 1¹/₂ pints (850ml)

If you've ever been to Greece or even to a Greek restaurant, you know how tempting this cucumber and yoghurt mixture is when scooped on to bread, eaten alone or used as a sauce. And don't forget that the cultures in yoghurt fight off bacteria like E. coli, the most common cause of "traveller's diarrhoea". I normally eat yoghurt but I make it a special point to do so when I travel in foreign countries where upset stomach and gastrointestinal bugs are apt to be problems. This tzatziki is a delicious way to get protection—at home or away. Thanks to Mary and Lee Koromvokis, who have made this authentic tzatziki more times than they can remember.

3 cucumbers, peeled, seeded, and finely chopped
1 small onion, finely chopped
2 garlic cloves, finely chopped (more if desired)
1lb 10oz (735g) natural very-low-fat yoghurt

Mix all ingredients together and refrigerate for at least 2 hours so flavours blend.

Note To make a thicker tzatziki, use 2–2¹/₂lb (900g–1.1kg) yoghurt and let it drain for two or three hours, as in making yoghurt cheese. (See page 73).

Per 4 tablespoons (60ml) serving:

Calories	31
Total fat	.1g
Saturated fat	.06g
Cholesterol	1mg
Sodium	35mg

Chickpea Dip
(Hummus)

Serves 6

Of all the hummus recipes I have seen, I think this is the best. You can make it in a jiffy and feel virtuous eating it because chickpeas are one of the richest sources of anticancer compounds called protease inhibitors. *Chickpeas also help lower blood cholesterol. Use this as a dip for vegetables or spread for all kinds of bread; the traditional one is pitta. It's great as an appetizer, sprinkled with parsley or a snack or sandwich. It also freezes well. Nearly all the fat, of which 87 per cent is unsaturated, comes from the tahini, which is high in antioxidant vitamin E.*

> 1lb (450g) can chickpeas, drained
> 8 tablespoons tahini (sesame seed paste)
> Juice of 2 lemons
> 1 teaspoon chopped garlic
> Salt to taste
> 1/4 teaspoon ground cumin
> Chopped parsley to garnish

Place all ingredients except the parsley in the bowl of a food processor or blender. Process until the mixture is smooth. Serve chilled or at room temperature, sprinkled with chopped parsley.

Per serving:

Calories	212
Total fat	11g
Saturated fat	1.6g
Cholesterol	0
Sodium	249mg

✔

FOOD PHARMACY FACT
Olive Oil: The Winner!

Olive oil is better than a low-fat diet in lowering cholesterol, report researchers at the Catholic University of Nijmegen in the Netherlands. In the study of forty-eight healthy people, half ate a low-fat diet (22 per cent of calories from fat) and the other half ate a high-fat diet (41 per cent of calories from fat) but the fat was almost entirely monounsaturated, as in olive oil. After thirty-six days the average blood cholesterol of the low-fat group fell seventeen points, with the good-type HDLs down three points. The cholesterol of the olive-oil eaters, although they had eaten nearly twice as much fat per day, dropped even more—by twenty points, with no reduction in protective HDLs. (These figures are given in milligrams per 100 millilitres and on this scale an average Western blood cholesterol level is 212.)

The point is not to overdose on olive oil, which can add lots of unwanted calories, but to substitute olive oil for other saturated animal fats and polyunsaturated oils (like corn and safflower). In other words, when you must eat fat, make it olive oil.

Rena's Syrian Baba Ghanouj
(Aubergine Dip)

Serves 4

What makes this Baba Ghanouj so authentic is both its first-generation Syrian origin and the plentiful amount of lemon juice, which, Rena Dweck says, is what makes it taste so good. She has been making it for fifty years, just as her grandmother did but it's not only taste that makes it special. Aubergine, several studies show, has properties that help protect the arteries and lower blood cholesterol, even helping fight some ill effects of high saturated fat in meat and dairy products.

1 large aubergine, pierced with a fork in several places
8 tablespoons tahini (sesame seed paste) or more to taste
3 medium garlic cloves, finely chopped
Salt to taste
1/4 pint (140ml) lemon juice (more if needed)
1/2 teaspoon ground cumin
Chopped parsley for garnish

Preheat the grill, then grill the aubergine, turning it at least once, until it is soft to the touch. The skin will be charred.

When cool, split the aubergine lengthwise and remove the pulp, discarding the skin.

In a bowl, combine the aubergine pulp, tahini, garlic, salt and lemon juice, stirring well to blend flavours. Add cumin and stir again.

Sprinkle parsley on top. Serve with toasted or heated pitta bread.

Per serving:

Calories	173
Total fat	11g
Saturated fat	1.5g
Cholesterol	0
Sodium	38mg

Radicchio with Garlic

Serves 4

For a taste adventure, try lightly grilling or barbecuing radicchio as Italians do. This red leaf chicory is full of carotenoids, as revealed by the reddish colour. The garlic and olive oil are good for your cardiovascular system. Balsamic vinegar is a dark mellow vinegar with a sweet-sour flavour. It is only made around Modena in northern Italy and is concentrated, fermented grape juice aged in wooden barrels. It is expensive but a little goes a long way. It is available from Italian delicatessens and quality grocers.

2 orange-size heads radicchio
1 tablespoon olive oil
4 garlic cloves, finely chopped
4 teaspoons balsamic vinegar or to taste
Salt and freshly ground pepper to taste

Cut the heads of radicchio in half. Sprinkle the cut side of each piece of radicchio with ³/₄ teaspoon of olive oil and a quarter of the garlic.

Preheat the grill and place the radicchio halves under the heat source on the lowest position for 2–3 minutes or until the top is slightly browned. Or put cut side down on a barbecue for a minute or two. The radicchio should be slightly heated but still crisp.

Drizzle a teaspoon of balsamic vinegar or more on each half. Add salt and pepper to taste. Serve as an appetizer, salad or vegetable.

Per serving:
Calories	55
Total fat	3.7g
Saturated fat	.5g
Cholesterol	0
Sodium	11mg

Bruschetta

Serves 6

"Once you've lived in Italy, one thing you can never do without is bruschetta," says my friend Kathleen Drew. It's the original garlic bread. She prepares it in summer on the barbecue and in winter under the grill. In both cases you can just serve the ingredients and let the guests make their own. Be sure to use good-quality olive oil. This simple appetizer is undoubtedly one more reason for Italians' healthy hearts.

> 6 slices crusty Italian bread
> 3 garlic cloves, peeled and cut in half
> 2 tablespoons extra-virgin olive oil
> 1–2 tablespoons chopped fresh basil
> Salt and freshly ground pepper to taste
> 6 plum tomatoes, chopped

Toast the bread. While the bread is still hot, rub cut garlic over one side of each slice. Drizzle on a teaspoon of olive oil. In the meantime, add the basil, salt and pepper to the tomatoes.

Top the bread with a portion of the seasoned tomatoes.

Per serving:
Calories	126
Total fat	5 g
Saturated fat	.7g
Cholesterol	.3mg
Sodium	169mg

FOOD PHARMACY FACT
Garlic vs. Cancer

In tests by Sidney Belman at New York University Medical Center, animals that had garlic and onion oils rubbed on to their skin were not as likely to develop skin cancer. Similarly, Michael Wargovich at the University of Texas System Cancer Center in Houston exposed animals to cancer-causing agents, then fed half of them a dose of diallyl sulphide, a compound in garlic. The garlic chemical prevented colon cancer in 75 per cent of the animals.

I Matti's Beans and Onions

Serves 4

What makes these beans distinctive is the large amount of onion, says Roberto Donna, a distinguished chef and owner of I Matti and Galileo, two of Washington, D.C.'s highly-rated Italian restaurants. I have had the dish often at I Matti and made it many times. You can serve the beans as a side dish or as an appetizer heaped on to a slice of thick, sturdy Italian bread, as they do at the restaurant. Then it's called bruschetta al fagioli e cipolla and unquestionably it's good for your health.

    1 large onion, chopped
    2 tablespoons olive oil (less if desired)
    19oz (540g) can cannellini beans with liquid
    1¹/₂ tablespoons chopped fresh sage *or* 1 teaspoon dried, crushed
        1 teaspoon dried thyme
    1 teaspoon balsamic vinegar (optional)

In a large skillet, sauté the onion in the olive oil over medium heat until the onions are translucent and soft. Add the beans, sage and thyme and cook over low heat for about 20–30 minutes. Add the vinegar if desired. Serve at room temperature or lightly chilled with Italian bread.

    Per serving:
        Calories   184
        Total fat   7g
        Saturated fat   1g
        Cholesterol   0
        Sodium   468mg

Dr. David's Caponata
(Aubergine Appetizer)

Serves 12 (3½–4 pints/2–2.2 litres)

*Caponata is a kind of ratatouille, except it has vinegar and sugar and I
can definitely say this version is the best I have ever had. It is made often
by Dr. David Rall, former director of the American National Institute of
Environmental and Health Sciences, the government group that does all
those studies to ferret out which compounds may cause cancer. You can
be sure this recipe has all the right cancer-fighting stuff.*

2 medium aubergines, total weight 2lb (900g)
Salt
2–3 tablespoons olive oil
3 medium onions, thinly sliced
4 celery stalks, sliced
4–8oz (115–225g) Calamata or other black olives, stoned and halved
28oz (795g) can plum tomatoes, chopped
5 tablespoons drained capers
3 tablespoons raisins
3 tablespoons pine nuts
4 tablespoons red wine vinegar
1 tablespoon sugar
Salt and freshly ground pepper to taste

Peel the skin from one aubergine. (This is for variety so some pieces
still have skin.) Cut both into 1 inch (2.5cm) cubes. Put the cubes in a
colander and sprinkle generously with salt. Allow to stand for about 20
minutes to draw out moisture and bitterness. Rinse with cold water to
remove some of the salt.

Put the olive oil in a large saucepan and sauté the onions and celery
until translucent and soft. Blot the aubergine cubes with paper towels,

then add them to the pan and sauté for about 20–25 minutes, until the aubergine is cooked but not mushy.

Add the remaining ingredients and simmer for about 10 minutes.

Per serving:
Calories	93
Total fat	4.6g
Saturated fat	.6g
Cholesterol	0
Sodium	388mg

Gazpacho Vegetable Pâté

Serves 6

What a powerhouse of vitamin C is this brightly coloured and taste-filled appetizer or salad. And it's so refreshing—very pretty too, when served as part of a buffet dinner. Need I say that it has very high protective value for your cardiovascular system and a great deal of anticancer potential?

28oz (795g) can plum tomatoes
2 medium green peppers, or one green and one yellow
1 cucumber, peeled, and seeded
1 medium onion
2 tablespoons olive oil
3 tablespoons tomato purée
3 tablespoons red wine vinegar
Salt to taste
2 teaspoons ground cumin
$^1/_2$ teaspoon celery seed
$^1/_4$ teaspoon cayenne pepper
3 tablespoons (3 packages) unflavoured gelatine
4fl oz (115ml) dry white wine
1 ripe but not soft avocado, peeled, stoned and cubed
Watercress or shredded lettuce to garnish
Reduced-calorie mayonnaise for serving (optional)

In a food processor or blender, purée the plum tomatoes, 1 green pepper, the cucumber, onion, olive oil, tomato purée, vinegar, salt, cumin, celery seed and cayenne. Transfer to a large bowl.

In a small bowl, sprinkle the gelatine over the wine and place the bowl in a larger bowl filled with hot water. Stir until the gelatine is dissolved.

Stir the dissolved gelatine into the vegetable purée. Mix in the cubed avocado and remaining green pepper, finely chopped.

Oil a 9 x 5inch (23 x 13cm) loaf tin and pour in the mixture. Chill up to several days before serving or until the mixture is firm and set.

To unmould, run a small knife around the edges of the tin and dip the tin into hot water for a couple of seconds. Invert on to a flat surface. Slice the pâté about 1 inch (2.5cm) thick and place on individual salad plates garnished with watercress or shredded lettuce. Add a dollop of reduced-calorie mayonnaise if you wish.

Per serving:
Calories	157
Total fat	10g
Saturated fat	1.5g
Cholesterol	0
Sodium	272mg

✔

FOOD PHARMACY FACT
Veggies vs. Cataracts

In a group of people between ages forty and seventy, those who had the highest levels of carotenoids in their blood were only 18 per cent as likely to have cataracts as those with the lowest carotenoid levels, reported researchers at U.S. Agriculture Department's Human Research Center on Aging at Tufts University in Boston. Nearly half of all Americans over age seventy-five have cataracts, which causes the lens to become opaque, reducing eyesight. Carotenoids in the blood come from eating fruits and vegetables—especially tomatos, carrots and dark green leafy vegetables.

Yoghurt Cheese

You can easily convert yoghurt into a soft, creamy "cheese" without the calories and fat of ordinary cheese and with lots of medicinal value. If you have never done this, try it, for it will give you a whole new world of possibilities for using this ancient medicinal food with its newly documented benefits.

All you do is take natural very-low-fat or low-fat yoghurt made without gelatine or other setting agent and drain it until it loses most of its liquid and becomes like a soft cheese. Low-fat yoghurt forms a slightly firmer, thicker cheese than very-low-fat yoghurt.

Put the yoghurt in a colander or strainer lined with a porous material— for example, several layers of muslin or a cotton tea towel. You could also use a jelly bag. Put the colander or strainer in a bowl to collect the excess moisture. Refrigerate overnight or for at least five hours. The longer you strain the yoghurt, the thicker it tends to become. 2lb (900g) of yoghurt will make from 12oz–1lb (340–450g) of yoghurt cheese.

Use this cheese as a base to make spreads, dips, low-fat desserts, cheese balls or logs and sauces. It can almost double for fat-rich cream cheese. It is also an excellent substitute for soured cream or crème fraîche. Use a dollop of yoghurt cheese to top soups and omelettes instead of soured cream.

Yoghurt Cheese and Lox

Serves 8

This can really satisfy people who love cream cheese and lox but don't like all the saturated fat in cream cheese. Most people think it is a high-fat cheese but it has the rich taste of cheese without the fat. And the fat you get from the lox is good fat that helps your heart and the rest of your body. You can use it as a dip or as a spread on crackers—or, of course, on bagels, where it belongs.

8oz (225g) very-low-fat yoghurt cheese (see page 73)
2oz (55g) lox or smoked salmon, chopped
4 tablespoons finely chopped spring onions, including green tops
Salt and freshly ground pepper to taste

Combine all ingredients and chill for at least an hour to let flavours blend.

Per serving:

Calories	35
Total fat	.4g
Saturated fat	.1g
Cholesterol	3mg
Sodium	173mg

Herbed Yoghurt Cheese

Serves 8

If you love Boursin or herb-flavoured goat cheese but don't love the all saturated fat and calories, this is an excellent substitute. Serve it with crusty French bread, crackers, or vegetables. It is also excellent served with fresh tomatoes.

8oz (225g) very-low-fat yoghurt cheese (page 73)
1 tablespoon finely chopped spring onion
1 tablespoon finely chopped parsley
1 tablespoon finely chopped fresh basil
1 teaspoon finely chopped garlic
Salt and freshly ground pepper to taste

Put the yoghurt cheese into a small bowl. Stir in the spring onion, parsley, basil, garlic, salt and pepper.

Per serving:
Calories	27
Total fat	.1g
Saturated fat	.1g
Cholesterol	1mg
Sodium	31mg

Yoghurt Roquefort Walnut Dip

About 7fl oz (200ml)

Try this dip using slices of fruit as a scoop. It's marvellous with pears. You can also slice fresh pears and put a dollop of the dip on top. Or halve pears, scoop out the cores, and fill with dip. It's also good with crackers but it makes a superb appetizer surrounded by slices of apple and pear. The Roquefort adds some saturated fat but not much because little Roquefort is needed to produce a strong flavour.

4oz (115g) very-low-fat yoghurt cheese (page 73)
³/₄oz (20g) Roquefort cheese
1oz (30g) chopped walnuts

Blend together the yoghurt and Roquefort cheeses. Mix in the walnuts and refrigerate the dip.

Per tablespoon:
Calories	26
Total fat	1.7g
Saturated fat	.4g
Cholesterol	1.4mg
Sodium	31mg

PHARMACEUTICAL NUTS

Some people shun nuts because they are high in fat. True, they are. But nuts are a terrific pharmacological package. Nuts are definitely not just a high-fat, empty-calorie food. If you do not eat nuts, you may cheat yourself of vitamin E, an antioxidant linked to lower rates of cancer. Walnuts also are extremely high in the marvellous omega-3 fatty acids, as well as antioxidants, such as ellagic acid. Almonds, hazelnuts and pistachio nuts are all rich sources of mono-unsaturated fat, in particular oleic acid, which has recently been revealed as an antioxidant. Eating almonds has lowered blood cholesterol in human tests. One major study decidedly linked low rates of heart disease with consumption of nuts. People who eat nuts seem to have a lower risk of Parkinson's disease.

As Dr. David Jenkins, University of Toronto, points out, the almond is full of the right stuff; most of its fat is monounsaturated; it is exceptionally low in saturated fat (even lower than olive oil); it is full of vegetable protein and fibre. It also helps keep blood sugar and insulin levels steady and thus may help fight high blood pressure, diabetes, obesity and general atherosclerotic damage. Nuts also have anticancer compounds.

This does not mean, of course, you should risk gaining weight by eating a large quantity of nuts. But it does suggest that nuts, as Dr. Jenkins says, are a potent pharmaceutical food and should be included in a healthy diet.

✔

FOOD PHARMACY FACT
Shellfish Vindicated

It's official. It's okay—in fact, advisable—to eat oysters, clams, mussels and crabs. That's what Dr. Marian Childs, a lipid expert at the University of Washington, says after feeding the shellfish to men with normal cholesterol. When a group of eighteen men substituted these shellfish for the protein they usually got from meat, cheese and eggs, their total cholesterol dropped significantly. Clams depressed cholesterol an average of 13 per cent; crabs, 10 per cent; oysters, 9 per cent and mussels, 5 per cent. More dramatic was the drop in triglycerides, falling 59 per cent from eating clams, 52 per cent from oysters, 51 per cent from mussels and 25 per cent from crabs. Further, oysters and mussels improved the good-type HDL ratios, thought to help protect against heart disease. All-around best for cholesterol-lowering ability, said Dr. Childs, were oysters, clams and mussels.

In the study, shrimp and prawns neither raised nor lowered cholesterol; squid was detrimental.

Steamed Clams Portuguese

Serves 4

Contrary to popular opinion, clams are not laden with cholesterol and forbidden to people who are concerned about their cardiovascular systems. In fact studies done at the University of Washington found that eating clams twice a day depressed triglycerides—a blood fat linked to heart disease—by an astonishing 61 per cent.

3lb (1.4kg) or 3 dozen steamer clams
2oz (55g) prosciutto ham
2 tablespoons olive oil
1 medium onion, diced
2 garlic cloves, finely chopped
2 teaspoons paprika
2 tomatoes, peeled, seeded and coarsely chopped
3 tablespoons chopped parsley
8fl oz (225ml) dry white wine or more if needed
1 tablespoon wine vinegar

Scrub the steamers. Cut the prosciutto into tiny slivers. Heat the oil in a large saucepan and sauté the ham, onion and garlic for 3–4 minutes or until the onions are translucent and soft but not browned. Pour off any fat.

Add the remaining ingredients, cover the pan and cook over high heat for 4–6 minutes or until the steamer shells just open. (Discard any clams that have not opened.) Serve at once, with crusty bread for dipping in the juices and a bowl for the empty shells.

Per serving:

Calories	188
Total fat	8.8g
Saturated fat	1.9g
Cholesterol	34mg
Sodium	432mg

Cucumber Rounds with Anchovy Topping (Tapenade)

About 20 pieces

Here's a way to work anchovies, rich in omega-3 oils, into your diet along with tuna, also high in the health-promoting oils. Plus, cucumbers have been known to help lower blood cholesterol. These appetizers do get a high proportion of their calories from fat—but all of it is from either beneficial fish oil or olive oil, which helps lower blood pressure and cholesterol. Go easy on these if you're on a sodium-restricted diet.

8 anchovy fillets
2oz (55g) canned white water-packed tuna, drained
3 tablespoons drained capers
Freshly ground black pepper
1 teaspoon lemon juice or to taste
Approximately 4 tablespoons olive oil
2 cucumbers, cut in ½ inch (1.5cm) slices
20 black olives, stoned (optional)

In a blender or a food processor, purée the anchovies, tuna, capers, pepper, lemon juice and enough olive oil to make a thick paste.

Using a piping bag fitted with a wide star nozzle, pipe the anchovy mixture on to the cucumber slices. Or heap the mixture on with a teaspoon. Decorate each piece with an olive if desired.

Per piece:

Calories	34
Total fat	2.9g
Saturated fat	.4g
Cholesterol	2mg
Sodium	103mg

FOOD PHARMACY FACT
Fish is an Anti-Arthritis Drug

The oil in fish helps relieve the symptoms of rheumatoid arthritis, according to six well-conducted clinical investigations, says Dr. Joel Kremer, associate professor of medicine, Albany (New York) Medical College and a leading researcher in the field. There's no doubt that fish oil is an anti-inflammatory agent, says Dr. Kremer. Furthermore, in an exciting new discovery he found that fish oil also acts directly on the immune system to suppress the release of trouble-causing compounds called *cytokines* that help destroy joints. When patients with rheumatoid arthritis took moderate doses of fish oil in addition to their normal medication for six months, Dr. Kremer found their production of a certain cytokine (interleukin 1) dropped by 40–55 per cent.

He also found in his study of forty-nine patients that fish oil suppressed various symptoms of arthritis. Fish-oil eaters had fewer tender and swollen joints and less pain and fatigue as well as other improvements based on twenty-four different measurements.

The dose was 5–6g of fish oil daily. That's comparable to a couple of cans of sardines a day or a 7oz (200g) serving of fresh salmon or mackerel, says Dr. Kremer. "There's no reason to think the oil from eating fish will not work the same way," he says.

Mackerel Salad Spread

Serves 8 as an appetizer, 4 as sandwiches

If you think mackerel is not addictive, try this sandwich or cracker spread. I couldn't stop eating it. Canned mackerel is one of the best, least expensive oily fishes that can help fight blood clots, lower your blood pressure and help protect you from psoriasis, rheumatoid arthritis, migraine headaches and other health problems. This also is not low-sodium diet fare, although studies have shown that canned mackerel lowers blood pressure despite its higher sodium content.

2 teaspoons lemon juice
15oz (425g) can mackerel, drained and flaked, any skin removed
2oz (55g) celery, diced
3oz (85g) onion, diced
1 tablespoon sweet or dill pickle relish
8 tablespoons reduced-calorie mayonnaise
Salt and freshly ground pepper to taste
1 teaspoon Dijon mustard

Add the lemon juice to the mackerel. Combine the remaining ingredients, add them to the mackerel and mix thoroughly. Chill.

Spread on bread or eat with crackers. For a sharper taste, add 1–1½ teaspoons Dijon mustard.

Per serving:

Calories	115
Total fat	6.8g
Saturated fat	1.7g
Cholesterol	39mg
Sodium	281mg

Molly's Chopped Herring

Serves 4

If you're not accustomed to making chopped herring—or even if you are—I heartily recommend this simple and delicious version given to me by Molly Schuchat, who often makes if for her husband, Michael, and her children. It's an old family recipe from Mike's mother. I have served it to chopped herring aficionados, who proclaimed it superb. And it's a snap to make in a food processor. There is no better way to get lots of omega-3s than from herring, which is one of the leading sources of the healthy oils.

2 medium *or* 1 large cooking apple, peeled, cored and cut into
    chunks
12oz (340g) jar pickled herring, drained and skin removed
2–3 hard boiled eggs, shelled and thickly sliced
White or red wine vinegar to taste

In a food processor chop the apples. Add the herring and pulse quickly to chop, then add the eggs and pulse again. Do not overprocess or the mixture will become too smooth. It should be chunky.

Stir in the vinegar a teaspoon at a time, tasting until the flavour is to your liking.

Serve with a dark bread, bagels or pitta bread.

Note The Schuchats usually discard any onion that comes with the herring but you can chop the onion along with the herring if you wish. Also, if you accidentally add too much vinegar, you can counteract it by adding a 1/2 teaspoon sugar, says Molly. The herring also keeps well in a closed jar in the refrigerator.

Per serving:

Calories	207
Total fat	14g
Saturated fat	2.5g
Cholesterol	141mg
Sodium	564mg

Salmon Pâté

6 servings

Salmon pâté is a classic, so good for company and for you. Here is a favourite of mine. It's thickened with gelatine or agar-agar (a seaweed gelatine available in health food shops) which makes it exceptionally low in saturated fat. Serve with raw vegetables or crackers. Thanks to nutritionist Ann Louise Gittleman; this recipe is adapted from her book, Beyond Pritikin.

15½oz (440g) can salmon, bones and skin removed, rinsed, liquid reserved
2 tablespoons lemon juice
1 teaspoon dried dill *or* 1 tablespoon chopped fresh dill
1 tablespoon agar-agar or unflavoured gelatine
3oz (85g) onion, chopped
½oz (15g) parsley, chopped
1 tablespoon rinsed and drained capers

Place the salmon, lemon juice and dill in a food processor or blender. Blend for 10 seconds.

Sprinkle the agar-agar or gelatine over 2 tablespoons of the reserved salmon liquid in a saucepan and heat to dissolve. Add the dissolved agar-agar or gelatine to the salmon mixture. Stir in the onion, parsley and capers. Refrigerate for about 4 hours before serving.

Per serving
Calories	113
Total fat	4.5g
Saturated fat	1g
Cholesterol	0
Sodium	445mg

✔
FOOD PHARMACY FACT
Fish Oil Keep Arteries Unclogged.

Heart surgeons are excited to discover that fish oil may help keep arteries open longer after angioplasty, a common surgical procedure to unclog arteries. Dr. Mark R. Milner, Washington (D.C.) Hospital Center, found that giving patients fish oil capsules for six months after surgery cut in half the rate at which arteries tended to become clogged again. In a study of eighty-four angioplasty patients those who took fish-oil capsules and ate a low-fat diet had a 19 per cent arterial reclosure rate compared with twice that of another group eating a low-fat diet but not taking fish oil.

The effective therapeutic dose equalled 4.5g of fish oil—or about two small cans of sardines or 4¹/₂oz (130g) of fresh mackerel.

Dr. Milner says fish oil retards the inflammation and scarring of arterial walls that lead to the buildup of plaque and reblockage. He says he gives fish oil capsules as an "emergency measure" but that if patients ate fish regularly this would be unnecessary. "After three to six months I tell patients, 'Stop taking the capsules and eat fish once a day or every other day,'" he says.

Oriental Tuna-Stuffed Mushrooms

About 20

Since fresh and frozen tuna steaks are now fairly readily available, here's an imaginative way to use the tuna to make appetizers, buffet fare or party nibbles. You can use large button mushroom caps or preferably shiitake or other Oriental mushroom caps, which have specific cardio-vascular protecting properties. Remember that tuna is one of the most concentrated sources of the marvellous omega-3 fatty acids.

> 8oz (225g) fresh or frozen tuna, thawed if frozen and coarsely chopped
> 2 spring onions, finely chopped
> 2 tablespoons light soy sauce
> 3/4 teaspoon ground ginger
> 20 large mushroom caps, preferably shiitake

Preheat the grill. Mix the tuna, spring onions, soy sauce and ginger. Clean the mushroom caps and stuff them with the tuna mixture.

Place the stuffed mushrooms on a baking sheet and grill for about 7–8 minutes. Serve with extra soy sauce.

Per piece:

Calories	23
Total fat	.6g
Saturated fat	.1g
Cholesterol	4mg
Sodium	65mg

Sardine and Avocado Sandwich

2 sandwiches

I grew up on sardines, thanks to my grandmother. So when Lynn Fischer, coauthor of the cookbook Low Cholesterol Gourmet, *told me about this new sardine sandwich she had devised, I was eager to try it. It gets raves from me. The flavours blend perfectly. You can also use plain sardines if you cannot find or do not care for the spicy ones. It also works as an open-face sandwich and I have packed it into a pitta bread pocket.*

1–2 teaspoons Bengal-style hot chutney
4 slices wholemeal bread
^{1}/4 ripe avocado, peeled and cut into thin slices
4^3/4oz (124g) can sardines in spicy sauce or plain sardines, drained
4 wafer-thin onion slices
2 large leaves crisp or cos lettuce *or* several watercress sprigs

Spread chutney over two slices of bread. Add the avocado and half the sardines. Top with onion slices and lettuce and other slices of bread. Cut in half and serve.

Note Bengal-style hot chutney has a jam consistency. You can substitute other mango or fruit chutney but chop large pieces of fruit.

Per sandwich
Calories	278
Total fat	11g
Saturated fat	1.7g
Cholesterol	77mg
Sodium	524mg

Soups

Easy Pumpkin and Apple Soup

Serves 6

Everybody needs a fantastic recipe for pumpkin soup—what better way to get all the fabulous health-promoting benefit from pumpkin's cancer-fighting beta-carotene! Pumpkin is one of the highest of all foods in beta-carotene. In this case you get a bonus: the heart-protective benefits of apples. This soup is so easy to make with storecupboard ingredients yet it has an elegant flavour fit for a dinner party. I like it hot but you can also serve it cold. My thanks for this adaptation to Maxine Rapoport and Nina Graybill, coauthors of Cold Soups *and other cookbooks.*

1 teaspoon butter or margarine
3oz (85g) onion, chopped
4oz (115g) celery, finely sliced
1lb (450g) pumpkin flesh, cubed
8oz (225g) peeled and sliced dessert apple
1½ pints (850ml) chicken stock
1 teaspoon dried marjoram, crushed
Salt to taste
6 tablespoons natural very-low-fat yoghurt mixed with grated lemon
   zest to taste, for garnish (optional)

Place the butter, onion and celery in a small bowl. Microwave on HIGH until the vegetables are softened and translucent—about 5 minutes.

Put the pumpkin and apple in a bowl with 3 tablespoons of water, cover and microwave on HIGH for 7–8 minutes or until soft. Purée in a food processor or blender.

Transfer the onion and celery mixture to a large saucepan. Stir in the pumpkin and apple purée, chicken stock and seasonings. Cook, covered, over low heat for about 20–30 minutes, stirring occasionally. Taste for seasoning.

Ladle the soup into bowls and garnish with yoghurt if desired. Or refrigerate for several hours or overnight and serve cold.

Note The zest is the coloured part of the rind of citrus fruits. Be sure not to use any of the white pith, which is bitter.

Per serving:

Calories	77
Total fat	2g
Saturated fat	.8g
Cholesterol	2mg
Sodium	431mg

FOOD PHARMACY FACT
Orange Vegetables, New Heart Savers

That stuff that makes carrots and pumpkins orange—beta carotene — seems to have unexpected abilities to protect the heart. In a major 10-year study of 22,000 male physicians, Harvard investigators have been giving high doses of beta carotene, mainly to test its powers to prevent cancer.

Then researchers decided to look at a small group of men who had entered the study with signs of heart disease, such as angina (chest pain). To their great surprise, the researchers found that beta carotene appears to slow down the process of atherosclerosis—stiffening and clogging of arteries — and to cut the risk of heart attacks dramatically.

Such men taking 50 milligrams (about 80,000 international units or IUs) of beta carotene every other day for six years suffered only half as many heart attacks and strokes as similar men who took a placebo—a harmless "sugar pill".

The daily dose used in the study is comparable to the beta carotene in about 10oz (285g) of carrots per day.

Spiced Carrot Soup

Serves 6

Believe it or not, carrots give you an even better jolt of life-preserving beta-carotene when they are cooked. That's because more of the beta-carotene is released from the carrot's cell walls and this soup is off the charts for high levels of beta-carotene. This wonderful spicy soup is a favourite of mine and of diners at Leigh Stone-Herbert's family-owned Gravetye Manor Restaurant at Sharpthorne, West Sussex, recognized for its healthy food. Thanks to the restaurant for the recipe from which this was adapted.

6 large carrots, thinly sliced
2½ pints (1.4 litres) chicken stock
½oz (15g) butter or margarine (optional)
⅛ teaspoon ground cumin or to taste
⅛ teaspoon ground coriander or to taste
⅛ teaspoon ground cinnamon or to taste
⅛ teaspoon cayenne pepper or to taste
Salt and freshly ground pepper to taste

Simmer the carrots in a heavy saucepan with ¼ pint (140ml) of the chicken stock and butter or margarine if desired, until the carrots are tender. Or place in a large bowl, cover and microwave on HIGH for 10 minutes or until tender.

Purée in a blender or food processor. Return the purée to the pan or microwave bowl.

Add the spices and stir. Add the remaining chicken stock and salt and pepper and simmer for 20 minutes on the stove or cook on HIGH for about 10 minutes in the microwave.

Per serving:
Calories	74
Total fat	1.7g
Saturated fat	.4g
Cholesterol	0
Sodium	88mg

Curried Broccoli Soup

Serves 4

Green is the colour researchers are raving about in evaluating foods as potential inhibitors of cancer. The green vegetables are exceptionally high in certain compounds believed to combat cancer-causing agents, according to U.S. Department of Agriculture studies. Broccoli, they say, is one of the best. In this recipe you get chunks of broccoli awash in a broccoli base. It's delicious. You can also substitute other green vegetables—peas, green beans or asparagus—for the broccoli.

1½lb (680g) chopped fresh or frozen broccoli
1 pint (570ml) chicken stock
1 large onion, chopped
2 large garlic cloves, chopped
1 teaspoon curry powder (more if desired)
Salt to taste
8fl oz (225ml) low-fat buttermilk mixed with 1 teaspoon flour

Set aside half the chopped broccoli. Place the remaining broccoli, chicken stock, onion, garlic, curry powder and salt in a heavy saucepan. Cover and bring to the boil. Lower the heat and simmer for 20 minutes. Cool for 10–15 minutes.

Purée the mixture in a food processor or blender. Return the purée to the saucepan and bring to a simmer, uncovered. Add reserved broccoli and buttermilk. Bring to a simmer (do not boil), adjust seasonings and serve immediately.

Note The soup can also be served lightly chilled.

Per serving:
Calories	89
Total fat	2g
Saturated fat	.6g
Cholesterol	2.5mg
Sodium	122mg

BROCCOLI—AN AMAZING FOOD PILL

Broccoli is one of the most amazing pharmaceutical packages in nature's food pharmacy.

If it had a pharmacological label, it would read like this. Contains high concentrations of beta-carotene (suspected lung cancer antagonist); carotenoids (general anticancer agents); quercetin (antioxidant and anticancer agent); glutathione (antioxidant and anticancer agent); indoles (anticancer and detoxification compounds); vitamin C (powerful antioxidant); Folate (anticancer agent); chromium (antidiabetic and anti-heart-disease medication); readily absorbable calcium (to help prevent osteoporosis—also a suspected anticancer and high blood pressure medication); calcium pectate fibre (lowers blood cholesterol). It is also a member of the famous cruciferous family of vegetables, closely tied to lower rates of cancer, notably colon cancer. In numerous studies broccoli shows up as a vegetable most preferred by those with lower rates of all kinds of cancer.

Potato and Kale Soup

Serves 6

Full of dense green kale, this soup has been described as "vigorous and deeply satisfying". It's the national soup of Portugal. I'm attracted to it mainly because kale is so underused yet is one of the super sources of carotenoids, believed to help fight off numerous diseases—from cancer to cataracts. Kale, for example, contains twice as many carotenoids as spinach, another super source. And combined with potatoes and onions, it makes a rich and flavourful soup.

1 tablespoon olive oil
1 medium yellow onion, finely chopped
1 leek, trimmed, washed and chopped
3 garlic cloves, finely chopped
3 large potatoes, peeled and diced
2½ pints (1.4 litres) water
Salt and freshly ground pepper to taste
4oz (115g) chorizo or linguica (Portuguese) sausage (optional)
1lb (450g) kale, trimmed and shredded

In a large, heavy saucepan, heat the olive oil. Add the onion, leek and garlic and cook over medium heat for 3–4 minutes or until the onions are translucent and soft.

Add the potatoes, water, salt and pepper. Bring to the boil, reduce the heat and simmer gently, covered, for 20 minutes or until the potatoes are very soft. With a potato masher, mash the potatoes in the stock or purée in a food processor or blender.

If you are using the sausage, prick it all over with a pin and place in cold water to cover. Gradually bring to the boil, reduce the heat and simmer gently for 6–8 minutes or until cooked. Allow to cool and cut into ¼ inch (0.5cm) slices. Add the sausage to the potato mixture and simmer for 3 minutes.

Stir in the kale and simmer for 1–2 minutes or just until the kale is tender. Do not overcook. The kale should remain bright green. Correct the seasonings and serve.

Note To shred kale, after you have stemmed and washed the leaves, roll them into a tight cigar and then slice across into the slenderest slivers.

Per serving:

Calories	175
Total fat	4g
Saturated fat	.5g
Cholesterol	0
Sodium	38mg

Minted Pea Soup

Serves 6

It's hard to resist peas when you can so quickly make them into a fabulous, fragrant soup like this. One night I made this soup and ate half of it myself. Peas are one of those green vegetables included in the diets of people more likely to escape cancer. The pea is also surprisingly high in fibre, which may be one more reason for its therapeutic qualities.

1lb 4oz (570g) frozen peas
1 pint (570ml) chicken stock
1oz (30g) mint leaves, chopped
1 medium potato, baked or boiled, peeled and cut into chunks
2 teaspoons lemon juice
8fl oz (225ml) very-low-fat buttermilk
Salt and freshly ground pepper to taste
1 tablespoon natural very-low-fat yoghurt for garnish (optional)

Put the frozen peas and half the chicken stock in a large saucepan. Heat for about 5 minutes until the peas are thawed.

Put the pea mixture in to a blender or a food processor. Add the mint, potato and lemon juice and process to a smooth purée.

Return the purée to the saucepan. Stir in the buttermilk, remaining stock and salt and pepper. Cook just until heated through; do not boil. If desired, serve topped with a small dollop of yogurt.

Per serving:
Calories	128
Total fat	1.4g
Saturated fat	.5g
Cholesterol	1.6mg
Sodium	173mg

Tomato and Basil Soup

Serves 4

The best time to make this soup is when both ripe, juicy fresh tomatoes and fresh basil leaves are plentiful. It's delicious served either cold or hot. Tomatoes are a super source of the powerful cell defenders vitamins A and C and the compound lycopene, as well as potassium, which some experts believe counters high blood pressure and strokes.

> 1 tablespoon olive oil
> 2lb (900g) tomatoes, peeled, seeded and finely chopped
> 3 garlic cloves, finely chopped
> 1oz (30g) fresh basil leaves, chopped
> 1¼ pints (710ml) chicken stock
> Salt and freshly ground pepper to taste
> Seasoned croutons or natural very-low-fat yoghurt to garnish
>   (optional)

Place the olive oil and tomatoes in a saucepan and cook over medium heat for 5 minutes. Add the garlic and basil and cook for a further 10 minutes, stirring occasionally.

Pour in the chicken stock, season and bring to the boil. Reduce the heat and simmer for 5 minutes.

If you are serving the soup cold, chill it for several hours or overnight. Serve topped with seasoned croutons or a dollop of yoghurt.

Note Skin tomatoes by dipping them in to boiling water for 1 minute. Run under cold water to stop cooking process. Peel away skin. Cut in half. Scoop out the seeds, then chop the flesh.

Per serving:
Calories	101
Total fat	4g
Saturated fat	.8g
Cholesterol	0
Sodium	58mg

✔

FOOD PHARMACY FACT
The Red Tomato Alert

Eating tomatoes may help protect you from pancreatic cancer, a virulent malignancy that kills 22,000 Americans annually, suggests a study at Johns Hopkins University. Investigators found that the blood of a group of such cancer victims was markedly low in levels of a vegetable compound called *lycopene*—a red pigment found in red vegetables and fruits, notably tomatoes and strawberries. In fact those with the least lycopene in their bloodstreams were five times more likely to develop pancreatic cancer than those with the highest blood levels of lycopene.

My Favourite Lentil Soup

Serves 6

Lentil soup is irresistible, especially on a cold day. But you can also eat this soup cold on a hot day. Lentils are one of nature's pharmacological gems, keeping blood sugar and cholesterol down and probably blood pressure too. Lentils also, as a member of the legume family, are full of a variety of anticancer agents. They have another virtue in that unlike other legumes, they do not need soaking and thus are quicker to prepare, although the soup is richer if allowed to simmer for a few hours.

2 teaspoons olive oil
1 medium onion, chopped
1½ pints (850ml) chicken or vegetable stock
7oz (200g) lentils
1½oz (45g) spinach leaves, coarsely chopped
1 carrot, chopped
1oz (30g) celery, chopped
8oz (225g) fresh or canned tomatoes with juice, chopped
2 garlic cloves, finely chopped
½ teaspoon ground allspice
½ teaspoon dried thyme
Salt and freshly ground pepper to taste
Juice of 1 lemon

Place the olive oil and onions in a large saucepan and sauté until the onions are translucent and soft.

Add the remaining ingredients except the lemon juice. Cover and bring to the boil. Reduce the heat and simmer for 1 hour or until the soup is of desired thickness, up to 3 or 4 hours, stirring occasionally.

Add the lemon juice just before serving or squeeze a splash of lemon juice into each bowl.

Per serving:
- Calories: 149
- Total fat 2g
- Saturated fat .2g
- Cholesterol 0
- Sodium 23mg

✔

FOOD PHARMACY FACT
Beans vs Pancreatic Cancer

Seventh-Day Adventists who ate the most lentils, peas and beans (including soya bean products) as well as dried fruit were much less likely to develop fatal pancreatic cancer, according to a study by Paul K. Mills, Department of Preventive Medicine, Loma Linda University School of Medicine. Specifically, those who ate beans, lentils and peas more than three times a week had only 40 per cent the chance of dying of pancreatic cancer of those who ate legumes less than once a week. Heavy eaters of raisins, dates and other dried fruits (more than three times a week) had equally low odds. The anticancer agents in dried fruits were unclear, said Dr. Mills but he credited protease inhibitors in legumes with warding off the deadly cancer.

Mariana's Salmon and Corn Soup

Serves 6

This is such a pretty soup, flecked with colourful vegetables. And it's a simple, inexpensive way to get lots of omega-3-type fish oils, especially if you use lower-priced pink canned salmon. Each serving contains about 1,200 milligrams of health-promoting omega-3s. This low-fat soup is adapted from a recipe given to me by my friend Mariana Gosnell, who first tasted it during a visit to wintry northern Canada.

1oz (30g) celery, chopped
1 garlic clove, crushed
3oz (85g) onion, chopped
¾ pint (425ml) chicken stock
6oz (170g) potato, peeled and diced
6oz (170g) carrots, diced
15½oz (440g) can salmon, drained and flaked, liquid reserved
½ teaspoon dried thyme
Salt and freshly ground pepper to taste
3oz (85g) broccoli, chopped
10oz (285g) frozen sweetcorn
12fl oz (340ml) evaporated skimmed milk

In a large saucepan, sauté the celery, garlic and onion in ¼ pint (140ml) chicken stock until the onions are translucent and soft.

Add the potatoes, carrots, the remaining chicken stock, salmon liquid, thyme, salt and pepper. Cover and simmer for about 30 minutes, until the vegetables are tender. Add the broccoli and cook for a further 5 minutes.

Add the flaked salmon, corn and evaporated skimmed milk. Heat through and serve.

Per serving:
Calories	239
Total fat	5.5g
Saturated fat	1.4g
Cholesterol	2.5mg
Sodium	512mg

Oyster Chowder

Serves 6–8

Oysters are the opposite of what many people think—they are good, not bad, for your heart and cholesterol. They are extremely rich in the trace minerals copper, zinc, chromium and selenium, all of which have been linked to better cardiovascular functioning. In addition selenium is an antioxidant, thought to help prevent cancer. Spinach and potatoes are also well endowed with pharmacological properties.

1 tablespoon olive oil
3 shallots, finely chopped
2 celery stalks, finely chopped
1 tablespoon flour
1½ pints (850ml) fish stock
1lb (450g) shucked fresh oysters, strained and liquor reserved
2 large potatoes, peeled and diced
8fl oz (225ml) skimmed milk
Salt and freshly ground black pepper to taste
5oz (140g) fresh spinach, stemmed, washed and cut into ½ inch
    (1.5cm) strips

Heat the oil in a large saucepan and cook the shallots and celery over medium heat for a few minutes or until translucent and soft but not brown. Stir in the flour. Stir in fish stock and reserved oyster liquor and bring the chowder to the boil. Add the potatoes and simmer gently for 6–8 minutes or until tender. Add the milk and salt and pepper to taste. (The chowder can be prepared up to 24 hours ahead to this point.)

Just before serving, add the oysters and simmer for 2 minutes or until the oysters are cooked—but just barely. Stir in the spinach. The heat from the chowder should be sufficient to cook the spinach, but if not, simmer the soup for a few seconds more. Taste and correct the seasonings.

Per serving:
Calories	158
Total fat	5g
Saturated fat	1g
Cholesteol	48mg
Sodium	493mg

✔

FOOD PHARMACY FACT
More Oysters, Please

Oysters are one of the highest of all foods in the trace mineral chromium. That may make them good heart food. In studies at Bemidji State University of Minnesota and Mercy Hospital in San Diego, researchers gave 200 micrograms of chromium supplements to people with high cholesterol—6.9mmol/litre or higher—for forty-two days in a double-blind study. The chromium reduced the undersirable-type LDL cholesterol by 11 per cent and slightly increased desirable HDLs. About 90 per cent of Americans do not get enough chromium every day, according to the American National Academy of Sciences. Other high-chromium foods are whole grains, liver, nuts, prunes, asparagus, egg yolks, potatoes, mushrooms, rhubarb, beer and wine.

Seafood Minestrone

Serves 6

This mélange of seafood with Italian seasonings and vegetables helps ensure you get your daily quota of omega-3, which all your cells will appreciate. They can function better when they are supplied with good fats instead of bad fats. Shellfish, especially scallops, are quite low in fat; both mussels and clams help lower blood cholesterol. This is a hearty soup that can also serve as a main course. It's one of many low-fat, low-calorie recipes in Ellen Brown's The Gourmet Gazelle Cookbook.

1 dozen mussels
1 dozen small hard-shelled clams
2 tablespoons cornmeal
1 tablespoon olive oil
1 leek, cleaned and chopped
3oz (85g) onion, chopped
1 garlic clove, finely chopped
1oz (30g) celery, chopped
2 small mushrooms, sliced
4 large tomatoes, skinned, seeded and diced
3/4 pint (425ml) chicken stock, preferably unsalted
8fl oz (225ml) fish stock
2 tablespoons chopped fresh basil *or* 2 teaspoons dried
1/4 teaspoon freshly ground pepper
3oz (85g) kale, chopped
1oz (30g) macaroni
4oz (115g) prawns, peeled and deveined *or* crab meat
4oz (115g) fillet of sole or other white fish, cut into
    1/2 inch (1.5cm) pieces
4 oz (115g) scallops
3 tablespoons freshly grated Parmesan cheese

Scrub the mussels and clams under cold running water with a stiff brush, discarding any that are not firmly shut. Scrape off the beard from each mussel with a sharp paring knife. Place the mussels and clams in a bowl of cold water and sprinkle cornmeal on top. Place in the refrigerator for at least 2 hours.

Heat the olive oil in a large pan over medium heat. Add the leek, onion, garlic, celery and mushrooms. Sauté over medium heat, stirring frequently, for 5 minutes or until the onions are translucent and soft. Add the tomatoes, chicken and fish stock, basil and pepper. Bring to the boil, reduce the heat to low and simmer the soup, uncovered, for 15 minutes. Add the kale and macaroni and simmer for a further 5 minutes.

Drain the mussels and clams, then wash again. Raise the heat to high, add the shellfish and cover the pan. Steam the mussels and clams with the pan tightly covered for 5–7 minutes, depending on the size of the seafood. Shake the pot occasionally to redistribute the clams and mussels.

Remove the clams and mussels with a slotted spoon, discarding any that did not open. Set aside.

Return the soup to the boil and add the shrimp, sole and scallops. Cover the pan and turn off the heat. Leave the pan to stand undisturbed for 5 minutes.

To serve, ladle the soup into shallow flat soup bowls, arrange the clams and mussels on top and sprinkle with Parmesan cheese.

Per serving:

Calories	193
Total fat	5g
Saturated fat	1g
Cholesterol	54mg
Sodium	308mg

Dr. Ziment's Garlic Chicken Soup
for Colds and Coughs

Serves 4

*Brought to you by popular demand, this soup has helped countless people
fight colds and chest congestion. The recipe appeared in* The Food
Pharmacy *and so many people attested to its therapeutic benefits that it
is reprinted here. It comes from Dr. Irwin Ziment, professor of pulmonary
medicine, University of California at Los Angeles, who says he finds it
more healing than most modern drugs. He advises taking it at the beginning of a meal, one to three times a day.*

    $1^{1}/_{2}$ pints (850ml) homemade chicken stock
    1 garlic bulb, about 15 cloves, peeled
    5 parsley sprigs, finely chopped
    6 fresh coriander sprigs, finely chopped
    1 teaspoon lemon pepper
    1 teaspoon finely chopped fresh mint leaves
    1 teaspoon dried basil, crushed, *or* 1 tablespoon chopped fresh
    1 teaspoon curry powder
    Hot red pepper flakes to taste, sliced carrots, bay leaves (optional)

Place all ingredients in a pan without a lid. Bring to the boil, then simmer for about 30 minutes.

Strain the soup—or, better still, remove the solid garlic cloves and
herbs and put them in a blender or food processor, then return the purée to
the soup. Serve hot. Be sure to inhale the fumes from the soup during its
preparation, urges Dr. Ziment.

    Per serving:
        Calories   52
        Total fat   1.6g
        Saturated fat   .4g
        Cholesterol   0
        Sodium   258mg

FOOD PHARMACY FACT
Chicken Soup Fights Cold Symptoms

Let's not forget that several years ago a study in the prestigious medical journal *Chest*, to the surprise of researchers, revealed that chicken soup really is "good for you, especially if you have an upper respiratory infection". As researcher Dr. Marvin Sackner, pulmonary specialist at Mount Sinai Medical Center in Miami Beach, concluded, "There's an aromatic substance in chicken soup, not yet identified, that helps clear your airways."

He meticulously measured the effects of cold water, hot water and hot chicken soup on the rate of flow of mucus and airflow through nasal passages. Hot water cleared congestion in airways better than cold water but best of all was hot chicken soup. Even cold chicken soup worked to a lesser extent.

Dr. Weil's Miso Soup

Serves 4

A few years ago Japanese scientists found that those who ate miso soup regularly were about one-third less likely to have stomach cancer. There's apparently something in miso itself, which is fermented soya bean, rice, or barley paste, that is protective. No book with pharmacological recipes would be complete without one for miso soup. Luckily, I discovered this recipe in a superb book, Natural Health, Natural Medicine, by Dr. Andrew Weil, well-known medical author and faculty member at the University of Arizona College of Medicine. He says the soup recipe was developed for one of his food and nutrition workshops.

- 2 teaspoons rapeseed oil
- 3 thin slices fresh root ginger
- 1 large onion, thinly sliced
- 2 carrots, peeled and thinly sliced
- 2 celery stalks, thinly sliced
- 10oz (285g) cabbage, coarsely chopped
- 2 pints (1.1 litres) water
- 4 tablespoons light or dark miso
- Spring onions, including green parts, chopped, to garnish

Heat the oil in large saucepan. Add the root ginger and onion and sauté over medium heat for 5 minutes. Add the carrots, celery and cabbage. Stir well. Add the water. Bring rapidly to the boil, then lower heat and simmer, covered, until the carrots are just tender, about 10 minutes.

Remove the soup from the heat. Place the miso in a bowl, add a little of the soup and stir well to a smooth paste. Add more soup to thin the mixture, then add it to the rest of the soup. Leave to stand for a few minutes.

Serve the soup in bowls with chopped raw spring onions. You may wish to remove the sliced ginger and/or add a few drops of roasted (dark) sesame oil to each bowl.

Per serving:
Calories	105
Total fat	4g
Saturated fat	.3g
Cholesterol	0
Sodium	670mg

Eat Less, Live Longer.

Could there be any connection between the fact that the typical Japanese eats the fewest calories and yet has the longest life expectancy among inhabitants of industrialized nations?

The average Japanese man lives 75.2 years, the average woman 80.9 years, for a combined life expectancy of 78. The U.K. ranks tenth with a life expectancy of 75.2 years, below Sweden (77), Switzerland (77), Canada (76.5), Netherlands (76.4), Norway (76.2), Australia (76), Spain (76), France (75.6), and equal with West Germany, according to figures from the United Nations Secretariat. The Japanese have remarkably low rates of heart disease and all cancers except stomach cancer.

And what do they eat in Japan? Less fat and meat and fewer calories. And more fish and complex carbohydrates like rice, vegetables and soya bean products. Strikingly, the average Japanese eats a mere 2,600 calories daily compared with about 3,500 daily calories for Britains. In Japan about 25 per cent of the calories come from fat. In the U.K. it's about 37 per cent.

A main dish in Japan is often carbohydrates like rice and noodles with meat and vegetables as condiments. In the U.K., of course, meat is the centrepiece of most meals, complemented by carbohydrates and vegetables.

That restricting calories leads to a longer life has substantial support in animal studies. Trim, lean—but not undernourished—mice that eat about 65 per cent as many calories as normal mice live about 50 per cent longer. Why? Nobody is sure; the subject is under intense scrutiny. One theory is that the processing of calories boosts glucose or blood sugar as well as insulin levels. High amounts of glucose and/or insulin circulating in the system seem to promote cell destruction and disease, particularly heart disease, according to some experts.

Chicken or Turkey Stock

About 3 pints (1.7 litres)

Making your own chicken or turkey stock allows you to control its amount of sodium and fat, reducing them to virtually zero if you wish. You can use this recipe for the chicken stock in the recipes in this book. And you can vary the seasonings and richness to your taste.

3lb (1.4kg) chicken necks, wings and backs, or turkey wings
4½ pints (2.5 litres) water
1 large yellow onion, chopped
3 large celery stalks, including leaves, chopped
2 carrots, peeled and chopped
2 bay leaves
5 parsley sprigs (more if desired)
1 tablespoon whole black peppercorns
1 tablespoon dried thyme (optional)
2 garlic cloves, chopped (optional)
Salt to taste

Place all ingredients in a large saucepan and bring to the boil. Simmer over very low heat for abut 3½ hours. Skim the surface from time to time to remove any scum that forms.

When the flavour is of the required strength, remove the pan from the heat. Let the stock cool slightly, then strain it into a large bowl, using a colander lined with muslin or a fine strainer. Refrigerate for at least 3 hours, preferably overnight.

Skim off all congealed fat that has risen to the top. Keep the stock refrigerated or put into small containers and freeze. The frozen stock will keep for about 6 months.

Per ½ pint (285ml)
Calories	55
Total fat	2.25g
Saturated fat	0
Cholesterol	0
Sodium	10mg

Vegetable Stock

About 2¹/₂ pints (1.4 litres)

You can substitute vegetable stock for chicken stock called for in recipes. Practically any vegetable will work. Here's a suggested version.

1 medium yellow onion, chopped
2 carrots, peeled and chopped
2 celery stalks, including leaves, chopped
2 parsnips, peeled and chopped
1 small turnip, peeled and chopped
Salt and freshly ground pepper to taste
3¹/₄ pints (1.8 litres) water

In a large saucepan, combine all ingredients, bring to the boil, lower the heat and simmer for 1 hour, skimming occasionally.

When the vegetables are very soft, remove from the heat and strain through a muslin lined colander or fine strainer. Using a potato masher, mash the vegetables to extract all liquid.

Discard the vegetables and store the stock in the refrigerator or freezer.

Per ¹/₂ pint (285ml)
Calories	13
Total fat	0
Saturated fat	0
Cholesterol	0
Sodium	10mg

Grapefruit and Vegetable Gazpacho

Serves 6

This grapefruit-based cold soup is one of the most unusual and refreshing I have ever come across. You get loads of fibre from the membranes and juice sacs of the grapefruit, a unique fibre shown to help lower blood cholesterol and perhaps even help reverse damage that has already occurred to arteries. The soup is low in calories and is virtually fat free.

4 grapefruits, peeled, pips removed and quartered
3 tomatoes, halved and seeds removed
2 cucumbers, peeled, seeded and cut into chunks
3 celery stalks, including leaves
2 red or green peppers, cut into chunks
1/2oz (15g) parsley, chopped
Salt to taste
1/4 teaspoon Tabasco sauce or to taste
Grapefruit juice as needed

Purée the grapefruit quarters in a food processor or blender and pour into a large bowl or jug.

Purée the tomatoes and cucumbers and add them to the grapefruit purée. Purée the celery, peppers and parsley and add to the bowl or jug. Stir the puréed pulp together. Stir in the salt and hot pepper sauce and add grapefruit juice as needed.

Per serving:
Calories	83
Total fat	.5g
Saturated fat	.03g
Cholesterol	0
Sodium	34mg

FOOD PHARMACY FACT
Citrus Against Cancer

Nomilin—a compound that brings the sour and bitter taste to citrus fruits—may help block cancer, according to Dr. Luke K. T. Lam at the University of Minnesota. Mice given nomilin and then a potent cancer-causing agent in cigarette smoke were much less likely to develop stomach cancer. One hundred per cent of the mice not given nomilin developed malignancies, compared with only 28 per cent of the nomilin-treated mice.

Some experts have long speculated that the falling rate of stomach cancer in the U.S. is tied to the year-round consumption of home-grown citrus fruits. They generally credit vitamin C; nomilin may be another reason. Dr. Lam explains that nomalin probably works by tripling the activity of an enzyme that helps detoxify poisons in the body, including carcinogens.

Grape Gazpacho
(Ajo Branco)

Serves 4

Even if red grapes were not super sources of quercetin and other anti-cancer and cell-protecting compounds, this soup would still be an all-time favourite because of its unusual texture and pleasing taste and colour. It's even a favourite of my friend Daryl, who cannot abide grapes in any other form. You can use white seedless grapes but I prefer red because they are so concentrated in the antioxidant quercetin and other known antibacterial, antiviral substances. Almonds, too, are good for you; although high in fat, most of it is heart-protective and cholesterol-lowering monounsaturated fat. This recipe, which I have modified to use red instead of white grapes, is the inspiration of Steven Raichlen, an American food writer based in Miami, who specializes in ethnic foods.

1lb (450g) seedless grapes, preferably red
2¹/₂ oz (70g) white bread, crusts removed and cubed
12fl oz (340ml) cold water (more if needed)
3oz (85g) blanched almonds
2–3 garlic cloves, peeled or to taste
2 tablespoons olive oil
2–3 tablespoons white wine vinegar
1–2 drops almond essence
Salt and freshly ground black pepper to taste

Remove the stems from the grapes. Place the bread cubes in a bowl with the water. Soak the bread until soft.

Place the grapes in a food processor or blender with the remaining ingredients and purée until smooth. Add the bread and water and purée. Chill the soup for at least 1 hour before serving.

Just before serving, correct the seasoning, adding salt, pepper or vinegar to taste. The sweetness of the grapes should be balanced by the pungency of the vinegar and garlic.

Per serving:

Calories	309
Total fat	19g
Saturated fat	2g
Cholesterol	.5mg
Sodium	80mg

DON'T UNDERESTIMATE GRAPES

Nutritionally speaking, the grape does look puny. It has only a smidgen of vitamin C and not much potassium to speak of—and those are its strong points. That has caused some conventionally minded nutrition experts to write off or denigrate the grape. But to scientists who see beyond nutrients to other molecular aspects of food power, the grape is far from a wimp.

Red grapes are one of the richest of all foods in a powerful antioxidant called *quercetin* that can protect animals against cancer. It is also high in caffeic acid, another anticancer agent in animal and lab studies. Blue grapes, commercial grape juice and pure tannins extracted from grapes have been found extremely potent in inactivating viruses in test tubes. Wine, notably red wine, is an antibiotic; it contains compounds shown to work in similar fashion to penicillin. Grapes are also rich in boron, a newly discovered trace mineral linked to keeping bones strong and the brain alert. Dietary surveys link grapes to a lower incidence of gum disease (considered an infection) and raisins—dried grapes— to lower rates of both cancer of the pancreas and deaths from all cancers.

So don't neglect grapes just because they are "nutritionally" lightweight; researchers insist that in other ways they are capable of delivering knockout punches to save your cells from damage.

FOOD PHARMACY FACT
Almonds—Good for the Heart

Almonds, though high in fat, still may help fight heart disease, according to Dr. Gene A. Spiller, a noted researcher and director of the Health Research and Studies Center in California.

In an experiment Dr. Spiller asked a group of men and women with moderately high cholesterol (average about 6.25) to eat 3³/₄oz (100g) of almonds a day for three to nine weeks. Other groups in the study ate the same amount of fat from cheese or olive oil. Everybody ate equal amounts of grains, vegetables and fruits.

Surprise! The almond-eaters' cholesterol dropped from 10–15 per cent compared with the cheese eaters' cholesterol. Olive oil also reduced cholesterol but almonds were slightly better.

Dr. Spiller explains it this way. Most of the fat in almonds is the same type as that in olive oil—monounsaturated, which is linked to healthier blood and less heart disease. However, this does not give you licence to eat tons of almonds to lower blood cholesterol—because almonds, like olive oil, are high in fat—1oz (30g) almonds has about 175 calories. The point is that almonds, like olive oil, can substitute for other fats in a health-promoting diet.

Other nuts that are exceptionally high in monounsaturated fat are hazelnuts and pistachios.

Avocado Ceviche

Serves 4

I flipped over this when I found it on the menu of the Four Seasons Hotel in Beverly Hills. I had it as an appetizer at dinner and again the following day at lunch and immediately asked the chef for the recipe. It is like a gazpacho with a marvellous hot spicy flavour offset by the mellowness of the avocado. It's full of vitamin C from the tomatoes and limes, the best cell-protecting vitamin known, with horseradish and jalapeños to clear your sinuses and avocado to help keep your blood pressure down. Many thanks to Pascal Vignau, executive chef at the Four Seasons Hotel.

6 plum tomatoes, seeded and diced
1 small cucumber, seeded and diced
1 avocado, peeled, stoned and diced
¹/₂ red onion, finely diced
2 jalapeño peppers, seeded and diced
1 large bunch fresh coriander, chopped (at least 2oz/55g)
Juice of 2 limes
1¹/₂ pints (850ml) tomato juice
1 teaspoon horseradish
Salt and freshly ground pepper to taste
Additionally avocado slices for garnish (optional)
Tortilla chips for serving (optional)

Combine all ingredients, Adjust the seasoning and chill. Garnish with a fan of avocado slices and serve with crisp tortilla chips.

Note Low-sodium tomato juice was used in the analysis. Sieved canned tomatoes would be a perfect substitute.

Per serving:

Calories	151
Total fat	8g
Saturated fat	1.3g
Cholesterol	0
Sodium	38mg

Peachy Ginger Soup

A lovely-to-look-at, mellow blend of peaches and ginger, this is a most pleasant way to get some beta-carotene, plus the other largely unidentified health-promoting compounds in peaches. The ginger, in case you have forgotten, is a rather potent blood "thinner," according to tests and a stomach soother. This chilled soup is glorious on a hot summer day. It is definitely not too sweet as a prelude to dinner, although the degree of sweetness depends on the natural sugar in the peaches. You can sweeten it to use as a dessert soup.

    5–6 large peaches (2lb/900g) peeled and stoned
    2oz (55g) crystallised ginger, finely chopped
    2oz (55g) natural very-low-fat yoghurt
    1/2 pint (285ml) skimmed milk
    Salt to taste
    1/4 teaspoon ground nutmeg (preferably freshly grated)
    1/4 teaspoon ground cinnamon

Reserve one whole peach, then in a food processor or blender, purée the remaining peaches and ginger until smooth. Transfer the peach mixture to a large bowl. Add the yoghurt, milk, salt, nutmeg and cinnamon. Blend well.

Cut the reserved fresh peach into small dice. Stir in the diced peach. Chill until serving time.

If desired, garnish with a small dollop of yoghurt sprinkled with some additional slivers of crystallised ginger.

Per serving:

Calories	109
Total fat	.3g
Saturated fat	.1g
Cholesterol	1mg
Sodium	40mg

Chilled Cantaloupe Soup

Serves 6

Lovely to look at, this soup is also lovely for your heart and cells in general because it is packed with vitamin A (beta-carotene), vitamin C and potassium and is virtually fat free.

3 very ripe cantaloupe melons, peeled and seeded
6oz (170g) can frozen orange juice concentrate
6oz (170g) honey
$1/2$ teaspoon ground cardamom
$1/2$ teaspoon ground cinnamon
4 tablespoons peach brandy (optional)
Fresh mint leaves, if available, for garnish

Place the melon chunks in a food processor or blender and purée. Add the remaining ingredients except the mint leaves and blend until smooth.

Pour into a large jug or container and serve in small bowls, mugs or goblets, garnished with mint. Serve well chilled.

Per serving:
Calories	237
Total fat	1g
Saturated fat	0
Cholesterol	0
Sodium	26mg

Cranberry Soup

Serves 6

*A cranberry soup recipe is a must for anyone interested in the pharmaco-
logical properties of food. And this delicately flavoured blend of fruit,
vegetables and Indian spices makes a wonderful hot ot cold soup for any
season. Cranberries have been used to prevent and treat bladder and
urinary tract infections for at least a century. Even cranberry juice that
has been watered down to 1 per cent has shown some pharmacological
activity in lab tests but the whole berry is more potent.*

12oz (340g) fresh cranberries
12oz (340g) carrots, chopped
3oz (85g) onions, chopped
8fl oz (225ml) water
1¼ pints (710ml) chicken stock
4oz (115g) canned tomatoes, sieved to remove seeds
4 tablespoons frozen unsweetened orange juice concentrate
½ teaspoon ground cinnamon
¾ teaspoon ground cardamon
3 tablespoons sugar
Salt to taste

In a heavy saucepan, simmer the cranberries, carrots and onions in the
water for 25–30 minutes or until all liquid is absorbed and carrots are soft.
Stir in the remaining ingredients. Purée in a blender or a food processor. Taste for seasoning. Serve hot or refrigerate and serve well chilled.

Per serving:
Calories   121
Total fat   1g
Saturated fat   .2g
Cholesterol   0
Sodium   74mg

Salads, Relishes and Chutneys

Cabbage and Pepper Coleslaw

Serves 8

Coleslaw is one of the best ways to eat cabbage. Some studies suggest that raw cabbage and peppers have more of certain cancer-fighting compounds than the cooked vegetables. Also, you won't get any possibly cancer-promoting fat in this recipe. Absolutely no fat is added, making it as low-fat as a coleslaw can get. Yet I find it exceptionally good. One of the keys to its excellent flavour is the balsamic vinegar.

1½lb (680g) green cabbage, cut into chunks
1 medium onion, quartered
1 green pepper, cut into chunks
1 yellow pepper, cut into chunks
1 red pepper, cut into chunks
Salt and freshly ground pepper to taste
3 tablespoons balsamic vinegar
2 teaspoons sugar

Finely shred the cabbage or use the slicing disc of a food processor. Finely slice the onions and peppers by hand or using a food processor.

Transfer the vegetables to a bowl and add the salt and pepper, vinegar and sugar. Marinate in the refrigerator for at least an hour.

Per serving:
Calories	36
Total fat	.3g
Saturated fat	.01g
Cholesterol	0
Sodium	16mg

Apple Coleslaw with Peanuts

Serves 6

Adding apples, carrots and nuts to cabbage gives more variations of crunch and disease-fighting properties. Peanuts are high in boron, a trace mineral thought to help keep bones strong and the brain alert. The lemony yoghurt gives this salad an appealing taste without the fat found in typical coleslaw. This easy dressing is also terrific served on other fruit and vegetable salads.

   8oz (225g) cabbage, shredded
   4oz (115g) carrots, coarsely grated
   1 large cooking apple, cored and diced
   1¹/₂oz (45g) raisins
   1oz (30g) dry-roasted peanuts, chopped

Dressing

   4oz (115g) lemon low-fat yoghurt
   1 tablespoon low-calorie mayonnaise
   1 tablespoon lemon juice

   Combine the coleslaw ingredients in a bowl and toss together with the dressing ingredients.

   Per serving:
   Calories   118
   Total fat   4g
   Saturated fat   .7g
   Cholesterol   1.6mg
   Sodium   39mg

✔

FOOD PHARMACY FACT
Strong-Bone Foods

Nuts, particularly peanuts and almonds, as well as dried fruits, surprisingly may help prevent the crippling bone disease osteoporosis. These foods are high in the trace mineral boron, now thought critical in producing hormones that help regulate calcium metabolism. Tests by Dr. Forrest H. Nielsen, at the U.S. Department of Agriculture's Human Nutrition Research Center in Grand Forks, North Dakota, found that women on low-boron diets were more apt to lose calcium and magnesium, essential for keeping bones strong. But when given three milligrams of boron a day for three months, their calcium losses dropped by 40 per cent. People who eat lots of fruits and nuts get an average three milligrams daily, says Nielsen. One of the richest sources is peanuts, $3^1/2$oz (100g) contains two milligrams of boron.

Dr. Duke's Anticancer Slaw

Serves 8

Dr. James Duke, chief of the medicinal plants section at the U.S. Department of Agriculture, eats cabbage slaw every other day. He's convinced it may help ward off colon cancer, prevalent in his family. Here's one of his favourite recipes and he notes that every single ingredient has shown anticancer potential. For example, radishes, like cauliflower, are a member of the cabbage family well endowed with anticancer compounds. "Hot peppers contain capsaicin, another potent chemopreventive. Ginger absorbs and neutralizes gastrointestinal toxins and acids and is an immune stimulant," he says. And, of course "onions and garlic were added because they contain sulphurous compounds with cancer preventive properties".

1 small firm green cabbage, shredded
1 large carrot, shredded
7oz (200g) cauliflower florets, steamed until tender-crisp
1/2 green pepper, chopped
4 radishes, thinly sliced
4 spring onions, thinly sliced

Dressing

2 teaspoons grated root ginger *or* 1/2 teaspoon ground ginger
2 garlic cloves
1/4–1/2 teaspoon hot red pepper flakes
4fl oz (115ml) white wine vinegar
2 tablespoons tamari or light soy sauce
2 tablespoons olive oil or dark sesame oil
2 tablespoons toasted sesame seeds or slivered almonds (optional)

Place all the salad ingredients in a large bowl.

Place all dressing ingredients except the optional sesame seeds or almonds in a blender and process until smooth. Stir in the sesame seeds or almonds if desired.

Add the dressing to the vegetables to taste and toss. Refrigerate any remaining dressing.

Per serving:
Calories	71
Total fat	3.6g
Saturated fat	.5g
Cholesterol	0
Sodium	276mg

Turnip Slaw with Banana Dressing

Serves 4

"Turn on to turnips" might be a slogan of some researchers. Turnips are one of the cruciferous vegetables known to have several compounds believed to help cells resist damage leading to cancer. Frankly, I love raw turnips and the addition of apples and the banana dressing in this recipe makes it outstanding—a real treat. Many thanks to my friend Pat Krause for this imaginative combination.

1lb (450g) white turnip, peeled and grated
2oz (55g) onion, grated
2 unpeeled apples, preferably cooking, chopped
2 tablespoons frozen unsweetened orange juice concentrate
2 tablespoons lemon juice
1 teaspoon celery seeds
1 teaspoon caraway seeds
Salt and freshly ground black pepper to taste
8fl oz (225ml) Banana Dressing (recipe follows)

Combine all ingredients and refrigerate for at least 3 hours, preferably overnight.

Per serving:

Calories	138
Total fat	.7g
Saturated fat	.1g
Cholesterol	0
Sodium	93mg

Banana Dressing

1 pint (570ml)

2 medium bananas
2 small onions, chopped
4 tablespoons unsweetened concentrated apple juice
12 drops Tabasco sauce
Freshly ground black pepper to taste

Purée all the ingredients in a blender and refrigerate

Per 1-tablespoon serving:
Calories   9
Total fat   .02g
Saturated fat   .01g
Cholesterol   0
Sodium   .73mg

✔

FOOD PHARMACY FACT
Pineapple for Strong Bones

To preserve strong bones and guard against the crippling bone disease osteoporosis, you need not just calcium but also other minerals, including manganese. And pineapple is full of manganese, says Dr. Jean Freeland-Graves, professor of nutrition at the University of Texas at Austin. "When we want to up the levels of manganese in the diet, we tell women to eat pineapple or drink pineapple juice," she says.

Her studies find that women with osteoporosis have about one third less manganese in their blood than healthy women. Further, when given manganese the diseased women absorbed twice as much, proving their bodies needed it. There's no question animals deficient in manganese develop severe osteoporosis, says Dr. Freeland-Graves.

Other good sources of manganese are oatmeal, nuts, cereals, beans, whole wheat, spinach and tea. However, you're not as likely to absorb the mineral as well from these foods as you are from pineapple, says Dr. Freeland-Graves.

Cold Grated Carrot Salads

"A fluffy pile of orange shreds, light, cold, moist as snow" is the way
Phyllis Richman, restaurant critic of **The Washington Post**, describes
freshly grated carrots, saying she has loved them since childhood. But
now she combines them with a variety of fruits, vegetables, nuts and
flavours. Grating or shredding raw carrots, say experts, is one of the best
ways to obtain their therapeutic benefits, because grating breaks down
cell walls. This enables you to absorb more beta-carotene, the carrot
compound that is thought to help protect against cancer and some of the
effects of ageing.

With some imagination there's virtually no end to combinations you
can think up to make with grated carrots. Here are some of Richman's
suggestions: diced orange sections, crushed pineapple, diced red or
green peppers, diced banana, shredded red cabbage, raisins, grapes,
cantaloupe melon, green or black olives, coconut, onion, avocado, shredded cucumbers, nuts, parsley, spring onions, garlic, diced crystallised
ginger, shredded mint, dill, caraway seeds, cumin seeds, celery seeds,
nutmeg, mustard, hot pepper, oregano, paprika, anise, oil and vinegar,
citrus juice, yoghurt, low-fat mayonnaise.

Here are some of my favourite combinations.

Carrots with Pineapple, Raisins
and Walnuts   Serves 4

12oz (340g) carrots, grated
9oz (255g) canned, crushed pineapple in unsweetened juice
1 teaspoon lemon juice or to taste
1oz (30g) walnuts, chopped

In a bowl, mix all ingredients together. This salad needs no dressing; the pineapple juice takes care of that.

Per serving:
Calories	121
Total fat	4.8g
Saturated fat	.4g
Cholesterol	0
Sodium	30mg

✔

FOOD PHARMACY FACT
Surprising Anti-Parkinson's Foods

It's a small study, but it offers a hint about what foods may ward off Parkinson's disease, a nervous-system disorder characterized by shaky hands and a shuffling gait. Researchers at the University of Medicine and Dentistry of New Jersey asked eighty-one Parkinson's patients (average age sixty-five) and their same-sex siblings of similar age who were free of the disease which foods they were most likely to have eaten in earlier years. Those free of Parkinson's were more apt to have eaten nuts and seeds, particularly walnuts and sunflower seeds and salad oil or dressing.

The researchers speculate such foods share a common protective factor: vitamin E, which is concentrated in nuts, seeds and oils. A study of actual Parkinson's patients at Columbia University did find fewer symptoms in those taking megadoses of vitamin E. Thus some researchers conclude that vitamin E may help prevent Parkinson's and reduce its severity.

Carrots with a Touch of Cumin   Serves 4

4 large carrots, peeled and grated
1–3 tablespoons frozen orange juice concentrate diluted
   with half as much water
$^1/_2$ teaspoon ground cumin or to taste
2–3 tablespoons pine nuts (optional)

Put the grated carrots in a bowl and pour the diluted concentrate over them. Add the cumin and pine nuts if using and mix well.

Per serving:

Calories	58
Total fat	.2g
Saturated fat	0
Cholesterol	0
Sodium	36mg

✔

DOCTOR'S ADVICE

If you're a smoker or have ever been one, eat lots of deep orange foods high in beta-carotene; they may cut your chances of lung cancer, says Phyllis Bowen, associate professor of nutrition and medical dietetics at the University ot Illinois at Chicago and an expert in beta-carotene. Studies show, she says, that smokers and former smokers who consume the most beta-carotene foods are only half as likely to develop lung cancer as those who skimp on such foods. Foods highest in beta-carotene are deep orange vegetables like carrots and deep green leafy vegetables like spinach.

Minted Carrots with Lime Juice   Serves 4

Thanks for this suggestion to Molly O'Neill, food writer, The New York Times.

  4 large carrots, shredded or grated
  1oz (30g) fresh mint leaves, shredded
  2–3 teaspoons lime juice
  2 teaspoons olive oil
  Black pepper to taste, preferably freshly ground

Combine all ingredients and allow to marinate in the refrigerator for 30–60 minutes.

Per serving:
  Calories   65
  Total fat   2.5g
  Saturated fat   .3g
  Cholesterol   0
  Sodium   35mg

Tomatoes and Onions with Fresh Basil

Serves 4

My family loves this summer treat, claiming to have a craving for it. It's an excellent way to get the cholesterol-fighting benefits of raw onions and the varied protection from raw garlic. The fresh basil makes it all a very pleasant combination indeed.

2 large ripe tomatoes, cut into 1 inch (2.5cm) cubes
1 large mild onion, such as Spanish or red, chopped
6–8 large fresh basil leaves, shredded
2 tablespoons raspberry vinegar
3 tablespoons olive oil
2 garlic cloves, crushed
Salt and freshly ground pepper to taste

Combine the tomatoes and onions and add the basil.

Combine the vinegar, olive oil, garlic and salt and pepper. Add the dressing to the tomato onion mixture and chill for an hour before serving.

Per serving:
Calories	136
Total fat	10g
Saturated fat	1.4g
Cholesterol	0
Sodium	8mg

✔

DOCTOR'S ADVICE

Be sure to eat at least some of your garlic and onions raw, advises Dr. William Blott, Ph.D., epidemiologist and biostatistician at the U.S. National Cancer Institute. It's unclear, he says, whether garlic and onions work equally well raw and cooked. "Nobody knows for sure," he says "but we suspect that the active cancer-fighting compounds in garlic and onion are most potent in the raw form. In animal studies researchers usually use garlic or onion oils or garlic and onion extracts from raw bulbs to test anticancer potency, not the cooked version. Garlic and onion may also be anticancer when cooked but we just don't know at this time."

Footnote: quercetin, an anticancer agent in yellow and red onions, is not destroyed by heat. Allicin, in garlic, is.

Red and Yellow Onion Rings

About 4 servings

If you are in constant quest of the raw onion, as you should be, here's a treat that can be eaten as a relish with meat or poultry or added to green salads—it comes complete with its own low-calorie vinegar dressing. If it needs repeating, raw onions may boost your good-type HDL cholesterol and both yellow and red onions are incredibly rich sources of quercetin, an antioxidant and anticancer agent.

1 tablespoon balsamic vinegar or cider vinegar
1 tablespoon rice vinegar or white wine vinegar
4 teaspoons honey
2 teaspoons Dijon or any spicy mustard
Freshly ground pepper to taste
1 small red onion, thinly sliced
2 small yellow onions, thinly sliced

In a small bowl, thoroughly mix together the vinegars, honey, mustard and pepper.

Separate the onions into rings and add the dressing. Cover and allow to stand at room temperature for 30 minutes or refrigerate until serving time.

Note You can also coarsely chop the onions to make a relish.

Per serving:

Calories	36
Total fat	.2g
Saturated fat	0
Cholesterol	0
Sodium	76mg

Raw Onion Salsas or Relishes

*In California they call them salsas and they are like what most people
know as relishes—chopped-up fruits and vegetables, spiked with herbs
and a little vinegar and/or oil. Regardless, they are wonderful accom-
paniments to almost any main course. And I love them because they can
be a vehicle for getting a daily quota of raw onions, shown in tests by Dr.
Victor Gurewich, professor of medicine at Tufts, to boost good-type HDL
cholesterol by an average whopping 30 per cent. Consequently people are
always asking me, "How can I get more raw onions into my diet?" The
following five salsas are one of the most pleasant ways I know. Try them;
you'll love them too, not just for their health qualities but also for their
unique flavour and great colours.*

*They can turn a plain grilled fish, for example, into a spectacular
event. Heap the salsa on top of or beside the fish. You can also use salsas
as a colourful accompaniment to many vegetables or meat main dishes or
to liven up sandwiches.*

Peach, Onion and Pepper Salsa   Serves 4

---

3 unpeeled peaches, cut into ¹/₂ inch (1.5cm) dice
1oz (30g) spring onions, sliced, including some of the green
1oz (30g) red pepper, diced
1oz (30g) green pepper, diced
2–3 tablespoons lime juice
¹/₂oz (15g) chopped parsley or fresh coriander
3 tablespoons chopped flat-leaf parsley
1 tablespoon olive oil
¹/₂ teaspoon ground cumin
Salt and freshly ground pepper to taste
Finely chopped jalapeño pepper or hot red pepper
    flakes to taste (optional).

Combine all ingredients and allow to stand for about 30 minutes.

Per serving:

Calories	51
Total fat	.2g
Saturated fat	0g
Cholesterol	0
Sodium	4mg

✔

FOOD PHARMACY FACT
Onion Juice for Bronchial Asthma

German studies at the University of Munich by Dr. Walter Dorsch have shown that onion juice may be antiallergenic, helping ward off bronchial asthma attacks. In one test those who drank onion juice prior to being exposed to irritants had about half the number of bronchial asthma attacks. Also, when onion juice solution was rubbed on arms that had been exposed to allergens, there was delayed swelling and less inflammation in nine out of twelve cases. Onion compounds are known to inhibit the formation of prostaglandins in the blood; prostaglandins are cellular messengers that can encourage the allergic process.

Cantaloupe and Pear Salsa   Serves 4

3oz (85g) cantaloupe melon, diced
1oz (30g) celery, finely chopped
2oz (55g) red onion, chopped
2 spring onions, including some green, finely chopped
4 tablespoons lime juice
1 tablespoon olive oil
1 tablespoon finely chopped fresh mint
1/2oz (15g) parsley or fresh coriander, chopped
1 teaspoon hot chilli oil
1 tablespoon grated fresh root ginger
4oz (115g) pear, half peeled and all cut in 1/2-inch (1.5cm) dice
Salt and freshly ground pepper to taste
Pinch of sugar to taste

Mix all the ingredients except the pears, salt, pepper and sugar. Add these last ingredients just before serving.

Per serving:

Calories	80
Total fat	3.7g
Saturated fat	.5g
Cholesterol	0
Sodium	18mg

✔

FOOD PHARMACY FACT
The Vidalia Phenomenon

The county in Georgia, U.S.A. famous for producing Vidalia onions (a large mild variety) has an unusually low death rate from stomach cancer. Residents of the county are only one third as likely to die of stomach cancer as other Americans and one half as likely to die of the disease as other Georgians. Experts can only speculate it's because the residents who grow so many onions also eat more of them, helping protect them from the cancer.

Tomato and Onion Salsa   Serves 4

3 large tomatoes, peeled, seeded and finely chopped
1/2 large red onion, finely chopped
1 red pepper, finely chopped
1 cucumber, finely chopped
2 tablespoons lime juice
3–4 tablespoons chopped flat-leaf parsley, fresh coriander or fresh
    basil *or* 2 tablespoons chopped fresh oregano
2 tablespoons dark brown sugar
1 tablespoon olive oil
Salt and pepper to taste
Tabasco sauce to taste

Mix all ingredients in a bowl and marinate for 30 minutes

Per serving:
   Calories   99
   Total fat   3.8g
   Saturated fat   .05g
   Cholesterol   0
   Sodium   16mg

Confetti Jicama Salsa   Serves 4

Jicama is a crisp, juicy root vegetable native to Central America. It is also used in Oriental cooking. Try specialist or Oriental greengrocers.

1 small jicama or apple, peeled and diced
2 carrots, peeled and diced
1 red pepper, diced
1 medium onion, chopped
1 jalapeño pepper, seeds and veins removed, finely chopped
2–3 garlic cloves, finely chopped
4fl oz (115ml) rice vinegar
Salt and freshly ground pepper to taste
1/2 teaspoon hot red pepper flakes
1 teaspoon dried oregano
3 tablespoons chopped parsley or fresh coriander *or* 1 tablespoon
    each chopped fresh parsley, basil and mint
1 teaspoon dark brown sugar (optional)

Put the diced vegetables in a bowl.

Using a fork, beat together the garlic, vinegar, salt and pepper, pepper flakes, oregano, parsley or coriander and optional sugar. Pour the dressing over the diced vegetables and marinate for at least 2 hours before serving.

Per serving:
Calories	60
Total fat	.4g
Saturated fat	0
Cholesterol	0
Sodium	23mg

✔

FOOD PHARMACY FACT
Proof of Onion's Anticancer Powers

Experimenters at Harvard have found that putting minced yellow onions in the drinking water of hamsters saves them from oral cancer. Every day for four weeks the researchers put fresh onion in the animals' drinking water. Other hamsters were given no onions. Then the scientists painted a cancer-producing agent inside the mouths of both sets of animals. The onion-eating hamsters had only one third as many oral cancers and much smaller tumours than carcinogen-painted hamsters given no onions. The onion reduced the "total tumour burden" by about tenfold.

The researchers suspect that several compounds in the onions, including allicin, the chemical that brings tears to the eyes, are active cancer-preventive agents.

Onion and Rhubarb Salsa   Serves 4

2lb (900g) fresh rhubarb, diced
4oz (115g) onion, chopped
2oz (55g) green pepper, chopped
2oz (55g) yellow pepper, chopped
1 jalapeño pepper, finely chopped
1 tablespoon grated fresh root ginger
2 tablespoons lime juice
2 tablespoons dark brown sugar or to taste
Salt and freshly ground pepper to taste
2 tablespoons balsamic vinegar or to taste
Chopped parsley, fresh coriander, fresh oregano, or
    fresh mint to taste

Blanch the rhubarb in boiling water for 10–20 seconds. Drain and submerge in cold water for a few minutes.

Thoroughly drain the rhubarb and combine it with the onion, peppers, ginger, lime juice, sugar, salt and pepper. Add just a little balsamic vinegar to taste.

Add the chopped herbs last, using just one or a combination of them.

Note Since this salsa quickly loses its crunch, it is best to use it fairly soon after making it.

Per serving:
Calories	93
Total fat	.6g
Saturated fat	.01g
Cholesterol	0
Sodium	14mg

Chopped Broccoli and Pepper Salad

Serves 4

Here's a broccoli salad with a simple, no-fat tomato juice dressing. Broccoli is one of the best-tested and best-analysed vegetables, full of disease-fighting vitamins and minerals as well as at least half a dozen antioxidants and anticancer agents.

1lb (450g) broccoli, trimmed and broken into small florets, upper stems peeled and cut into 1/2 inch (1.5cm) pieces
4oz (115g) red peppers, cut into 1 inch (2.5cm) long strips
3oz (85g) red onion, finely chopped

Tomato Dressing

6fl oz (170ml) tomato juice
10–12 large fresh basil leaves, torn in half
2 teaspoons fresh thyme or oregano
2 teaspoons prepared mustard
1/4 teaspoon pepper, preferably freshly ground (more to taste)

Place broccoli in a microwave dish. Cover and cook for 1 minute on HIGH. Remove and plunge broccoli into cold water, drain and pat dry.

Toss the broccoli, red pepper strips and chopped red onion together in a bowl.

In a blender or food processor, mix together the tomato juice, herbs, mustard and pepper. Blend just until the leaves are finely chopped. Pour the dressing over the vegetables and toss to coat. Chill before serving.

Per serving:

Calories	58
Total fat	.7g
Saturated fat	.1g
Cholesterol	0
Sodium	230mg

HOW CARROTS, CABBAGE AND BROCCOLI CAN LOWER CHOLESTEROL

Peter D. Hoagland, Ph.D. and Philip E. Pfeffer, Ph.D., at the U.S. Department of Agriculture's regional research centre in Philadelphia, have discovered a major cholesterol-lowering constituent in carrots, cabbage and broccoli. It is a peculiar type of pectin fibre called *calcium pectate*. It works just like some cholesterol-lowering drugs, such as cholestyramine.

In laboratory experiments Drs. Hoagland and Pfeffer have demonstrated that both carrot pectin and particularly calcium pectate bind to bile acids. This is critical, for bile acids are digestive substances in the intestine made from cholesterol. Bile acids are normally reabsorbed after use but small amounts are lost and the body must make more by drawing cholesterol out of the system. Thus, if vegetable fibre grabs on to bile acids and whisks it out of the body, the body is forced to take cholesterol out of the blood to make more bile acids. Consequently cholesterol levels in the blood drop. Carrot fibre is very potent in binding to bile acids; both broccoli and cabbage have high amounts of calcium pectate.

Broccoli and Cauliflower Garlic Salad

Serves 4

What makes this salad so special is that the cruciferous vegetables are totally raw, meaning that all the antioxidant glutathione and indoles so plentiful in broccoli and cauliflower are totally intact and at full power. Add to that the antioxidant quercetin in red onions and all the therapeutic benefits of raw garlic and this salad is a real health winner. It is not for the timid; the garlic gives it real zing but if the garlic is too overwhelming for your taste, you can reduce the amount. It is always better to get some garlic than none at all.

12oz (340g) broccoli florets
8oz (225g) cauliflower florets
3oz (85g) red onion, chopped
½ quantity Garlic Dressing (recipe follows)

Combine all ingredients and toss.

Per serving:

Calories	69
Total fat	.5g
Saturated fat	0
Cholesterol	.6mg
Sodium	53mg

Garlic Dressing

8oz (225g) natural very-low-fat yoghurt
4 large garlic cloves, roughly chopped
½oz (15g) fresh basil leaves
2 teaspoons frozen orange juice concentrate (optional)
Salt and freshly ground pepper to taste

Put half the yoghurt in a blender or a food processor with the garlic and basil and process until blended. Stir in the remaining yoghurt, orange juice concentrate if using and salt and pepper. Use half on the salad and save the rest for another salad.

Lynn's Caesar Salad

Serves 4

Who doesn't love Caesar salad? Scientifically it is a favourite because cos lettuce is one of the darkest green varieties and therefore overstuffed with carotenoids, chlorophyll and other disease-fighting agents. Here's a fantastic-tasting version by Lynn Fischer, coauthor of The Low Cholesterol Gourmet, *that lacks all that traditional fat and cholesterol except for the good fat of anchovies and olive oil. Spraying the leaves with oil coats them with the minimum amount of oil possible. Use a new plant watering spray.*

1 head chilled cos lettuce
1 teaspoon olive oil (approximately)
$^1/_2$ teaspoon Worcestershire sauce
$^1/_2$ teaspoon anchovy paste *or* 4 anchovy fillets, patted dry
2 large garlic cloves, finely chopped
2 tablespoons lemon juice or to taste
4 tablespoons freshly grated Parmesan cheese
Coarsely ground black pepper to taste
Garlic croutons (recipe follows)

Wash and shake dry the lettuce. Spray the leaves all over with olive oil.
In a separate dish, mix the Worcestershire sauce, anchovy paste, garlic and lemon juice. Toss the salad and sprinkle with cheese, black pepper and garlic croutons.

Per serving:
Calories	102
Total fat	3.4g
Saturated fat	1.38g
Cholesterol	7.4mg
Sodium	342mg

Garlic Croutons

2 slices bread
1 large garlic clove, cut in half
$1/2$ teaspoon olive oil

Preheat the grill and toast the bread. Rub the toast with the garlic. Spray lightly with olive oil. Put under the grill until browned a little more. Remove, cut into cubes and add to the salad.

Spinach with Strawberries and Honey Dressing

Serves 4–5

It's hard to say enough for spinach pharmacologically, since it more than any other green leafy vegetable except broccoli and kale is full of identified compounds that protect cells in numerous ways. For example, it is extremely high in beta-carotene, being tested for its anticancer properties. Strawberries also contain disease-fighting antioxidants and frequently turn up in the diets of people who have less heart disease and cancer. I'm also crazy about this no-fat dressing and I use it on many other green salads.

6oz (170g) fresh spinach, torn into bite-size pieces
6oz (170g) strawberries, thickly sliced
1 tablespoon toasted sesame seeds *or* 4 tablespoons
  chopped pecans (optional)
1 small red onion, thinly sliced (optional)

Honey Mustard Dressing

2 tablespoons balsamic vinegar
2 tablespoons rice vinegar
4 teaspoons honey
2 teaspoons Dijon mustard
Salt and freshly ground black pepper to taste

Wash and throroughly dry the spinach.

In a separate container, whisk together the vinegars, honey, mustard, salt and pepper. Add to the spinach and toss lightly.

Add the strawberries and optional ingredients and toss again lightly.

Note You can also spray the spinach leaves with olive oil, then add the mixture of vinegar, garlic and salt before tossing.

Per serving:
Calories	47
Total fat	.4g
Saturated fat	0
Cholesterol	0
Sodium	111mg

DOCTOR'S ADVICE

Eat the greenest vegetables you can find. Cancer-fighting vegetables have shown their true colours—and one is definitely dark green. The deeper the green colour, the more cancer-inhibiting carotenoid compounds a vegetable has, says Dr. Frederick Khachik of the U.S. Department of Agriculture's Research Service. His analysis found that kale, known for its deep green colour, has the highest concentrations of three important carotenoids, twice as much as spinach. Fortunately, in tests, he says cooking by boiling, steaming or microwaving did not lessen the protective carotenoids in broccoli, green beans or spinach. "Even after boiling green beans for one hour, we ended up with the same amounts," he says. It's unlikely heat destroys the carotenoids in other green vegetables either, he says.

Mixed Leaves with Tangy Avocado Dressing

Serves 6

All kinds of dark green leafy vegetables appear tops on the diets of people who escape numerous diseases. That's probably because the greens are so high in carotenoids as well as folic acid and often vitamin C—all three disease-fighting antioxidants. Here's a particularly good way to use a variety of flavourful green leaves with a salad dressing that gives you only the beneficial monounsaturated fats in the avocado; it's the same type as is in olive oil. You can also add reddish radicchio for contrast; its red colour reveals that it too has carotenoids.

½ head escarole
½ head frisée
1 head radicchio
1 bunch watercress
2 seedless oranges, peeled and cut into 1 inch
    (2.5cm) chunks (optional)
½ quantity Tangy Avocado Salad Dressing (recipe follows)

Wash and dry the leaves thoroughly and tear them into bite-size pieces. In a large bowl, just before serving, toss the leaves (and oranges if using) with the avocado dressing or until the leaves are well coated.

Per serving:

Calories	81
Total fat	3g
Saturated fat	.5g
Cholesterol	.4mg
Sodium	125mg

Tangy Avocado Salad Dressing   About 12fl oz (340ml)

---

1 ripe avocado, peeled, stoned and cut into chunks
2 tablespoons white wine vinegar
3 tablespoons lemon juice
2 teaspoons Dijon mustard
10 drops Tabasco sauce or to taste
1/4 teaspoon salt or to taste
8fl oz (225ml) skimmed milk

Put all the ingredients in a blender or food processor and process until smooth and creamy.

Note Use half of the dressing for the mixed leaf salad. Save the rest by putting it in a tightly closed container and refrigerating for 1–2 days.

Per tablespoon:
Calories	18
Total fat	1.3g
Saturated fat	.2g
Cholesterol	.2mg
Sodium	43mg

A GUIDE TO GREENS

The greening of the diet may be as important to survival as the greening of the planet, say some authorities. The green stuff is packed with a variety of compounds—carotenoids, chlorophyll, glutathione, folic acid, vitamin C—all thought to protect cells from myriad types of damage.

Here are some of the green leaves you should be including in your diet:

Rocket: Dark green leaves with a pungent, peppery bite. Use rocket as a salad green alone or to add spice to other salad greens. Tear leaves into pieces and toss into soups and stir-frys.

Round (Butterhead): A small, roundish head lettuce with delicate, buttery-flavoured pale green to dark green leaves. Use in salads with a light dressing.

Cabbage lettuce: Larger than (Butterhead) lettuce, with a similar taste but slightly less crunchy texture and usually deeper green leaves. Use in salads with a light dressing.

Spring Greens: Similar to kale, but with straighter, smoother leaves, this maybe the so-called "cabbage" beloved among ancient Romans, according to Waverley Root's book *Food*.

Frisée (Curly Endive): A stalk with frizzled, curly green leaves, cultivated in ancient Egypt and probably referred to in the Bible as "bitter herbs". Because of its distinctive taste, it is often mixed with other lettuces in salads.

Escarole (Broad-leafed Endive): Large, broad leaves with a slightly bitter, tangy taste but not as bitter as curly endive. Add to other salad leaves or sauté as a vegetable or tear into pieces and add to soups and stews.

Kale: A member of the cruciferous or cabbage family, kale leaves are slightly curled and crimped (kale in French is "curly cabbage") and strongly flavoured. Kale is often sautéed, steamed or boiled alone or with other leafy green vegetables. Shred it and add to soups, stews and stir-frys. To eat it raw in salads, remove the stems and centre veins and tear into small pieces.

Lamb's Lettuce (Mâche, Corn Salad): Small, delicately flavoured long tongue-shaped leaves with a light, creamy texture. Serve with very lightly flavoured dressings and herbs.

Cutting or Looseleaf Lettuce: Sweet, delicate and crisp, with green and/or reddish leaves. Excellent for salads. Lollo Rosso or Lollo Biondo are the two main types.

Chinese Mustard Cabbage (Gai choy): The leaves are a vivid green and not surprisingly have a somewhat sharp, mustardy taste. Used in soups, cooked with vinegar or preserved like sauerkraut.

Parsley: One of the world's oldest and most universal greens, widely used in ancient Roman cuisine. Common supermarket parsley with its frilly, curly leaves has a pleasant light, peppery taste; Italian parsley, with broader flat leaves, tastes stronger and sharper. Use parsley in salads, sauces and dressings, to stuff fish, to sprinkle on vegetables and as a vegetable on its own.

Radicchio (Red Chicory): Actually this "green" usually is bright red and crunchy with a mild to bitter taste. Commonly used in Italian dishes. Heads are small and tightly wrapped, ranging from golf-ball to grapefruit size. Add to other green salads for colour and distinctive taste.

Cos (Romaine): Large dark green crunchy leaves with a strong, nonbitter taste. Ideal for salads and very versatile. Used in the classic Caesar salad, cos lettuce derives its name from the fact that it was cultivated by the ancient Greeks on the island of Kos or Cos.

Spinach: Becoming increasingly popular. Leaves vary from large to small and flat to crinkly and are of a sharp taste and strong texture. Spinach is of fairly recent cultivation, not known in ancient cultures. Wash and dry it thoroughly and use it in salads, steam it, stir-fry or toss it into soups, casseroles, stews, sauces and meat loaves of all types.

Swiss chard (Leaf Beet): Actually the leaf of the beet plant, chard is similar to spinach and is most popular in France. It is usually steamed, sautéed or cooked like spinach.

Watercress: Almost always available, watercress was cultivated in ancient China and is still used extensively in stir-fried dishes. Its peppery taste adds spice and pungency to salads as well as soups, stews, stir-frys and casseroles.

Green Salad with Apples and Blue Cheese Dressing

Serves 6

Mixing fruit with green salad is always a good idea and apples are a natural. Among lettuces, dark green cos and cabbage are among the best, far better choices than pale iceberg, because darker green lettuces have more disease-fighting compounds. In this salad the leaves and fruit are complemented with a pungent blue cheese low-fat dressing that produced raves among tasters. You can also use the dressing on other green or fruit salads.

> 1 large bunch dark green cutting lettuce, cleaned and torn into bite-size pieces
> 1 large head cos or cabbage lettuce, cleaned and torn into bite-size pieces
> 4oz (115g) celery, diced
> 3 apples, cored and diced
> Blue Cheese Dressing (recipe follows)

Put the leaves in a large salad bowl. Sprinkle the celery and apple over the leaves. Pour the dressing over the salad or serve separately.

Per serving:

Calories	128
Total fat	2.4g
Saturated fat	1.2g
Cholesterol	5mg
Sodium	148mg

Blue Cheese Dressing

1¹/₂oz (45g) blue cheese
1 teaspoon vinegar
¹/₄ teaspoon Worcestershire sauce
¹/₂ teaspoon prepared mustard
¹/₂ teaspoon sugar
2 tablespoons frozen orange juice concentrate.
8oz (225g) natural very-low-fat yoghurt

Put the blue cheese in a small bowl and mash with a fork. Add the remaining ingredients and combine. Cover and chill for several hours so flavours blend.

FOOD PHARMACY FACT
Vitamin C vs. Breast Cancer

Surprisingly few foods or nutrients have been linked to the prevention of breast cancer. But a recent analysis of sixteen breast-cancer studies by researchers at Canada's National Cancer Institute found that eating lots of vitamin-C-rich foods, like green leafy vegetables and fruits, may provide striking protection.

The institute's Dr. Geoffrey R. Howe estimated that if all women over age twenty were to eat enough fruits and vegetables to take in 380 milligrams of vitamin C a day, the breast-cancer rate might drop by 16 per cent. Eating more vitamin C seemed to have a greater impact on breast cancer than cutting back on saturated animal and dairy fats, longtime suspected promoters of breast cancer.

Dr. Howe predicted that if women past menopause cut consumption of saturated fats to 9 per cent of calories, their breast-cancer rate would probably go down 10 per cent. If they cut back on fat and ate foods containing 380 milligrams of vitamin C daily, their breast-cancer rate might fall a whopping 24 per cent.

Shredded Brussels Sprouts with Dates

Serves 6

It's not often you find recipes for raw Brussels sprouts but new tests find that some of the anticancer agents are more plentiful in uncooked sprouts. When I mentioned this to cookbook author Maxine Rapoport, she came up with this imaginative recipe for raw Brussels sprouts, which makes me wonder why we don't treat Brussels sprouts more like cabbage, which is commonly made into slaw. After all, Brussels sprouts are of the cabbage family and contain many of the same wonderful pharmacological agents, notably related to preventing cancer.

8oz (225g) Brussels sprouts, shredded or chopped
2 medium carrots, peeled and coarsely grated
15 stoned dates, coarsely chopped
1 tablespoon olive oil
2 tablespoons balsamic vinegar
2 tablespoons concentrated apple juice or citrus blend concentrate
$1/8$ teaspoon freshly ground pepper

Mix all ingredients together and chill at least 1 hour before serving.

Per serving:

Calories	114
Total fat	2.5g
Saturated fat	.3g
Cholesterol	0
Sodium	20mg

✔

FOOD PHARMACY FACT
Brussels Sprouts Zap Cancer

In tests at Cornell University, researchers fed one group of animals Brussels sprouts while a second group was fed ordinary rat feed. Both groups were injected with a powerful carcinogen. After fifteen weeks only 13 per cent of the Brussels sprouts eaters had developed breast tumours compared with 77 per cent of the feed-eaters. A possible reason could be that Brussels sprouts have high amounts of a compound called *glucobardssicin* that aids the liver in neutralizing and eliminating potential carcinogens.

Dilled Potato Salad

Serves 10

There must be enough different potato salad recipes to stretch to another galaxy but this one really is different and is always described as not just good but sensational. I like it because it combines so many healthy vegetables in an interesting way and of course the dill pickles give it that extra punch. The pickles also are high in sodium, which should be noted by those on a low-sodium diet.

4 large red potatoes, cooked and diced
4oz (115g) French beans, cut into 1 inch (2.5cm) pieces and cooked until tender-crisp
12oz (340g) carrots, sliced and cooked
10oz (285g) frozen peas, thawed, boiling water poured over them, then well drained
3 large dill pickles, diced
1 tablespoon finely chopped fresh dill *or* 1 teaspoon dried
1 teaspoon caraway seeds
2oz (55g) natural low-fat yoghurt
4 tablespoons reduced-calorie mayonnaise
2 teaspoons Dijon mustard
Salt and pepper to taste

In a large bowl, combine the potatoes, French beans, carrots, peas, pickles, dill and caraway seeds.

Mix the yoghurt, mayonnaise, mustard, salt and pepper together and add to the salad mixture. Mix thoroughly, cover and refrigerate for several hours before serving.

Per serving:
Calories	135
Total fat	2g
Saturated fat	.4g
Cholesterol	2.3mg
Sodium	535mg

Black Bean Salad with Feta Cheese and Mint

Serves 4

The beans, cheese and mint are a stunning combination and the mint is a well-documented carminative that helps counteract the gaseous qualities of the beans. I think you will be surprised how fantastic this salad is—I was. It's the fresh mint that makes the difference, so use every bit called for. Since the mint tends to lose flavour if stored for many hours or overnight, the salad needs to be eaten within a few hours of being made— but that has never been a problem in my house.

7oz (200g) dried black beans, soaked overnight, cooked and drained
    or 1lb (450g) canned, drained and rinsed
4oz (115g) feta cheese, drained and crumbled
2–3 teaspoons finely chopped red onion
$1/2$oz (15g) fresh mint leaves, finely chopped
3 tablespoons olive oil
Juice of 1 lemon or to taste
Salt and freshly ground black pepper to taste

Place the drained black beans in a large mixing bowl. Add the crumbled feta cheese and chopped onion. Stir in the mint leaves with the oil, lemon, salt and pepper. Let the beans marinate for 30–60 minutes. Correct the seasonings before serving.

Per serving:
Calories	333
Total fat	16g
Saturated fat	5.7g
Cholesterol	25mg
Sodium	320mg

Three-Bean Salad with Poppy Seed Dressing

Serves 6–8

One of the joys of beans is that you can so easily combine various types. In this salad I use one that is too often neglected in this country—soya beans. Soaked and cooked, they are as delicious in taste and texture as other commonly used legumes and yet have some added attributes. According to tests, soya beans are the most thoroughly documented among legumes for their singular anticancer capabilties. All legumes help fight blood cholesterol. Even if you substitute other beans for soya beans, you still get some soya beans from the tofu in the low-calorie, low-fat salad dressing.

4oz (115g) black-eyed peas, cooked *or* 15oz (425g) can,
   drained and rinsed
5oz (140g) black beans, cooked *or* 15oz (425g) can,
   drained and rinsed
6oz (170g) soya beans, cooked or chickpeas, any type of bean or
   even sweetcorn
1 large green pepper, chopped
1 large red onion, chopped
Salt and freshly ground pepper to taste
1–2 tablespoons fresh coriander, parsley, thyme, or other
   fresh herb (optional)
Poppy Seed Dressing (recipe follows)

Combine all ingredients in a large bowl. Add dressing and toss until all ingredients are well coated.

Per serving:
Calories	236
Total fat	5.9g
Saturated fat	.9g
Cholesterol	0
Sodium	8mg

Poppy Seed Dressing

    4oz (115g) firm tofu
    4 tablespoons frozen orange juice concentrate
    4 tablespoons rice vinegar
    1 garlic clove, finely chopped
    2 teaspoons lemon juice
    2 teaspoons poppy seeds

Put all the ingredients except the poppy seeds into a blender or a food processor and blend until smooth. Transfer to a jar or bowl and stir in the poppy seeds.

✔

FOOD PHARMACY FACT
The Soya Bean and Poppy Seed Cirrhosis Defence

Worried about liver damage from drinking alcohol? Lecithin, found in good supply in soya beans and poppy seeds, may be an antidote. That's the remarkable finding of a group of top alcohol researchers.

In a ten-year study, Dr. Charles S. Lieber and colleagues at Mount Sinai School of Medicine in New York City, fed baboons the human equivalent of eight cans of beer per day. They also gave some animals about three tablespoons a day of soy lecithin. The lecithin-fed baboons showed only slight liver scarring and no cirrhosis. However, seven out of nine baboons not given lecithin developed severe liver damage and two progressed to full-blown cirrhosis.

Although tests on humans need to be done, Dr. Lieber, a noted expert on alcohol, believes the new study indicates that lecithin delays and possibly prevents cirrhosis of the liver. It may also reverse the early stages of liver scarring.

Soya beans have 15,000–25,000 parts per million of lecithin; mung beans have about 16,000 ppm, peanuts have 5,000–7,000 ppm and poppy seeds have 28,000 ppm; dandelion flowers beat all with 29,700 ppm, according to U.S. Department of Agriculture expert, Dr. Jim Duke.

✔

FOOD PHARMACY FACT
Tofu vs. Cholesterol

Eat tofu instead of cheese and your blood cholesterol will most likely drop. That's what a study by nutritionists Carolyn Dunn and Michael Liebman, University of North Carolina at Greensboro, found. They asked twelve lacto-ovo-vegetarian men to eat tofu instead of cheese. At the end of three weeks the men's cholesterol had dropped around 7 per cent. The probable reason is that tofu contains mostly unsaturated fat, whereas cheese is packed with saturated fat – the type that boosts blood cholesterol.

✔

FOOD PHARMACY FACT
Cancer Drug in Soya beans

Why do Asian women have less breast cancer? Maybe it's their high diet of soya beans. Soya beans contain plant hormones (phytoestrogens) very similar chemically to a common drug tamoxifen, used quite successfully to block the spread of breast cancer in certain women. So discovered Dr. Stephen Barnes, associate professor of pharmacology and biochemistry at the University of Alabama.

He fed soya beans to one group of rats, regular feed to another group. Then he dosed them all with cancer-causing agents. Sure enough, the soya-bean-eating rats had 40–65 per cent fewer breast cancers than the non-soya-bean eating rats. Dr. Barnes suspected the anticancer agent to be plant hormones (phytoestrogens). But soya beans also contain anticancer compounds called *protease inhibitors*. So he removed the protease inhibitors from the soya beans—and the beans still curbed breast cancer in rats. "That told us it was probably the phytoestrogens blocking the cancer," says Dr. Barnes.

Soya bean products highest in anticancer phytoestrogens are whole soya beans, tofu (bean curd), miso (fermented soya bean paste) and soya milk. Processed soya flour may have some phytoestrogens, but soy sauce has none, says Dr. Barnes.

SALADS, RELISHES AND CHUTNEYS

Waldorf Salad with Sardines

Serves 4

This unlikely combination turns an old-time favourite into a modern source of fish high in the beneficial omega-3-type oils. Add walnuts—one of the best plant sources—and you have even more omega-3s. You can use plain sardines but smoked sardines are even more scrumptious, the smoky taste blending well with the apples and nuts. Don't worry about the fat, nearly all of it is the good omega-3-type from the fish. The rest is from the walnuts, also high in omega-3, vitamin E and beneficial antioxidants.

6oz (170g) diced apples
2 teaspoons lemon juice
2 x 2³/₄oz (78g) cans sardines, drained
2oz (55g) celery, diced
1oz (30g) chopped walnuts
2oz (55g) natural very-low-fat yoghurt or reduced-calorie
    mayonnaise or a mixture.

Toss the apples with the lemon juice to help the apples retain their colour. Cut sardines into bite-size pieces. Lightly mix the apples, celery, sardines, walnuts and yoghurt.

Per serving:
Calories	171
Total fat	10g
Saturated fat	1.13g
Cholesterol	65mg
Sodium	257mg

Herring Salad with Potatoes and Beetroot

Serves 6

"A land with lots of herring can get along with few doctors," goes an old *Dutch proverb. That's because people who feast on fish like herring, full of omega-3 fatty acids, are less likely to get heart disease, high blood pressure, cancer, diabetes, psoriasis, arthritis and migraine headaches. It's time to make herring more popular. For a start, try this appetizer salad with onions and apples that also give your heart a boost. Thanks to Joan Nathan, author of* Jewish Holiday Kitchen.

    8oz (225g) pickled herring, drained and cut into
        ½ inch (1.5cm) cubes
    2 cooked beetroot, cut into ½ inch (1.5cm) cubes
    4 medium potatoes, peeled, boiled and cut into
        ½ inch (1.5cm) cubes
    1 large unpeeled Granny Smith apple, cored and cut into ½ inch
        (1.5cm) cubes
    3 slices red onion, diced
    2 tablespoons chopped walnuts
    Lettuce leaves (optional)

Vinaigrette Dressing

    2 tablespoons balsamic vinegar
    2 tablespoons olive oil
    1 garlic clove, finely chopped or crushed
    Salt and freshly ground pepper to taste
    Pinch of sugar
    Herbs of your choice (optional)

Remove and discard any onion that might come with the herring. Combine the herring, beetroot, cooked potato, apple and onion.

For the dressing, whisk together the vinegar, olive oil, garlic, salt and pepper, sugar and herbs.

Add the vinaigrette dressing to the herring salad and toss. Sprinkle with walnuts. Serve on lettuce leaves if you wish.

Per serving:
Calories	221
Total fat	10g
Saturated fat	1.3g
Cholesterol	3mg
Sodium	218mg

Orange and Sangria Salad

Serves 6

Oranges are so good for you and not only because of their vitamin C, which is gaining a reputation as a health protector that not even its strongest advocate, Linus Pauling, thought possible. Vitamin C looks as if it can help zap a whole gamut of chronic diseases, including bronchitis, cancer and heart disease. Citrus, however, has other, newly discovered cancer-fighting compounds. This excellent recipe comes from food writer Elaine Hallgarten, as published in the Daily Mail. She advises serving it as a cold salad or as a warm accompaniment to poultry.

    6 oranges
    8fl oz (225ml) dry red wine
    8fl oz (225ml) fresh orange juice
    1 tablespoon sugar
    1 cinnamon stick
    4 cloves
    Sliver of orange zest

Peel the oranges and slice thinly. In a small saucepan, bring the remaining ingredients to the boil and simmer for 5 minutes.

Pour the hot wine and juice mixture over the sliced oranges. Serve warm or cold.

Per serving:

Calories	112
Total fat	.4g
Saturated fat	.04g
Cholesterol	0
Sodium	2.6mg

FOOD PHARMACY FACT
Oranges for High Blood Pressure?

Too little vitamin C may make you more susceptible to high blood
pressure. That's what a large-scale study by researchers in Finland
noted. They found "marked high blood pressure" among those with
the lowest blood levels of vitamin C and selenium. Both vitamin C
and selenium are antioxidants.

It's the first evidence that antioxidants may help depress blood
pressure, say the investigating scientists. For foods highest in vitamin C, see page 7.

Mango, Banana and Blueberry Salad

Serves 6

*At least six of the ingredients in this salad have been shown to be either
antibacterial or antiviral, according to laboratory tests. They are mango,
blueberry, yoghurt, ginger, cayenne and honey—a winning combination.
The dressing is one of my favourites, a rare treat with minimal fat and few
calories. Try it also on other fruit salads.*

1 large *or* 3 small ripe but firm mangoes, peeled and cut into chunks
   (about 1¹/₂lb/680g with seeds and skin)
2 bananas, sliced
8oz (225g) blueberries, rinsed and picked over
3 teaspoons lemon juice
1 bunch watercress or cutting lettuce

Honey and Ginger Dressing

6oz (170g) vanilla very-low-fat yoghurt
1 teaspoon honey or to taste
2 teaspoons finely chopped crystallised ginger
¹/₈ teaspoon ground cumin (optional)
Pinch of cayenne pepper or to taste

In a bowl, combine the fruit with the lemon juice to prevent discoloura-
tion. Combine all the dressing ingredients in a small bowl.

Place the prepared fruit on a bed of watercress or lettuce and top with
the honey and ginger dressing.

Per serving:
   Calories   145
   Total fat   .5g
   Saturated fat   .1g
   Cholesterol   .8mg
   Sodium   38mg

✔

FOOD PHARMACY FACT
Bananas vs. Ulcers

Bananas have some mysterious substances that prevent ulcers in animals. A recent study by researchers at the University of New England in Australia noted that rats fed bananas and then fed high amounts of acid to induce ulcers had very little stomach damage. The bananas prevented 75 per cent of the expected ulcers. Researchers believe the bananas somehow helped create a barrier between the stomach lining and the acid.

In other studies Indian physicians have successfully treated ulcers with powder made of unripe plantains, a larger member of the banana family.

✔

FOOD PHARMACY FACT
Mangoes Halt Herpes Virus

Scientists have found that in test-tube studies two components of the mango behaved like antiviral drugs against the herpes simplex virus. In fact the mango compounds (mangiferin and iso-mangiferin) were found to be superior to commonly used antiviral compounds—acyclovir, idoxuridine and cyclocytidine—which the scientists also tested. Apparently the mango compounds prevented the virus from replicating, causing it to die off.

Joanna's Cranberry Fantasy

Serves 8

Everyone thinks this tastes as if it took hours to make yet it's so easy, says my friend Joanna Simon who has served it often. You can, of course, make the sauce from fresh cranberries instead. So there's no excuse for not getting your quota of cranberries, now found to contain ellagic acid, an antioxidant that protects cells from various kinds of damage. Walnuts are also high in this beneficial antioxidant. Joanna says the combination is fabulous with any roast poultry or game, I agree.

29oz (820g) cranberry sauce
8oz (225g) canned crushed pineapple packed in natural juice
4oz (115g) walnuts, chopped

Mix all ingredients together and refrigerate for 2 hours before serving.

Per serving:
Calories	271
Total fat	9g
Saturated fat	.8g
Cholesterol	0
Sodium	32mg

✔

FOOD PHARMACY FACT
Doctors for Cranberries

Cranberry juice for urinary infections has passed muster with the American Medical Association, although it's still unclear, they say, exactly how the berry works. An article in the *Journal of the American Medical Association* speculated on possible mechanisms. Cranberry juice raises acidity of the urine, killing off infection-causing bacteria, but that effect appears temporary. Also, cranberry agents may help prevent bacteria from sticking to the lining of the urinary tract. Regardless, the journal noted research showing that 73 per cent of patients with such infections improved after drinking about ¾ pint (425ml) of cranberry juice daily for twenty-one days. Thus the AMA suggests using liberal amounts of cranberry juice in conjuction with drug therapy as a possible preventive for such urinary tract and bladder infections.

Spicy Indian-Style Fruit Salad

Serves 6

The spicy apple butter sauce turns this ordinary salad into a spectacular one. You can mix the sauce in with the fruit or serve the sauce in a bowl surrounded by freshly cut fruit for dipping. This recipe was inspired by a salad called Chat served at the Taste of India restaurant in Dayton, Ohio. The restaurant uses tamarind paste, a tart and tangy paste available in Indian grocers. The manager suggested to food consultant Howard Solganik apple butter (a thick spicy purée) would be a good substitute for tamarind. Howard came up with this delightful recipe.

1¹/₂lb (680g) sliced fruit (combination of bananas, strawberries, raspberries, blueberries, kiwi fruit, peaches, mango and papaya)
Juice of 1 lemon
8oz (225g) apples, peeled and chopped
4oz (115g) brown sugar
¹/₄ teaspoon allspice
¹/₈ teaspoon salt
¹/₂ teaspoon ground ginger
¹/₄ teaspoon ground nutmeg
¹/₄ teaspoon ground cinnamon
¹/₄ teaspoon cayenne pepper
¹/₄ teaspoon black pepper, preferably freshly ground

Place the sliced fruit in a large bowl. Toss with the lemon juice.

Cook the apples with 2–3 tablespoons of water in a pan with a tightly fitting lid. When soft, beat to a purée and stir in the sugar and allspice. Continue to cook over a low heat until the purée is very thick and no liquid separates out when a little is placed on a cold plate.

Whisk together the remaining ingredients with the apple purée. Toss gently with the fruit and serve chilled.

Per serving:
Calories	156
Total fat	.7g
Saturated fat	.07g
Cholesterol	0
Sodium	49mg

FOOD PHARMACY FACT
Fruit Every Day May Keep Cancer Away

An American National Cancer Institute study found that eating fruit such as apples, bananas, oranges, strawberries, orange juice or canned fruits only once a day cut the odds of developing pancreatic cancer by 40 per cent. Eating fruit twice a day cut the risk by 60 per cent. The study was done among residents in southern Louisiana, where the rate of pancreatic cancer is unusually high.

Indian Raitas

Raita is the classic yoghurt-based accompaniment to hot curried dishes in India. But you can serve it with any hot spicy food, even chilli. It soothes the palate and cools the fire in the mouth, taking away the burning sensation, according to experts. Not to mention that yoghurt also soothes the stomach and may help keep ulcers away, according to new French research. Here are three variations on raita.

Banana Raita   Serves 2

8oz (225g) natural very-low-fat yoghurt
1 teaspoon lemon juice
1/4 teaspoon grated fresh root ginger
1/4 teaspoon cumin seeds, toasted
1 ripe banana, diced

Combine all ingredients and chill for at least 1 hour.

Per serving:
Calories	117
Total fat	.45g
Saturated fat	.3g
Cholesterol	1.5mg
Sodium	87mg

Mint Raita   Serves 2

1oz (30g) fresh mint, chopped
3oz (85g) onion, finely chopped
1/2 green pepper, finely chopped
6oz (170g) natural very-low-fat yoghurt
Salt to taste

Combine all ingredients and chill before serving.

Per serving:
Calories	69
Total fat	.4g
Saturated fat	.1g
Cholesterol	2mg
Sodium	66mg

Green Pepper and Watercress Raita   Serves 4

4oz (115g) green pepper, finely chopped
1oz (30g) watercress leaves, finely chopped
1 teaspoon finely chopped garlic
8oz (225g) natural very-low-fat yoghurt
1–2 teaspoons ground cumin
$1/2$ teaspoon sugar
Salt and freshly ground pepper to taste

Combine all ingredients and refrigerate.
Note Best made a day in advance.

Per serving:
Calories	45
Total fat	.4g
Saturated fat	.1g
Cholesterol	1mg
Sodium	80mg

FOOD PHARMACY FACT
Greens to the Rescue

Mice fed cabbage or spring greens and then injected with breast cancer cells had fewer spreading (metastasized) cancers, according to experiments at the University of Nebraska's Eppley Cancer Institute. Greens in other tests have exhibited extraordinarily active antimutagenic agents that help block genetic changes in cells that promote tumours.

RAW OR COOKED—WHICH IS BETTER?

Eating vegetables raw, as our Stone Age ancestors did, is undoubtedly a good idea—sometimes. Numerous studies indicate that some of the powerful antioxidants, body detoxifiers and anticancer agents are diminished by cooking. On the other hand, recent evidence shows that cooking vegetables is not as detrimental to certain pharmacological compounds as previously thought and in fact cooking in some cases can boost absorption of life-enhancing chemicals. Also, too much of a raw vegetable, as in the case of garlic, may cause trouble.

Here's the latest evidence on the pros and cons of eating vegetables both raw and cooked.

• Raw crucifers have more anticancer indoles. Canadian scientists at the University of Manitoba found that indole glycosinolates in cruciferous vegetables, such as cabbage, cauliflower, broccoli and Brussels sprouts, sank by 30–50 per cent when steamed for 10 minutes or boiled for 40 minutes. These indoles are known to prevent a broad array of cancers in laboratory animals and are thought to be active anticancer agents in humans. The Canadian researchers think any vegetable protection against stomach and colon cancer should be credited to "the consumption of raw vegetables".

• Indeed experts at the American National Cancer Institute suspect that raw vegetables are highly responsible for keeping certain cancers in check. Numerous epidemiological studies single out raw vegetables and salads as protective. A study of Seventh-Day Adventists done by Harold Kahn in 1984 found that eating "green salads" was linked to lower death rates from all types of cancer.

Similarly a 1988 study by Belgian researcher Albert J. Tuyns of the International Agency for Research on Cancer declared that "all raw vegetables had a clear protective effect for both colon and rectal cancer". Eating a mere 3oz (85g) of raw vegetables a week appeared to cut the odds of colon cancer by about 40 per cent.

• One of the powerful antioxidants and anticancer agents, glutathione, heavily concentrated in green leafy vegetables, is 25–50 per cent lower in cooked vegetables, according to tests by Dr. Dean P. Jones, associate professor of biochemistry, Emory University School of Medicine. Protective glutathione is almost entirely wiped out when vegetables are canned, he notes.

• The discovery that vitamin C is a powerful antioxidant dramatically elevates its role as a disease preventer and makes conserving it even more critical than ever. Unfortunately vitamin C in vegetables appears more fragile than previously suspected. New U.S. Department of Agriculture tests found that freezing, boiling, blanching, steaming or cooking broccoli in any fashion cuts its vitamin C content roughly in half.

However, contrary to long-standing belief, says USDA researcher Dr. Joseph T. Vanderslice, vegetables do not lose more vitamin C when cooked in large amounts of water than when steamed in very little water. His tests showed that a stalk of broccoli retained the same amount of vitamin C when cooked in 4fl oz (115ml) of water or 32fl oz (900ml) of water. The best way to conserve vitamin C in cooked vegetables, he says, is to microwave them. Microwaved broccoli lost a mere 15 per cent of its vitamin C.

• Dr. Victor Gurewich, professor of medicine at Tufts University School of Medicine, finds that half a raw onion a day or a comparable amount of onion juice boosts beneficial HDL cholesterol in most people by an average 30 per cent. But this particular therapeutic benefit of onions lessens with cooking and disappears when onions are cooked to the limp stage. However, cooked onions retain their anticoagulant powers, he says.

• Garlic, too, loses some of its therapeutic benefits when cooked but not nearly as much as generally believed, says Dr. Robert I. Lin, chairman of the first international scientific conference on garlic held in Washington, D.C., in August 1990.

Allicin, the major antibiotic in garlic, is destroyed by heat but it's a myth to think allicin is the only, or even the major, medicinal compound in garlic, argues Dr. Lin. He says that most of garlic's therapeutic benefits come from the bulb's 200 or so other chemicals, most of which survive heat and do not have a strong taste or smell. Garlic does not have to give off the heavy allicin-inspired garlic odour to be good for you, he says. He explains that garlic is often pickled in China, which destroys the allicin. Yet studies show Chinese who eat the most garlic have lower rates of certain cancers.

Furthermore, Dr. Lin notes that eating too much raw garlic could be hazardous. Chewing on raw garlic cloves could injure the mouth, stomach and oesophagus, he says. In an experiment he also found healthy men who ate a special garlic powder equal to seven-and-a-half raw garlic cloves a day developed diarrhoea that lasted a week. "In high doses the allicin in raw garlic can be toxic," he warns.

Dr. Lin favours cooking garlic for two or three minutes, as is common in stir-frying, especially if you eat much of it. He makes it a point to average a large garlic clove daily but thinks that "two or three cloves a day are okay".

A recent study in India by researcher-cardiologist Arun Bordia of Tagore Medical College backs up Dr. Lin. In the test Dr. Bordia had half of 432 patients with heart disease eat two or three garlic cloves a day for three years. The other half got no garlic. In the second year fatalities among garlic eaters dropped by 50 per cent and sank by 66 per cent in the third year.

It made no difference in warding off heart attacks whether the garlic was eaten raw or cooked, concluded Dr. Bordia. Both worked equally well, indicating that garlic's heart-protective powers were not compromised by cooking. However, the raw garlic eaters complained more about side effects, such as flatulence.

• Nor does cooking destroy the "blood thinning" abilities of garlic and onions, according to Drs. Amar Makheja and John M. Bailey, biochemists at George Washington University School of Medicine. They found that a chemical called *adenosine* is mainly responsible for the allium vegetables' powers to reduce blood platelet stickiness (aggregation). Adenosine is not harmed by heat, they say.

There's other evidence that vegetables' disease-fighting properties can survive cooking. Studies by Dr. Terrance Leighton, University of California at Berkeley, found that quercetin, an antioxidant and anti-cancer agent heavily concentrated in onions, broccoli, red grapes and yellow squash, is not damaged by cooking.

Similarly, experiments at the U.S. Department of Agriculture find that the widely acclaimed family of carotenoids, found in tomatoes, green leafy vegetables and orange vegetables like carrots, is not ruined by cooking. Additionally, tests show that your body is better able to absorb one of the carotenoids, beta-carotene, from vegetables like carrots and broccoli that have been cooked lightly and moderately.

Researchers are still in the early stages of sorting out how these newly discovered exotic natural compounds in food are affected by cooking and modern processing. In the meantime it makes sense to eat vegetables both raw and cooked.

Vegetables and Legumes

Whole Roasted Garlic

Serves 4

If you have never had this, you are in for a treat. And don't be overwhelmed by the amount of garlic. It mellows with the cooking. For the ultimate garlic bread, squeeze the soft garlic cloves on to toasted Italian bread. Or use the garlic on vegetables or meat.

4 large bulbs garlic
4 tablespoons olive oil

Preheat the oven to 180°C/350°F/Gas 4.

Pull off the loose papery layers around the top of the garlic and stand the heads upright in the baking dish. Drizzle the olive oil over the garlic, letting it run between the cloves.

Bake, covered, basting from time to time, for 30–40 minutes or until the garlic is soft.

Place each garlic bulb on a plate. To eat, pull off a garlic clove and squeeze out the garlic paste on to bread, vegetables or meat.

Per serving:
Calories	137
Total fat	3.7g
Saturated fat	.5g
Cholesterol	0
Sodium	12mg

QUICK, EASY WAYS TO USE GARLIC

• Add a couple of crushed or finely chopped garlic cloves to cheese or yoghurt dips.

• Add two cloves of fresh crushed or finely chopped garlic to all standard salad dressings.

• Rub a salad bowl with a cut clove of garlic before adding other ingredients.

• To make instant aïoli—the French garlic mayonnaise—simply put two or three crushed or finely chopped garlic cloves in one cup of reduced-calorie mayonnaise. You can use this as a dip or sauce for cooked or raw vegetables or with meats and fish.

• Add slivers of garlic to a bowl of ripe stoned olives. Mix in a couple of tablespoons of olive oil and refrigerate for two or three hours until the oil and olives have absorbed the garlic flavour. The garlic slivers will also stick to the olives and be eaten along with them when served as appetizers.

• Toast Italian or French bread slices in the oven. Serve the bread with fresh peeled garlic cloves and a small jug of olive oil. Rub a garlic clove over the toast and top with a little olive oil.

• Sauté peeled garlic cloves, sprinkled with oregano, in a little oil until the cloves are slightly browned. Drain and sprinkle with alittle coarse salt if desired. Serve as nibbles with drinks.

• When steaming or microwaving fresh or frozen vegetables, add a clove or two of crushed or finely chopped garlic.

• Use garlic to thicken sauces. Simply toss unpeeled garlic cloves into a stew or soup. When done, remove the cloves, put them through a fine-mesh sieve and return to the stew.

• Make a garlic and olive oil paste by putting five bulbs of peeled garlic cloves in 1½ pints (850ml) of good-quality olive oil. Store for a week, then put the cloves and oil through a food processor to form a paste. Use to spread on bread, to toss into stews or casseroles or pastas or to rub on meat or poultry before roasting.

• Add a little fresh garlic to vegetable juices, such as tomato or V8 juice. Put juice and garlic in a blender until the garlic is puréed.

• Sprinkle chopped garlic over salads before tossing.

✔

FOOD PHARMACY FACT
Oriental Cancer Fighters

Chinese who eat about 3oz (85g) a day of garlic, onions, spring onions and leeks are only 40 per cent as likely to develop stomach cancer as those who eat only 1oz (30g) of the allium vegetables daily. That's what a group of National Cancer Institute and Chinese scientists found in Shandong Province, a region of China known for its high stomach cancer rates. The researchers believe that regularly eating garlic and onion since childhood accounts for the protection. A medium onion weighs about 3oz (85g).

Italian Baked Onions

Serves 4

It's impossible to imagine how wonderful these onions taste just from looking at the recipe. I was completely and pleasantly surprised when I first tasted them in the test kitchen of food consultant and TV chef Howard Solganik in Dayton, Ohio. I find them particularly good at festive meals when you need all the help you can get in trying to counteract some of the ill effects of eating saturated fat. And onions, studies show, can help rev up your clot-dissolving capabilities, helping defeat the detrimental effects of fatty foods.

4 medium onions
2 tablespoons olive oil
2 tablespoons balsamic vinegar
$^1/_2$ oz (15g) parsley, finely chopped
$^1/_2$ oz (15g) fresh breadcrumbs
1oz (30g) Parmesan cheese, freshly grated
$^1/_2$ teaspoon Italian seasoning (more if desired)
Salt and pepper to taste

Preheat the oven to 190°C/375°F/Gas 5. Cut the onions in half horizontally. Peel and trim the ends so they stand flat. Use the large end of a melon baller and remove a scoop from the centre of each onion half. Reserve the onion centres.

Place 1 tablespoon of the olive oil in the bottom of a roasting tin and rub the onions in it to coat their tops and sides. Place the onions upright in the dish and sprinkle each half with balsamic vinegar. Cover with foil and bake for 15 minutes.

Meanwhile, finely chop the reserved onion balls. Mix them with the parsley, breadcrumbs, Parmesan and seasonings. Stir in the remaining tablespoon of olive oil.

Remove the dish from the oven, remove the foil, and place about 1 tablespoon of filling in the centre of each onion, mounding it slightly on top. The dish can be prepared in advance up to this point and left covered until baking time. (If you are not going to bake them immediately, preheat the oven again before baking.)

Bake, uncovered, for 15–20 minutes or until the onions are golden brown.

Per serving:
Calories   126
Total fat   9g
Saturated fat   2g
Cholesterol   4.9mg
Sodium   133mg

✔

FOOD PHARMACY FACT
Vegetables vs. Chest Pain

Who would have guessed that a trio of vitamins might help protect against heart disease and in particular chest pain? Yet, that's what Dr. Rudolph A. Riemersma at the University of Edinburgh has discovered. The big three are vitamin C, beta-carotene and most important, vitamin E.

In a study of 500 middle-aged men, Dr. Riemersma found that those with higher than average blood levels of these three nutrients were less likely to have chest pain or angina, a common sign of heart disease. Most powerful seems to be vitamin E. Those with the lowest blood levels of vitamin E in the study were two-and-a-half times more likely to suffer from angina than those with the highest blood levels of vitamin E.

The suspected reason is that all three are antioxidants (see page 3) that are thought to help keep cholesterol from clogging and destroying arteries.

Dr. Riemersma's advice is to eat more fruits and vegetables, high in vitamin C and beta-carotene, plus cereals, nuts and vegetable oils rich in vitamin E. He adds that vitamin-poor diets among middle-aged men in Scotland may help explain why the country has one of the world's highest rates of heart disease.

Carrot Purée

Serves 6

Simple yet dazzling is this purée of carrot with its rich grainy texture and touch of dill. Experts say cooking and puréeing carrots is the best way to guarantee that your body absorbs and utilizes carrots' enormous amounts of health-promoting beta-carotene.

2lb (900g) carrots, cut into ¹/₂ inch (1.5cm) rounds
4 teaspoons butter or margarine
1 teaspoon dried dill (more if desired)
Salt and freshly ground pepper to taste

Boil the carrots for 25 minutes. Drain. Cool slightly, then purée in a food processor.

In a nonstick saucepan, brown the butter, add the purée, dill, salt and pepper and heat gently.

Note For a more exotic taste, substitute ¹/₂ teaspoon ground cardamom for the dill.

Per serving:
Calories	88
Total fat	2.8g
Saturated fat	1.6g
Cholesterol	6.9mg
Sodium	79mg

COOK'S ADVICE
Smash That Carrot

To get the most beta-carotene from a carrot you need to break down its cellular structure. That releases more beta-carotene for absorption, says James Olsen, a leading expert on carotenoids at Iowa State University. There are two ways to do it, either by cooking carrots slightly or by chopping, grating, puréeing and liquefying them. This allows your digestive juices to come in better contact with the carrot's beta-carotene. "If you actually nibble on a raw carrot Bugs Bunny style, you absorb very little of the carotene—about 5 per cent," says Olsen. "Cooking it makes 25–30 per cent of the beta-carotene available and puréeing cooked carrots allows your body to absorb 50 per cent," he says.

Honey Lemon Carrots and Apples

Serves 4

The sweet-tart-lemony flavour of this side dish makes it unusually appeal-
ing, as do its festive colours. It's also a winning combination for health.
Both carrots and apples (partly because of their fibre) and the high
monounsaturarted fat in the olive oil have been shown to help reduce
blood cholesterol levels and possibly protect the heart in other ways.
Carrots, apples and lemon peel all contain cell-protecting antioxidants.

4 medium carrots, peeled and cut into $1/4$ inch (0.5cm) rounds
2 tablespoons honey
1 tablespoon olive oil
1 teaspoon grated lemon peel
Salt to taste
2 tablespoon water
2 unpeeled Golden Delicious apples, cored and quartered.

Put the carrots, honey, olive oil, lemon peel, salt and water into a
saucepan and simmer, covered, for 20 minutes.

In the meantime, cut the apple quarters in half crosswise, then into
$1/4$ inch (0.5cm) slices. Add the apple slices to the carrots and stir. Cover
and simmer gently for about 10 minutes or until the carrots and apples are
just tender.

Per serving:
Calories	144
Total fat	3.8g
Saturated fat	.5g
Cholesterol	0
Sodium	26mg

✔

FOOD PHARMACY FACT
Carrot Compound Stimulates Immunity

Beta-carotene, the stuff in carrots and green leafy vegetables, can increase immune functioning. Tests show that in cell cultures beta-carotene boosted the ability of neutrophils (white blood cells) to kill bacteria and improved functioning of macrophages, immune system regulators of infection fighters such as interferon and tumour necrosis factor.

Scientists are particularly excited by animal research showing that feeding beta-carotene spurred the production of immune products that directly killed tumour cells; beta-carotene animals had tumours only one-seventh the size of those in animals not given beta-carotene. In men large doses of beta-carotene (180 milligrams daily for two weeks) increased the numbers of T helper cells that help produce antibodies.

CARROTS VS. CANCER

Why is the American National Cancer Institute giving a carrot compound in a capsule to thousands of people in fourteen large-scale studies to see if it helps ward off all types of cancer, in particular lung, colon, oesophageal and skin cancer? Because animal and dietary studies throughout the world link this carrot chemical, called *beta-carotene* (first isolated from carrots 150 years ago) with substantially lower risks of cancer, notably lung cancer.

In fact about twenty epidemiological studies, say experts, now show that the most prodigious eaters of foods high in beta-carotene have lung cancer odds that are about half those of people who skimp on these foods. Of twenty-two animal studies all but one found that beta-carotene blocked the development of cancer. Additionally, low levels of beta carotene in the blood—which is tied closely to low intakes of beta-carotene foods—are grisly predictors of who is more apt to get lung cancer. And what is the critical amount of beta-carotene that separates the low-risk from the high risk cancer candidates? Roughly the amount in one carrot, according to studies.

Squash Purée with Apricot

Serves 2

Acorn squash is one of those yellow-orange vegetables that constantly show up in the diets of those least likely to develop certain types of cancer. Here is a really simple but elegant way to prepare it without fat.

1 acorn squash (about 1¹/₂lb/680g
2–4 teaspoons apricot jam or preserve
Salt to taste

With a fork, pierce the squash. Place it on a paper towel in the microwave. Microwave on HIGH for 8–10 minutes, turning it after 4 minutes. Let it stand for 5–10 minutes before cutting.

Cut the squash in half, remove the seeds and scoop the pulp from the shell. Place the pulp in a food processor and blend with the preserve to desired sweetness. Mix in salt to taste. Serve warm.

Per serving:
Calories	130
Total fat	.3g
Saturated fat	0
Cholesterol	0
Sodium	9mg

Spinach with Soy and Sesame Seeds

Serves 6

You can never have too many simple recipes for spinach because of its great taste and its potential as a fighter of various diseases, including cancer and cataracts. It's all in the green stuff's heavy concentration of carotenoids and other anticancer compounds such as folic acid. Also, hardly anything can compare with the flavour of fresh spinach, either steamed or microwaved. I prefer the microwave because it is so simple and preserves more disease-fighting properties. You may want to do no more than add a little lemon juice but you can also toss the spinach in an Oriental sauce given here. Soy sauce has also been found, in test tubes, to have an anticancer effect. This recipe even makes young children like their spinach.

1¹/₂lb (680g) fresh spinach, stemmed and washed thoroughly

Sauce

1¹/₂ tablespoons light soy sauce
1 tablespoon rice vinegar
1 teaspoon dark sesame oil
1 teaspoon sugar
1¹/₂ tablespoons orange juice
1¹/₂ tablespoons white sesame seeds, toasted.

Put the spinach with the water clinging to its leaves in a large microwave bowl. Cover and microwave on HIGH for 3 minutes. Stir spinach, then microwave on HIGH for another 2–3 minutes. The leaves should be bright green and still hold their shape.

Drain spinach in a colander. Squeeze gently with a paper towel to remove any excess liquid, then chop spinach coarsely.

Whisk together all the other ingredients except the sesame seeds and pour the sauce over the spinach. Toss to coat the leaves and sprinkle with toasted sesame seeds.

Per serving:
Calories	45
Total fat	2.1g
Saturated fat	.3g
Cholesterol	0
Sodium	215mg

✔

FOOD PHARMACY FACT
Attention Smokers, Another Reason to Eat Your Spinach!

Green vegetables are full of so many compounds that may help lessen damage to your lungs. A recently discovered one is folic acid or folate, a vitamin concentrated in dark green leafy vegetables, notably spinach, spring greens, turnip and beetroot tops, broccoli and Brussels sprouts. According to tests by Dr. Douglas Heimburger and colleagues at the University of Alabama Medical Center, heavy smokers had much less lung cell injury after they took fairly high doses of folic acid.

Greens with Garlic and Walnuts

Serves 6

Proclaimed by one of my guests as "the best greens I ever tasted," this wonderful mixture of green leafy vegetables gives you bountiful amounts of cell-protecting carotenoids and other disease-fighting antioxidants. This recipe is raved about among people who profess not to like greens. It was inspired by Annemarie Colbin, director of the Natural Gourmet Cookery School Institute for Food and Health in New York City, and author of several books, including The Natural Gourmet.

1lb (450g) mixed greens, such as spring greens, kale and chard,
    washed and tough stems removed
8oz (225g) spinach, washed and trimmed
1 tablespoon olive oil (more if needed)
4 large garlic cloves, finely chopped
Salt and freshly ground pepper to taste
1¹/₂oz (45g) walnuts, chopped

Put half the washed greens with the water clinging to their leaves in a large microwave bowl. Cover and microwave on HIGH for 1 minute. Stir and microwave, covered, for another 30–60 seconds. The greens should be just wilted but still crisp.

Repeat the procedure above, using the remaining greens and then the washed spinach.

Drain the greens and spinach. Chop them coarsely and press them gently between paper towels to remove more liquid.

Heat the olive oil in a frying pan, add the garlic and sauté over medium heat for 2–3 minutes. Add all the greens and sauté until heated through.

Season with salt and pepper, sprinkle with the walnuts, stir and serve immediately.

Per serving:
Calories	93
Total fat	6.7g
Saturated fat	.7g
Cholesterol	0
Sodium	42mg

QUICK WAYS TO PUT GREENS IN YOUR DIET

- Tear or shred leaves and toss into soups and stews during the last few minutes of cooking.
- Mix chopped or shredded greens into meat loaf, turkey loaf or salmon loaf.
- Add chopped greens to yoghurt or reduced-calorie mayonnaise and whirl in a blender to add flavour, colour and health benefits to salad dressings.
- Serve grilled or barbecued seafood or poultry on a bed of raw or slightly cooked mixed greens.
- Sprinkle chopped greens over baked potatoes and other lightly cooked vegetables.
- Fold chopped greens into an omelette.

Spring Greens with Smoked Chicken

Serves 4

Spring greens are one of the best and most neglected vegetables in the food pharmacy. Here's a great way to get more of them in your diet. The darker green a leafy vegetable is, the more carotenoid-type health-promoting compounds it contains. Spring greens are one of the deepest, brightest greens of any edible leaf but memories of overcooked soggy "school greens" discourages many people from eating them. Here's a version that cooks them lightly, adding a delicious smoked flavour with chicken or turkey.

1 tablespoon olive oil
1 small onion, finely chopped
1 jalapeño pepper, seeded and finely chopped (optional)
1oz (30g) smoked chicken or turkey, cut into ¼ inch (0.5cm) slivers
1lb (450g) fresh young spring greens, washed, stems removed, and
   leaves cut into 1 inch (2.5cm) pieces
Salt and freshly ground black pepper to taste
2 teaspoons vinegar
1 splash of Tabasco sauce
4 tablespoons water

Heat the olive oil in a large sauté pan. Add the onion, jalapeño and chicken or turkey and sauté over medium heat for 2–3 minutes or until the onion is soft.

Add the greens, salt and pepper, vinegar, Tabasco and water. Cook, uncovered, over medium heat for 3–4 minutes or until the greens are just tender. Correct the seasoning, adding salt, vinegar or Tabasco to taste.

Per serving:
Calories	54
Total fat	3.8g
Saturated fat	.5g
Cholesterol	3mg
Sodium	87mg

Stir-Fried Kale

Serves 4

Kale, with its broad crimped leaves, is popular in many places of the world and is wonderful prepared Oriental style. In fact one study from China found that women who ate the most kale were less likely to have lung cancer. It's understandable because kale is full of beta-carotene and is twice as high as spinach in other types of carotenoids believed to help protect cells from cigarette smoke damage.

1 tablespoon light soy sauce
1 tablespoon dark sesame oil
1 tablespoon rice wine or dry sherry
2 tablespoons chicken stock or water
1 teaspoon cornflour
2 teaspoons vegetable oil
1 garlic clove, finely chopped
1 spring onion, finely chopped
$1/2$ inch (1.5cm) piece of fresh root ginger, finely chopped
1lb (450g) kale, washed, stems and ribs removed and leaves cut into
    1 inch (2.5cm) strips
1 jalapeño or serrano chilli pepper, finely chopped

Combine the soy sauce, sesame oil, rice wine, stock and cornflour in a small bowl and stir to dissolve cornflour.

Just before serving, heat the vegetable oil to almost smoking in a wok. Add the garlic, spring onion, ginger and chilli pepper and cook until fragrant, 15–30 seconds.

Add the kale and stir-fry for 1 minute. Add the soy sauce mixture to the kale in the wok and cook for 30 seconds or until the sauce is slightly thickened and the kale is tender. Serve at once.

Per serving:
Calories	86
Total fat	4.5g
Saturated fat	.6g
Cholesterol	0
Sodium	182mg

COOK'S ADVICE

Don't overcook greens. It will ruin the colour as well as some of the pharmacological properties. Greens cooked too long in too much water turn from bright green to brownish green. Also, cooking greens in an aluminium pan is detrimental to the colour and flavour of greens. Use stainless steel, other noncorrodible metal or glassware pots. When blanching greens, remove them from the hot water and immediately plunge them into cold water to preserve the green colour and stop the cooking process.

Chinese Mustard Cabbage

Serves 4

If you have never had Chinese mustard cabbage or gai choy, *you are in for a treat. Not surprisingly, the greens have a sharp but pleasant bite. They are great raw in salads and also wilted as in this recipe or added to soups. Chinese mustard cabbage is one of those deep green leafy vegetables packed with carotenoids and folic acid and reputed to help discourage cancer, especially smoking-related cancers.*

If you can't get Chinese mustard cabbage use shredded spring greens and a bunch of watercress for that peppery flavour. Add the watercress right at the end so it does not overcook.

    1lb (450g) fresh Chinese mustard cabbage, washed
    2 tablespoons raspberry or red wine vinegar (more if desired)
    1 teaspoon imitation bacon bits *or* 1oz (30g) chopped smoked
        chicken to taste

Put the Chinese mustard cabbage in a large bowl with just the water clinging to its leaves, cover and microwave on HIGH for 2 minutes. Stir greens, then microwave, covered, on HIGH for another 2–3 minutes or until wilted.

Toss the greens with the vinegar and bacon bits or smoked chicken.

Per serving:
Calories	33
Total fat	.3g
Saturated fat	0
Cholesterol	0
Sodium	39mg

Gingered Green Beans

Serves 6

Green vegetables of all types—and that includes French green beans—seem most likely to help ward off cancer, even breast cancer, according to recent research. Of all spices, ginger has been best scrutinized for its pharmacological properties and it appears to be a very versatile health tonic; new discoveries of its powers turn up regularly. That's what makes this dish a winner.

1½lb (680g) French or bobby beans, each bean cut into thirds
2 teaspoons groundnut or dark sesame oil
1 tablespoon fresh root ginger, finely chopped
1 garlic clove, finely chopped
1 teaspoon cornflour
1 tablespoon light soy sauce
4 tablespoons chicken stock
Dash of dry sherry
4 spring onions, sliced
1oz (30g) chopped walnuts (optional)

Blanch the green beans in boiling water for about 3 minutes. Drain. Plunge into cold water, drain again, and pat dry.

Heat the oil in a large frying pan or wok and add the ginger and garlic. Stir-fry over moderate heat for about a minute. Do not brown.

Add the green beans and cook for another minute.

In a small bowl, blend the cornflour, soy sauce, chicken stock and sherry. Add to the green beans. Bring to the boil, stirring constantly. Reduce the heat, cover and simmer for about 4 minutes.

Add the spring onions. Stir and toss briefly.

Transfer the beans to a serving dish. Sprinkle with chopped walnuts just before serving if wished.

Per serving:
Calories   59
Total fat   1.7g
Saturated fat   .3g
Cholesterol   0
Sodium   110mg

Sweet and Sour Cabbage

Serves 4

Cabbage with raisins was popular in biblical days and since ancient Roman days cabbage has been touted as a cancer fighter. Indeed eating cabbage but once a week has been shown to substantially reduce the chances of colon cancer. Here's my quick and easy modern version made in the microwave.

3oz (85g) raisins
4fl oz (115ml) apple juice
1/2 large head red cabbage, coarsely shredded or sliced
2 tablespoons balsamic vinegar
1 tablespoon honey
1/4 teaspoon ground cinnamon
2oz (55g) chopped pecans (optional)

Soak the raisins in the apple juice for 2 hours or until plumped.

Place the cabbage in a large microwave bowl. Add the vinegar and mix. Cover and microwave on HIGH for about 5 minutes.

Add the raisins, apples juice, honey and cinnamon and mix. Microwave, covered, on HIGH for a further 3–5 minutes. The cabbage should still be slightly crunchy.

Sprinkle with pecans if wished and serve.

Per serving:

Calories	140
Total fat	.6g
Saturated fat	.1g
Cholesterol	0
Sodium	25mg

Cabbage and Beans with Ham

Serves 6–8

*This old-fashioned, hearty dish combines two of nature's best medicines—
cabbage and beans—in a tomato sauce that you can make as spicy as you
want with the hot pepper flakes. I've served it at dinner parties as a vegetable side dish to my gourmet guests, Nancy and Kevin and they loved it.*

3 tablespoons olive oil
6oz (170g) lean baked ham, cut into 1 inch (2.5cm) julienne strips
2 tablespoons garlic, crushed
2 medium onions, coarsely chopped
$^1/_2$–1 teaspoon hot red pepper flakes or to taste
3 lb (1.4kg) green cabbage, coarsely shredded
4 tablespoons tomato purée
12fl oz (340ml) water
1$^1/_2$lb (680g) cooked cannellini or haricot beans
1oz (30g) parsley chopped
Salt and freshly ground pepper to taste

Place the oil in a large pan and sauté the ham, garlic and onions over a
low heat until the onion is translucent.

Add the hot pepper flakes to taste and stir for 30 seconds. Add the cabbage and mix well.

In a small bowl, blend the tomato purée with the water and pour over
the cabbage. Cover, reduce the heat to moderate and cook, stirring occasionally, until the cabbage is almost tender, about 20 minutes.

Add the beans and half the parsley. Cook, covered, until the cabbage is
tender and the beans are heated through, about 5 minutes.

Season with salt and pepper, sprinkle with the remaining parsley and
serve piping hot.

Per serving:
Calories	320
Total fat	9g
Saturated fat	1.6g
Cholesterol	15mg
Sodium	473mg

✔

FOOD PHARMACY FACT
Anticancer Cruciferous Secrets

Scientists have uncovered an important clue in the quest to establish why a vegetarian diet may protect against breast cancer. In human tests Drs. H. Leon Bradlow and Jon J. Michnovicz of the Institute for Hormone Research in New York found that compounds (indoles) in cruciferous vegetables, such as cabbage, broccoli, Brussels sprouts and cauliflower, bolster a process by which the body metabolizes (burns up) the female hormone oestrogen. Other research shows that women with such an elevated oestrogen metabolism have lower risks of hormone-dependent cancers, such as breast, uterine and endometrial cancer.

The researchers found oestrogen metabolism activity jumped about 50 per cent after daily doses of 500 milligrams of indole-3-carbinol. That's the amount in about 14oz (400g) of raw cabbage.

The researchers also fed the vegetable indoles to female mice; their rate of breast cancer dropped significantly.

Mapled Brussels Sprouts

Serves 6–8

Ever seeking variations of ways to prepare health-promoting Brussels sprouts, my friend Jane Stevens came up with this recipe. In case you haven't heard, the little green globes have substantial anticancer abilities.

2lb (900g) Brussels sprouts
3 tablespoons maple syrup
1 tablespoon whole grain German or Dijon mustard
1 tablespoon olive oil
3 tablespoons white vinegar
3 tablespoons sherry
Salt and freshly ground pepper to taste

Wash and trim the sprouts, cutting a cross in the stems.

Boil, steam or microwave the sprouts until just tender when pierced with a sharp knife—not mushy.

Whisk together the maple syrup, mustard, olive oil, vinegar, sherry, salt and pepper and pour over the cooked Brussels sprouts.

Per serving:
Calories	85
Total fat	.5g
Saturated fat	.1g
Cholesterol	0
Sodium	52mg

Spicy Curried Cauliflower

Serves 4

Put more cauliflower in your life, especially if your family has a history of colon cancer. Cauliflower is a member of the cruciferous family of vegetables, which are believed to have special abilities to ward off cell changes in the colon that give rise to cancer. One study in Norway showed that people who eat the largest proportion of their calories in cruciferous veggies like cauliflower were less likely to have polyps—colon growths that can erupt into full-blown tumours. In this recipe you get a health-promoting bonus of onion, garlic, ginger, pepper, tomatoes and lots of spices, all of which may also help inhibit various cancers. And there's very little fat.

1 tablespoon oil
1 medium onion, diced
2 garlic cloves, finely chopped
1 jalapeño pepper, seeded and finely chopped
1½ teaspoons finely chopped root ginger
Salt to taste
4fl oz (115ml) low-sodium tomato juice or sieved canned tomatoes
1 medium head cauliflower, broken into equal-size florets

Curry Spices

1 teaspoon ground ginger
1 teaspoon ground cumin
½ teaspoon ground cardamom
½ teaspoon coriander
¼ teaspoon turmeric
⅛ teaspoon cayenne pepper or to taste
¼ teaspoon mustard seeds

Put the oil, onion, garlic, jalapeño pepper and root ginger in a large microwave dish. Cover and microwave on HIGH for 3–4 minutes, until onions are tender and translucent.

Add the curry spices, salt and tomato juice. Microwave on HIGH for 1 minute.

Add the cauliflower and stir to coat it with the sauce. Microwave, covered, on HIGH for 5 minutes. Stir. Microwave on HIGH for another 5 minutes or until cauliflower is just tender but not mushy and the sauce is bubbling.

Note You can substitute 1–2 tablespoons good-quality curry powder for the curry spices.

Per serving:

Calories	74
Total fat	3.8g
Saturated fat	.5g
Cholesterol	0
Sodium	292mg

FOOD PHARMACY FACT
Cauliflower, Cancer and Men

Attention, all males! Eating more cruciferous vegetables, including cauliflower, may be your ticket to avoiding colon cancer. A study of more than 600 persons by researchers at the University of Utah School of Medicine found that men (but not women) who ate the most cruciferous vegetables were only 30 per cent as likely to develop colon cancer as those who ate the least of such vegetables.

It's one of the first studies to suggest that cruciferous vegetables (cabbage, including sauerkraut, cauliflower, Brussels sprouts, broccoli) may be specifically more beneficial to men. However, both men and women who ate the most fat were about twice as likely to develop colon cancer. And both sexes who ate the most high-beta-carotene foods also had about half the risk of colon cancer.

Roast Potatoes with Garlic and Rosemary

Serves 6

Potatoes are so entirely underrated but they are overflowing with potas-sium—more per calorie than even bananas—which makes them good candidates for lowering blood pressure and preventing strokes. This easy preparation includes garlic, which can also help lower blood pressure. Rosemary contains four potent antioxidants that may also help protect arteries.

2lb (900g) small red potatoes, scrubbed and quartered
1 tablespoon olive oil
3 garlic cloves, slivered
2 teaspoons dried rosemary, crushed
Salt and freshly ground pepper to taste

Preheat the oven to 230°C/450°F/Gas 8. Put the potatoes in a roasting tin that has been brushed with olive oil. Add the garlic, rosemary, salt and lots of pepper and toss the potatoes until they are all covered with oil, garlic and herbs.

Roast for about 30 minutes. Stir once during cooking so the potatoes don't stick.

Per serving
Calories	145
Total fat	2.6g
Saturated fat	.3g
Cholesterol	0
Sodium	12mg

COOK'S ADVICE

You do not lose vitamin C by peeling potatoes, say Cornell University analysts. Contrary to popular opinion, they did not find in tests that most of a potato's vitamin C is just under the skin or that you destroy much of a potato's vitamin C by scraping off the skin. With or without skin, a 7oz (200g) baked potato, they found, has about thirty milligrams of vitamin C. That's half the amount that conventional authorities say you need, but only one fifth of what some vitamin C researchers say is adequate.

Phyllis Richman's Garlic-Stuffed Potatoes

Serves 8

Everybody loves these potatoes! A version of garlic mashed potatoes, these are well worth your attention any day. They do have a little butter and cheese, giving them slightly more fat than most recipes in this book; even so, they are not ultra-caloric and the percentage of calories from fat is but 26 per cent, still relatively low and below the 30 per cent government guidelines. This soul-satisfying recipe comes from Phyllis Richman, restaurant critic for The Washington Post, *who says there is no food she loves more than these potatoes.*

4 large baking potatoes
1 whole bulb garlic
2 tablespoons butter or margarine
4fl oz (115ml) skimmed milk
1 spring onion, very finely chopped
Salt and freshly ground pepper to taste
1½oz (45g) freshly grated Parmesan or Emmental cheese

Preheat the oven to 190°C/375°F/Gas 5. Scrub the potatoes and dry them well. Pierce the skins with a fork.

Wrap the garlic in foil

Place the potatoes and garlic directly on the oven shelves and bake for 1 hour. Remove the garlic and continue baking the potatoes for up to 30 minutes more, until a fork pierces the centre of the potato easily.

Separate the garlic cloves and squeeze each so the pulp pops out of the skin into a large bowl. Discard the skin. Mash the pulp well and beat in the butter.

Halve the potatoes lengthways, scoop out the flesh and add it to the bowl with the garlic butter. Reserve the skins.

Add the milk, spring onion, salt and pepper, mashing and beating until smooth. Preheat the grill.

Refill the potato skins and sprinkle with cheese. Brown under the grill for about 5 minutes.

Per serving
Calories	144
Total fat	4.2g
Saturated fat	2.5g
Cholesterol	11mg
Sodium	108mg

FOOD PHARMACY FACT
Kudos for Starch

The starch in cooked potatoes, rice and partially ripe bananas may help ward off colon cancer. So finds John Cummings, a fibre expert at Cambridge University. He explains that starch, broken down in the lower gut, creates butyric acid, a substance that counteracts certain cancer-causing agents.

Genevieve's Italian Potatoes and Peppers

Serves 4–6

A heartwarming and satisfying dish as only the Italians can make, this is always a hit and combines three pharmacological superstars—onions, garlic and peppers. Thanks to Genevieve Trezza Hill for this recipe, which has been in her Italian family for many years.

2–3 tablespoons olive oil
3 medium baking potatoes, peeled, halved lengthways, then cut into
    eighths or quarters
1 medium green pepper, cut into ¹/₂ inch (1.5 cm) strips
1 medium red pepper, cut into ¹/₂ inch (1.5 cm) strips
2 medium onions, sliced
2 garlic cloves, crushed or to taste
Salt and freshly ground pepper to taste
2 tablespoons chopped fresh basil or 2 teaspoons dried (optional)

Preheat the oven to 200°C/400°F/Gas 6. Pour the olive oil into a roasting tin. Add the potatoes flat side down and cook for 15 minutes.

Add the peppers, onions, garlic, salt, pepper and basil and toss with the potatoes. Reduce the oven temperature to 170°C/325°F/Gas 3 and bake for 45 minutes to an hour, tossing occasionally or until all the vegetables are cooked.

Per serving:

Calories	187
Total fat	7.1g
Saturated fat	.1g
Cholesterol	0
Sodium	10mg

COOK'S ADVICE

Here's how to avoid the extra fat that comes with sautéing onions, garlic and peppers in a pan. Sauté in a microwave without any fat. Simply chop the onion, garlic or pepper, cover and zap them in a microwave for a few minutes. Then add them to casseroles and other dishes. You can also "sauté" garlic and onions in stock or wine, again eliminating the need for oil.

Shepherd's Pie with Curried Aubergine

Serves 8

This vegetarian version of shepherd's pie features aubergine instead of the traditional minced beef or lamb. I confess I adapted it from a meat-based recipe in The New York Times *a long time ago and it never fails to get acclaim. Aubergine has been shown in studies to help the blood and arteries resist damage from high-fat diets and is a vegetable high on lists of some people with lower rates of cancer.*

6 large potatoes (about 2¹/₂lb/1.1kg)
2 large aubergines (about 3¹/₂lb/1.6kg)
4oz (115g) onions, finely chopped
1 tablespoon finely chopped garlic
1 teaspoon olive oil
1–2 tablespoons good-quality curry powder
1 teaspoon ground cumin
1 teaspoon ground coriander
Salt and freshly ground pepper to taste
8oz (225g) can plum tomatoes, chopped
4fl oz (115ml) chicken stock
6fl oz (170ml) hot skimmed milk
¹/₂oz (15g) butter or margarine (optional)
6oz (170g) cooked fresh or frozen green peas

Boil the potatoes, salting the water if desired, until tender.

Meanwhile, cut one unpeeled aubergine into 1 inch (2.5cm) cubes. In a large covered bowl, microwave the aubergine cubes until soft. Pour off liquid. Pierce the other aubergine with a fork several times and microwave the whole aubergine until collapsed and very soft. Split and remove the pulp, discarding the skin. Combine the aubergine pulp and cubes.

Sauté the onions and garlic in a large nonstick saucepan with the oil until translucent and soft. Add the curry powder, cumin and coriander and cook about 3 minutes, stirring.

Add the aubergine, salt and pepper, tomatoes and stock. Cook, stirring occasionally, for about 20–30 minutes.

Drain the potatoes and mash or put through a ricer or food mill. Beat in the hot milk, some salt and pepper and butter, if using. Add the peas.

Preheat the grill. Spoon the aubergine mixture into a shallow 3 pint (1.7 litre) flameproof dish. Top with the hot mashed potatoes and smooth the top. Put the dish under the grill until the top is golden brown.

Per serving:

Calories	213
Total fat	1.3g
Saturated fat	.2g
Cholesterol	.4mg
Sodium	82mg

✔

FOOD PHARMACY FACT
Let's Hear it for Aubergine, Squash, Green Beans, Spinach and Cabbage!

All of these vegetables seem to ward off stomach cancer, according to a recent analysis in China. Scientists studied the eating habits of 482 residents of Heilongjiang Province; half had stomach cancer, half did not. Those free of cancer much preferred spinach, squash, aubergine, green beans and especially cabbage. In fact the amount of cabbage deemed protective against stomach cancer was minuscule, according to researchers—a mere 4oz (115g) raw or cooked cabbage per day—42 kilograms per year. Chinese cabbage is the principal vegetable eaten in the province.

Sweet Potatoes Amandine

Serves 4

These easy-to-make sweet potatoes are ever-popular at my family gatherings. The secret is the almond-flavoured amaretto liqueur, which adds sweetness, richness and an unusual flavour. It's a real shame sweet potatoes take such a back seat to ordinary white potatoes. The orange pigment comes from beta-carotene. 4oz (115g) of mashed sweet potatoes has enough beta-carotene to fulfil a person's daily requirement. Beta-carotene has been shown in studies to reduce dramatically the risk of smoking-related problems, especially lung cancer. It seems even to help "heal" the lungs for several years after a person has stopped smoking.

2½lb (1.1kg) sweet potatoes, scrubbed and pierced with a fork
A little skimmed milk, to mix (optional)
4 tablespoons amaretto liqueur
2 tablespoons flaked almonds toasted (optional)

Bake the sweet potatoes in conventional or microwave oven until soft. When cool enough to handle, split the potatoes and remove the flesh.

In a bowl, mash the sweet potatoes. If the mixture is too stiff, blend in a little skimmed milk. Add the amaretto and mash again. Top with toasted almonds if desired. Reheat in the oven or microwave if necessary.

Note To toast almonds, spread the nuts on a baking tray and toast in the oven at 180°C/350°F/Gas 4 or under the grill until a light golden brown. Move the nuts about frequently and do not overbrown.

Per serving:

Calories	255
Total fat	.6g
Saturated fat	.1g
Cholesterol	0
Sodium	26mg

Slow-Baked Plantains

Serves 4

In South American folk medicine plantains are used to treat ulcers.
There's truth to it, as numerous studies on both animals and humans
show. Dr. A. K. Sanyal, a pioneer in the study of plaintains for ulcers,
recommends they be cooked slowly at a low temperature, lest their
therapeutic properties be lost to high heat. Here is the secret to slow
cooking Latin American style.

    2 large ripe plantains
    2oz (55g) brown or white sugar
    4fl oz (115ml) water

Preheat the oven to 180°C/350°F/Gas 4. Cut the plantains in half across
and run a sharp knife lengthways down their skin, just deep enough to
touch the flesh. Pull the skin off. Slice the fruit in half lengthways.

Put the plantains in a baking dish and sprinkle evenly with the sugar.
Add the water.

Bake, covered, for about an hour until they are golden. Turn the plantains frequently so they brown evenly.

Note Plantains are excellent served with rice, such as Nutty Brown
Rice, page 258.

Per serving:
Calories	188
Total fat	.4g
Saturated fat	0
Cholesterol	0
Sodium	9mg

Scalloped Corn with Peppers

Served 4

This is a real temptation to make when fresh corn on the cob is in season, but you can substitute canned or frozen sweetcorn. Corn gives you lots of cellulose, a disease-fighting fibre that, in tests, has lowered cholesterol and helped combat infections. Corn, like other seeds, contains anticancer protease inhibitors.

3 fresh corn cobs *or* 9oz canned or frozen sweetcorn
2oz (55g) tortilla chips, crushed
1oz (30g) green pepper, finely chopped
1 heaped teaspoon very finely chopped hot red chilli pepper
2 eggs beaten
8fl oz (225ml) skimmed milk
¹/₂oz (15g) butter or margarine
Salt and freshly ground pepper to taste

Preheat the oven to 180°C/350°F/Gas 4. Cook the corn, cut the kernels from the cob and put into an ovenproof dish. (If you are using canned or frozen corn, drain or defrost.)

Add the tortilla chips, peppers, eggs, milk, butter, salt and pepper and mix together.

Bake for about 30 minutes or until browned.

Per serving:
Calories	201
Total fat	9.1g
Saturated fat	2.7g
Cholesterol	115mg
Sodium	180mg

FOOD PHARMACY FACT
Corn Fibre Reduces Cholesterol

Jerry Earll, an endocrinologist at Georgetown University Hospital, fed corn fibre to seven patients with high cholesterol (above 6.25). After six weeks the daily dose of 0.64oz (18g) of the fibre, reduced cholesterol by an average 20 per cent. One subject's cholesterol plunged by 41 per cent—down from 8.1 to 4.75. Another's dived 36 per cent. However, in one case cholesterol dropped only 1 per cent and it rose 4 per cent in another. Corn fibre also improved the ratio of heart-protective HDL cholesterol to total cholesterol.

Corn fibre's performance was a surprise because it is made up of 68 per cent hemicellulose and 21 per cent cellulose, both insoluble fibres that scientists did not think could cut cholesterol.

Turnips with Nutmeg

Serves 4

There are three basic things you should know about turnips, says my friend Joan Claybrook. Peel them before cooking. If you cook them unpeeled they have a slightly bitter taste some people find objectionable. Steam or microwave them; don't boil them in water because they are already a watery vegetable. Season them with lots of nutmeg. Here's her recipe for scrumptious turnips that has been served and enjoyed by several generations of her family. Don't forget that turnips are a crucifer cousin of broccoli and cabbage and share many of the same formidable pharmacological attributes.

> 4 medium turnips, peeled and cut into quarters
> 1 teaspoon butter
> Salt to taste
> Ground nutmeg to taste (preferably freshly grated)

Steam the turnips until soft. Mash them with a fork and add the butter, salt and several generous gratings of nutmeg.

Per serving:

Calories	33
Total fat	1g
Saturated fat	.6g
Cholesterol	3mg
Sodium	71mg

A SECRET CANCER FIGHTER IN BEANS, CORN, RICE, GRAINS AND NUTS

All so-called "seed" foods, like legumes, nuts, corn, rice and grains, possess agents called *protease inhibitors* that researchers believe help block the activity of enzymes that can instigate and promote cancer.

Legumes—chickpeas, soya beans, lentils, red and white beans— are particularly rich in one type of protease inhibitor, called the *Bowman-Birk inhibitor* (BBI), which is stirring up increasing excitement among cancer researchers. Researchers have long known that this legume compound survives cooking and digestion and thus was sure to end up in the colon, where it could conceivably help combat tumours. But what happened then was a mystery. Now researchers discovered a specific receptor for BBI in colon cells. That means BBI has a specific docking site from which it can wage biological war against cancer-prone cells.

New clues also reveal how BBI can get into the bloodstream and thus circulate to squelch cancer. Animal studies by a leading researcher in the field, Harvard's Dr. Ann Kennedy, have confirmed that BBI can travel to far-distant sites, helping prevent both liver and lung cancer.

Experts explain that it takes only one millionth of a gram of BBI to stop the conversion of a healthy cell to a cancerous one. Soya beans have about double the BBI of other legumes.

Mexican "Refried" Beans

Serves 4

Mexican-style refried beans, in my opinion, are one of the tastiest ways to eat disease-fighting, cholesterol-lowering beans. And they need not be high in saturated fat to be great-tasting, as this recipe demonstrates. There are a few canned refried beans on the market that do not contain lard (the traditional fat) but they are often hard to find. Better to make your own.

1³/₄lb (795g) cooked kidney or pinto beans
9oz (255g) onions, finely chopped
4fl oz (115ml) chicken stock
4oz (115g) canned tomatoes with juice
4 garlic cloves, finely chopped
1 teaspoon celery seeds
2 tablespoons lemon juice
10 drops Tabasco sauce (more if desired)
Salt and freshly ground pepper to taste

Combine all ingredients in a large nonstick pan. Simmer, covered, over low heat for 50–60 minutes or until the beans are soft and mushy and the liquid has been absorbed. Stir several times during cooking. Serve hot.

Per serving:
Calories	263
Total fat	1.4g
Saturated fat	.2g
Cholesterol	0
Sodium	65mg

QUICK WAYS TO SOAK DRIED BEANS

Don't be discouraged from using dried beans because of the soaking time. True, dried beans—except for lentils, split peas and black-eyed peas—must be soaked before cooking and although many cooks think that means overnight or for twenty-four hours, most beans do not need all that time. Actually, according to *The Brilliant Bean*, a wonderful cookbook by Sally and Martin Stone, most dried beans absorb as much water as they can hold within four hours. Even so, the Stones suggest quicker methods.

1. Simply put washed and picked-over beans in a large saucepan and cover beans with 2 inch (5cm) of fresh water. A rule of thumb is three to four times as much water as beans. Then boil for two minutes, remove from the heat and let the beans soak, covered, for an hour. Drain and add new water for cooking.

2. Cut more time by bringing the beans to the boil and then letting them boil at medium heat for ten minutes. Then they will need to soak for only thirty minutes to be reconstituted enough for proper cooking.

Soaking the Microwave Way. You may want to soak and cook beans the microwave way, which Barbara Kafka, author of the best-selling cookbook *Microwave Gourmet*, says meant the difference to her between "almost never cooking them from scratch and feeling free to use them as an ingredient".

Here's her advice for soaking dried beans and legumes in the microwave. Place 1/2–1lb (225g–450g) of dried beans or legumes in a 3½ pint (2 litre) soufflé dish with 3/4 pint (425ml) of water. Cover tightly and cook on HIGH for fifteen minutes. Take them from the oven and stand, covered, for five minutes. Then add 3/4 pint (425ml) of very hot water, re-cover, and stand for one hour. Drain and add new water before returning to the microwave for final cooking.

Caution Do not add salt to dried beans either during soaking or during cooking until they are tender. Salt tends to make the skin impermeable so the liquid is not absorbed as well, leaving the beans tough despite a long cooking time. Adding highly acidic ingredients, such as tomatoes and citrus juice, before the beans are tender has the same toughening effect.

Generally 8oz (225g) of dried beans makes 1lb (450g) when cooked—or enough for four servings. 8oz (225g) of dried soya beans or chickpeas becomes 1½ (680g).

Microwave Bean Burritos

4 burritos

For a quick cholesterol-lowering bean fix, especially for those who have frequent cravings for Mexican food, you can hardly beat this recipe. You can also use the "Refried" beans in the previous recipe.

12oz (340g) cooked pinto beans *or* 15oz (425g) can, drained
¼ teaspoon ground cumin
5 drops Tabasco sauce or to taste
4 flour tortillas
2 oz (55g) reduced-fat mature Cheddar cheese, coarsely grated
6fl oz (170ml) Salsa Cruda (page 385)

In a blender or a food processor blend the beans, cumin and Tabasco sauce until the bean mixture is smooth enough to spread but still slightly chunky.

Place the tortillas flat on a plate, cover with a paper towel and microwave on HIGH for 30–60 seconds until they are soft enough to fold without breaking.

Place a quarter of the beans on each tortilla. Reserving 2 tablespoons, cover with one quarter of the remaining grated cheese. Fold two opposite sides of the tortilla toward each other, then fold over from the other direction. Sprinkle the top of each burrito with a little of the reserved cheese.

Place the burritos in a shallow microwave dish. Cover and cook on HIGH for 2–3 minutes or until the cheese melts. Top with the salsa and serve immediately.

Per burrito:
Calories	263
Total fat	3g
Saturated fat	1.6g
Cholesterol	10mg
Sodium	318mg

Boston Baked Soya Beans

Serves 4

The ancient Chinese called the soya bean "the miracle bean" and indeed it seems to be. Highest of all beans in an anticancer compound called protease inhibitors, soya beans have retarded cancer in animals and performed numerous other therapeutic tricks to lower blood cholesterol, blood pressure and blood sugar. Making soya beans into the classic American baked beans is an excellent way to mainstream this much-neglected protector of health. In fact, some friends like these beans much better than the traditional baked beans.

12oz (340g) dried soya beans, soaked
4fl oz (115ml) chilli sauce
3 tablespoons dark molasses
1 teaspoon dry mustard or 1½ teaspoons prepared mustard

Drain the soaked beans, transfer them to a saucepan and add 1½ pints (850ml) water. Bring to the boil, then simmer, covered, for about 3 hours.

Mix together the chilli sauce, molasses, mustard and 4fl oz (115ml) water in a 2½ pint (1.4 litre) casserole dish.

Drain the cooked beans and stir them into the chilli mixture. Preheat the oven to 170°C/325°F/Gas 3.

Bake, uncovered, for 1½ hours, stirring occasionally.

Per serving:
Calories	360
Total fat	14g
Saturated fat	2g
Cholesterol	0
Sodium	473mg

✔

FOOD PHARMACY FACT
New Soya Bean Secret

Scientists know that soya beans contain several agents that can block cancer in animals and that people who eat more legumes, including soya beans, have lower rates of certain cancers. But a team of British and Egyptian researchers has discovered yet another anticancer secret in soya beans. The beans can block the formation of nitrosamines, one of the world's most dreaded cancer-causing agents. In fact soya beans worked better than vitamin C, which is added to cured meats expressly to prevent nitrosamines from forming.

In the study mice were given either soya beans, vitamin C or a standard diet and then subjected to nitrosamine-forming chemicals. The mice fed soya beans showed no abnormalities in the liver, the prime target of nitrosamines. There was some liver damage in mice given vitamin C and extensive damage, including tumours, in animals fed neither soya beans nor vitamin C.

Dr. Jenkins's Greek Bean Stew

Serves 4

According to Dr. David Jenkins, professor at the University of Toronto, "Food is our most intimate medicine". He and his wife and colleague, researcher Alexandra Jenkins, are particular devotees of beans, shown in Jenkins's studies as the best foods for regulating blood levels of insulin and blood sugar. This is important, says Dr. Jenkins, not only for diabetics but for everyone and has a favourable impact on blood cholesterol. This bean main course, served with a salad, is a favourite at the Jenkins's table. Among diners at my table it is also a hit, ranking number one in recipe requests.

14oz (400g) dried white haricot beans, soaked
2 medium onions, sliced
2 tablespoons olive oil
1 medium red pepper, sliced into strips
1 medium green pepper, sliced into strips
1 teaspoon minced garlic
28oz (795g) can tomatoes, chopped, juice reserved
2 tablespoons tomato purée
1 teaspoon dried marjoram
1 teaspoon Italian seasoning
Salt and freshly ground pepper to taste
2oz (55g) stoned, halved black olives, such as Calamata
2 tablespoons finely chopped parsley

Drain the soaked beans and simmer, covered, in plenty of fresh water for 1–1¼ hours, until almost soft. Drain and set aside.

In a large saucepan, sauté the onion in oil until brown. Add the peppers and garlic and cook gently for 10 minutes. Add the tomatoes, reserved tomato juice, tomato purée, beans, herbs, salt and pepper. Cover and simmer for 45 minutes.

Add the olives and parsley 5 minutes before serving

Per serving:
    Calories   513
    Total fat   10.6g
    Saturated fat   1.6g
    Cholesterol   0
    Sodium   555mg

David Taylor's Hoppin' John

Serves 8

My friend David says he can't stop eating this every time he makes it and I had the same reaction when he first gave me a taste. It's spicy and you can add even more cayenne pepper if desired. The pepper helps open up the air passages and the black-eyed peas and onions both contain compounds for keeping the heart healthy and inhibiting cancer.

10oz (285g) dried black-eyed peas, soaked
2–3oz (55–85g) imitation bacon bits *or* cubed smoked chicken
1 large *or* 2 medium onions, finely sliced
$1/4$ teaspoon cayenne pepper
2 tablespoons light soy sauce
2 tablespoons olive oil
3oz (85g) rice, soaked
Salt and freshly ground pepper to taste

Drain the soaked black-eyed peas, reserving $1^1/2$ pints (850ml) of the soaking liquid.

Put the peas, reserved liquid, half the bacon bits, onions, cayenne pepper, 1 tablespoon of the soy sauce and 1 tablespoon of the olive oil in a large pan. Cover and simmer for $1^1/4$ hours.

Drain the rice and add it along with the remaining soy sauce, olive oil and bacon bits, plus salt and pepper, to the black-eyed peas mixture. Simmer for 30 minutes or until the rice is cooked, then serve.

Per serving:
Calories	200
Total fat	4.8g
Saturated fat	.5g
Cholesterol	0
Sodium	286mg

✔

FOOD PHARMACY FACT
New Anticancer Agent in Legumes

It's long been known that legumes have "antinutrients" that some
feared were detrimental to health. Among the suspicious agents are
phytates or phytic acid. Now researchers have discovered that phytic acid, in fact, is an antioxidant that helps guard the membranes of
cells from becoming rancid and disintegrating, promoting diseases
of all types, according to Dr. Ernst Graf, a food scientist with the
Pillsbury Company in Minneapolis. Dr. David Jenkins suspects
phytic acid may also help regulate blood sugar and insulin levels
and consequently is a firm devotee of the bean.

Butter Beans with Apple and Cinnamon

Serves 4–6

An inspired combination of spices, beans and apple gives this North African dish a unique flavour. It's also an inspired pharmacological combination—both beans and apples lower blood cholesterol and beans, plus apples and cinnamon, help keep blood sugar in check. Beans, apples and turmeric also possess anticancer compounds. The cinnamony beans go especially well with rice. One of my favourite ways to serve it is with Rainbow Trout with Orange Rice Stuffing (page 286).

1 tablespoon olive oil
1 large onion, chopped
1 large cooking apple, diced
¹/₄ teaspoon turmeric
¹/₂ teaspoon ground allspice
³/₄ teaspoon ground cinnamon
1³/₄lb (795g) cooked butter beans, cooking liquid reserved

Heat the oil in a large saucepan, add the onions and sauté until the onions are golden.

Add the apple and seasonings and simmer until the apple is softened but not mushy.

Add the beans and a scant ¹/₂ pint (285ml) of the reserved liquid. Simmer for about 10 minutes.

Note This whole dish can be cooked in the same stages as above but in a microwave. There is no need to add liquid with the beans in the last step just add beans and microwave for a few more minutes until the beans are heated through.

Per serving:
Calories	287
Total fat	4.5g
Saturated fat	.6g
Cholesterol	0
Sodium	5mg

✔

FOOD PHARMACY FACT
A Toast to Cinnamon

Putting cinnamon in foods can boost the performance of insulin, a hormone that helps process sugar and carry it to the cells. So says biochemist Richard Anderson, U.S. Department of Agriculture's Human Nutrition Research Center in Beltsville, Maryland. In a survey of foods, to his great surprise, he found that those made with cinnamon seemed to stimulate insulin activity. In test tube experiments he discovered that most foods had little or no effect on insulin activity but cinnamon, cloves, turmeric, and bay leaves actually tripled insulin's activity. Cinnamon was the most potent.

Such spices, he says, probably help your body metabolize sugar more efficiently with less insulin, which could be of special benefit to those with Type II (adult-onset) diabetes who produce low-activity insulin. That means that eating cinnamon might increase insulin's efficiency, reducing the amount of insulin such diabetics need. Dr. Anderson is doing tests to find out.

L & N's Bean Casserole

Serves 6–8

My friends Nina Graybill, a four-time cookbook author, and Lisa Berger devised the recipe for this quick and tasty bean casserole while they were in a supermarket deciding what to serve to guests at a dinner party. It was so successful, it's become part of their regular repertoire. I like it because it's an easy, fast way to use beans, one of the most therapeutic but too often neglected items in nature's food pharmacy.

1 onion, diced
1 garlic clove, finely chopped
2 teaspoons olive oil
5 celery stalks, diced
1 green or red pepper, diced
4 × 15oz (425g) cans cannellini beans, drained and rinsed
28oz (795g) can tomatoes, chopped with juice
3/4 pint (425ml) chicken stock
1 teaspoon dried thyme or to taste
1 bay leaf
Salt and freshly ground pepper to taste

Preheat the oven to 180°C/350°F/Gas 4. In a flameproof casserole dish, sauté the onion and garlic in the olive oil until soft and translucent. Add the celery and pepper. Cook until limp. (All these vegetables can also be cooked to this point in a microwave.)

Add the beans, tomatoes, chicken stock, herbs, salt and pepper. Mix. Bake for 30 minutes.

Per serving:

Calories	387
Total fat	3.5g
Saturated fat	.7g
Cholesterol	0
Sodium	273mg

Cuban Black Beans and Rice

Serves 4

A favourite in my family for keeping cholesterol, blood sugar and insulin levels in check is legumes of all types. A combination of such beans and rice in various forms is popular all around the world as peasant or "ordinary people food". Now researchers are discovering how really good these high-fibre starchy foods are for you. I've adapted this recipe from that fabulous cookbook, The Brilliant Bean, *reducing the amount of oil and suggesting some hot peppers for those who also want a little pulmonary pick-me-up.*

1–2 tablespoons olive oil
1 medium onion, finely chopped
1 green pepper, finely chopped
2 teaspoons finely chopped garlic
2 large tomatoes, coarsely chopped, *or* 4 canned Italian plum
    tomatoes, drained and coarsely chopped
Salt and freshly ground pepper to taste
1/2 teaspoon hot red pepper flakes *or* Tabasco sauce to taste (optional)
1lb (450g) drained cooked black beans, *or* 15oz (425g) can, drained
    and rinsed
6oz (170g) long-grain rice (not easy-cook rice)

In a medium nonstick saucepan over moderately high heat, heat the oil, add the onion, pepper and garlic. Sauté, stirring frequently, until the onion is translucent and soft. Add the tomatoes and cook, stirring, until well blended and thickened, about 3–4 minutes. Season with salt, pepper and red pepper flakes or Tabasco, if using. Reduce the heat to simmer.

Stir in the beans, cover, and simmer gently while the rice is prepared. In a saucepan over high heat, bring 3/4 pint (425ml) salted water to the boil, add the rice, reduce the heat to simmer and cook, covered, for 18 minutes or until the rice has absorbed all the liquid.

Mound the rice on a warm serving plate and create a well in the centre. Pour the beans into the well and serve.

Per serving:

Calories	338
Total fat	4.4g
Saturated fat	.7g
Cholesterol	0
Sodium	9 mg

Spicy Tofu Stir-Fry with Vegetables

Serves 4

Tofu (soya bean curd) has most of the good stuff of soya beans, which makes it an ideal health food. Tofu has even been found in one study to make the stomach feel better by cutting down on the production of acid. Here's a way to put more tofu into your life, as well as health-promoting peppers, squash, garlic and ginger.

1lb (450g) firm or extra-firm tofu, cut into ½ inch (1.5cm) pieces
1 red or yellow pepper
1 green pepper
1 medium courgette
1 medium yellow summer squash such as pattypan or yellow
    courgette
1 large carrot
2–3 tablespoons olive oil
1 bunch spring onions, thinly sliced on the diagonal
1 tablespoon arrowroot
Soy sauce to taste (optional)
3 tablespoons sesame seeds, lightly toasted

Tofu Marinade

1 jalapeño pepper, finely chopped
2 garlic cloves, finely chopped
1 tablespoon finely chopped fresh root ginger
2 teaspoons dark sesame oil
1 tablespoon rice vinegar
2 tablespoons honey
2 tablespoons light soy sauce or tamari
3 tablespoons lemon juice

Combine the ingredients for the marinade in a glass bowl. Add the tofu and marinate while you cut the vegetables.

Cut the peppers, courgette, squash and carrot into matchstick slivers. Strain the tofu, reserving the marinade.

Heat a wok over a high heat. Add 1 tablespoon of the oil and when it starts to smoke, add the peppers, carrots and spring onions. Stir-fry for 1–2 minutes or until crispy tender. Transfer the vegetables to a bowl using a slotted spoon.

Reheat the wok, adding more oil if necessary. Add the courgette and yellow squash and stir-fry for 1 minute or until crispy tender. Transfer to the bowl using a slotted spoon.

Reheat the wok, adding 1 tablespoon oil. Add the tofu and stir-fry for 2 minutes, constantly moving the ingredients to prevent sticking.

Meanwhile, stir the arrowroot into the reserved marinade. Add this mixture to the wok along with vegetables. Cook for 1 minute or until the sauce thickens and the vegetables are thoroughly heated. Add soy sauce to taste if desired. Sprinkle the stir-fried tofu with sesame seeds and serve at once with rice or noodles.

Per serving:

Calories	377
Total fat	23g
Saturated fat	3.1g
Cholesterol	0
Sodium	332mg

Pizza, Pasta and Grains

Pissaladière (Onion Pizza)

Serves 6

In this unique version of the classic Provençal onion pizza, you get some anchovies, one of the richest of all fishes in disease-fighting omega-3-type oil and enough onions to make cancer researchers happy—fully one-and-a-half large onions or more than 3½oz (100g) cooked per serving. Studies in China found that people eating at least 3oz (85g) of onions and garlic a day were 40 per cent less likely to develop stomach cancer. Reprinted from the low-fat, low-calorie cookbook Mediterranean Light, *by Martha Rose Shulman.*

> 1 tablespoon olive oil (more as necessary)
> 4lb (1.8kg) (8–12 medium) onions, very thinly sliced
> 4 tablespoons dry red wine
> ¼ teaspoon dried thyme (more if desired)
> Salt and freshly ground pepper to taste
> 1 quantity Three-Hour Pizza Dough (recipe follows) or prepared
>   unbaked pizza crust 12–15 inches (30–38cm)
> 6 anchovy fillets, rinsed

Heat the olive oil over low heat in a large nonstick frying pan. Add the onions and cook, stirring from time to time, until they are translucent and soft. Add the wine and thyme and cook gently, stirring occasionally, for 1–1½ hours, until the onions are golden brown and beginning to caramelize. Add salt and pepper. The onions should not burn or stick to the pan. Add water if necessary. Preheat the oven to 240°C/475°F/Gas 9.

Top the pizza dough with onions.

Cut the anchovies in half and make a crisscross pattern over the onions. Bake the pissaladière for 20–25 minutes or until the crust is browned and crisp. Serve hot or allow to cool and serve at room temperature.

Per serving:

Calories	298
Total fat	6.2g
Saturated fat	.9g
Cholesterol	2.2mg
Sodium	338mg

Three-Hour Pizza Dough   Serves 6

---

2 teaspoons active dry yeast
7fl oz (200ml) lukewarm water
1 tablespoon olive oil
$^1/_2$ teaspoon salt
7oz (200g) wholemeal bread flour
3oz (85g) unbleached white plain flour

Mix the yeast with 4 tablespoons of the water and 1oz (30g) of the wholemeal flour. Cover the bowl and stand it in a warm place for 30 minutes to froth and rise.

Note If using easy-blend yeast do _not_ mix with water first, add directly to flour following package directions.

Add the remaining lukewarm water and olive oil and mix well. Add the salt, then stir in the remaining wholemeal flour, then the white flour.

Scrape the dough out of the bowl and knead it on a lightly floured surface for 10–15 minutes. The dough will be sticky, but keep flouring your hands and add only enough flour to prevent sticking to the surface.

Shape the dough into a ball and place in an oiled bowl; turn the dough in the bowl to coat with oil. Cover and allow to rise in a warm place for 2 hours.

Punch the dough down and allow to rise again for 40 minutes

Turn the dough out on to a lightly floured surface and roll it out until thin or press out and stretch with your hands. Use the dough to line and overhang an oiled pizza pan or a large baking tray and shape an attractive ridge around the edge with the overhanging dough.

Per serving:

Calories	166
Total fat	3g
Saturated fat	.4g
Cholesterol	0
Sodium	185mg

✔
FOOD PHARMACY FACT
Onions' Anticancer Compound

Red and yellow onions contain extraordinarily high concentrations of a compound called *quercetin*. Quercetin is an antioxidant; thus it helps protect cells from numerous attacks by rogue oxygen molecules.

Quercetin may also fight cancer in another way, says biochemistry professor Terrance Leighton, University of California at Berkeley. Cancer cells can escape normal growth controls—and thus proliferate—by activating a protein called *PKC*. Quercetin blocks the actions of PKC, thereby helping squelch the growth of cells and eventual formation of a tumour.

This is particularly critical for humans, because we all have genetically damaged cells vulnerable to action by PKC. By keeping PKC in check, quercetin may intervene when we most need it, nipping the control switch that allows such damaged cells to become truly wild and cancerous. Says Dr. Leighton, "There's enough quercetin in 2–3½oz (55–100g) of onions to give a pretty substantial dose."

Pasta Salad with Tuna and Grapes

Serves 4

Pasta salad has become a near staple in the diets of many of us. I like this one for its low fat, its use of canned tuna—one of the easiest ways to get the fabulous fish oils—and the red grapes, which you should not neglect to use because of their concentrations of antioxidants and other identified virus- and bacteria-fighting compounds. This recipe was developed by the U.S. Department of Agriculture as part of its campaign to get Americans to eat within the government's health-promoting dietary guidelines.

4oz (115g) macaroni
6¹/₂oz (185g) can tuna packed in water, drained
2oz (55g) celery thinly sliced
5oz (140g) seedless red grapes, halved
3 tablespoons reduced-calorie mayonnaise

Cook the macaroni until al dente according to the package directions, omitting salt. Drain thoroughly.

Toss the macaroni, tuna, celery and grapes together. Mix in the mayonnaise. Serve warm or chill until served.

Per serving:
Calories	174
Total fat	3.6g
Saturated fat	.8g
Cholesterol	21mg
Sodium	222mg

PASTA'S THERAPEUTIC PUNCH

Wheat flour made into pasta is quite different pharmacologically from the same white flour made into bread. Pasta, unlike white bread, helps keep blood sugar and insulin levels steady. This is good for your system because too much insulin coursing through the blood may be a curse for ordinary, normal people. "Just because it's good to have enough insulin doesn't mean it's good to have too much," says Dr. David Jenkins. He explains that high insulin levels are associated with obesity, high blood pressure, lesions on artery walls (independent of high blood cholesterol) and cancer. In animals insulin can promote cancer growth. Also in animals, too much insulin, needed to process calories, is thought to help shorten life.

So not only people with diabetes but everyone has a stake in eating foots like pasta that tend to keep blood sugar and insulin levels steady, says Dr. Jenkins.

Vegetable Confetti Pasta Salad

Serves 6

A colourful display of oodles of vegetables with popular pasta makes this an all-time favourite in taste and health. As a bonus, the dressing is virtually nonfat. For an even heartier—pun intended—main course, you can add fish. Try 1lb (450g) of salmon, sole or halibut fillet. Simply poach the fish, let it cool, then flake it and add it to the pasta and vegetables. You can also vary the vegetables depending on what you have on hand.

8oz (225g) medium pasta shells or wheels
2 tomatoes, diced
4 spring onions, diced
1 cucumber, peeled, seeded and diced
1 medium red onion, diced
1 medium yellow onion, diced
2 green and/or red peppers, diced
4 unpeeled medium red potatoes, cooked and diced
1 head broccoli, cooked briefly and diced
8oz (225g) French beans, cooked briefly and diced
1/2oz (15g) parsley, finely chopped
Fresh basil to taste, if available

Dressing

4 tablespoons balsamic vinegar
1/8 teaspoon Dijon mustard
Pinch of dried oregano
1/2 teaspoon freshly ground pepper or to taste
Salt to taste
1 tablespoon concentrated apple juice

Cook the pasta in boiling water until al dente and drain well. Toss the pasta with the prepared vegetables and herbs.

In a screw-top jar, shake the dressing ingredients until well blended, pour it over the other ingredients and toss again. Serve at room temperature or slightly chilled.

Note You can also use this low-calorie salad dressing for other pasta salad combinations.

Per serving:

Calories	313
Total fat	1.5g
Saturated fat	.2g
Cholesterol	0
Sodium	56mg

FOOD PHARMACY FACT
Broccoli Never Quits

Think you've heard every possible reason for eating broccoli? Here's another one. You and millions of others might save yourself from developing adult-onset (Type II) diabetes by eating more broccoli, which is extremely rich in the trace mineral chromium. Chromium, says Dr. Richard A. Anderson, a diabetes expert at the U.S. Department of Agriculture's Human Research Laboratories in Beltsville, Maryland, stimulates insulin to perform better in 85 per cent of people with a slight glucose intolerance, which makes them vulnerable to adult-onset diabetes.

In tests Dr. Anderson put seventeen volunteers on an ultra-low chromium dose of twenty micrograms a day—which is the skimpy amount eaten by 25 per cent of Americans. Then, for five weeks, Dr. Anderson put half the group on 200 micrograms of chromium daily. The chromium dramatically boosted insulin activity in those with a mild glucose intolerance. About a quarter of all Americans have this intolerance that is a precondition of diabetes.

Besides broccoli, other good sources of chromium are whole grains, especially wheat bran, oysters, offal, potatoes, nuts, prunes, asparagus, rhubarb, mushrooms, beer and wine.

Spaghetti with Broccoli, Pine Nuts and Parmesan

Serves 6

Think broccoli! It is one of the vegetables that consistently show up in dietary surveys as eaten by people less likely to develop cancer, especially lung and colon cancer. And I can hardly think of a more delicious way to eat broccoli than combined with pasta as in this marvellous recipe from that marvellous cookbook Mediterranean Light, *by Martha Rose Shulman.*

2lb (900g) broccoli, broken into florets
2 tablespoons olive oil
2 large garlic cloves, finely chopped or crushed
1 tablespoon pine nuts
Salt and freshly ground pepper to taste
1 teaspoon salt
12oz (340g) spaghetti, preferably wholemeal
3 tablespoons chopped parsley
4 tablespoons freshly grated Parmesan cheese

Steam the broccoli for 5–10 minutes, until tender-crisp. Refresh under cold water and set aside.

Bring a large pan of water to the boil.

Meanwhile, heat 1 tablespoon olive oil in a wide, heavy-bottomed frying pan over low heat and gently sauté the garlic and pine nuts until the garlic is golden. Add the broccoli and stir together over low heat until the broccoli is heated through. Set aside. Season to taste with salt and freshly ground pepper.

When the water comes to the boil, add 1 teaspoon salt, the remaining oil and the spaghetti. Cook the pasta until al dente, drain and toss at once with the broccoli mixture, parsley and Parmesan. Serve at once on warm plates.

Per serving:

Calories	275
Total fat	5g
Saturated fat	0
Cholesterol	3mg
Sodium	102mg

✔

FOOD PHARMACY FACT
High-Steppin' with Pasta

Athletes are in a better mood and perform better when they eat a high-carbohydrate diet, such as pasta, rice, potatoes and beans. So says Robert Keith, a nutrition professor at Auburn University. In tests he found that trained female triathletes could bicycle twice as far when they were on a high-carb diet instead of a low-carb diet.

Surprisingly, the women were also much calmer under stress when eating the high-carbohydrate diet. When they switched to a high-protein diet—lots of beef, pork, fish and chicken, nuts and cheese—they lost their cool and were more likely to become angry under stress. The high-carb eaters, on the other hand, scored high in vigour and low in anxiety, depression, hostility, fatigue and confusion—just what an athlete needs to win, says Professor Keith. Thus boosting carbohydrates and eating modest amounts of fat and protein is the diet most likely to maximize both physical and mental ability in athletes.

Pasta with Asparagus and Salmon

Serves 4

This quick pasta dish with Oriental flavourings is a blending of two healthy cultures, Asian and Italian, both known for their longevity and, in particular, low rates of heart disease. You also get raw garlic and ginger, both shown to have antibiotic and blood-clot-fighting activity. There's never enough to say for omega-3-rich salmon and asparagus is one of those green vetables linked to lower rates of cancer. Even soy sauce has been shown to have anticancer activity. You can substitute broccoli or green beans for the asparagus. And this is a good use for leftover salmon.

1 tablespoon olive oil
3 tablespoons light soy sauce
4 teaspoons rice vinegar or white wine vinegar
2 garlic cloves, finely chopped
$1/4$ teaspoon finely chopped or grated fresh root ginger
10oz (285g) small pasta wheels
1lb (450g) fresh asparagus, broken into $1^1/2$–2 inch (4–5cm) spears, not including the tough ends
8oz (225g) flaked cooked salmon or smoked salmon or canned salmon, skin removed
2–3 teaspoons sesame seeds
Freshly ground pepper to taste
Hot red pepper flakes or green nori (seaweed) flakes to taste (optional)

In a small bowl, combine the olive oil, soy sauce, vinegar, garlic and root ginger.

Cook the pasta until al dente according to the package directions. Five minutes before it is time for the pasta to be done, add the asparagus to the pot with the pasta and continue simmering for 5 minutes. Quickly drain the pasta and asparagus and put into a large serving bowl.

Add the salmon, soy sauce mixture, sesame seeds and seasoning to taste and toss until the pasta and asparagus are coated with the sauce. Serve immediately, while still hot.

Note Other combinations you can use with the same sauce are broccoli, poached scallops and walnuts; mangetout, red pepper slivers and crabmeat; beans, steamed prawns and almonds. Adjust cooking times for each vegetable.

Per serving:
Calories	401
Total fat	8.3g
Saturated fat	1.3g
Cholesterol	17.3mg
Sodium	478mg

Pasta with Tuna and Tomato Sauce

Serves 4

Canned tuna is one of the most popular and readily available ways to get the crucial omega-3-type fish oils. Water-packed tuna is better because you lose only 3 per cent of the precious omega-3s by draining away the water. When you drain oil-packed tuna, about 25 per cent of the omega-3 goes down the drain. For a quick main course, high in omega-3s, this is an answer in the Italian tradition.

14oz (400g) can tomatoes, drained, juice reserved
6oz (170g) onions, chopped
2oz (55g) green pepper, diced
2oz (55g) celery, finely chopped
3 garlic cloves, finely chopped
1½ teaspoons dried basil *or* 2–3 tablespoons chopped fresh
7oz (200g) can tuna packed in water (preferably albacore), drained
8oz (225g) spaghetti or small shells, cooked until al dente

Place the tomatoes in a heavy frying pan or flameproof casserole. Add the onions, peppers, celery, garlic and basil and simmer for 20–25 minutes.

Add the tuna and 4fl oz (115ml) of the reserved tomato juice. Stir to break up the tuna. Simmer only until the mixture is heated through. Serve over cooked pasta.

Per serving:
Calories	320
Total fat	2.5g
Saturated fat	.5g
Cholesterol	19mg
Sodium	215mg

✔

COOK'S ADVICE

When using canned fish, it's better to choose those not packed in olive oil or soya bean oil. When possible, choose sardines canned in their own oil (sild), mustard or tomato sauce or tuna packed in water. When you drain oil from canned tuna, you lose from 15–25 per cent of the omega-3s that have leached from the fish into the oil. Draining water-packed tuna washes away only 3 per cent of the omega-3s. Of course, you can also save the omega-3s by using the oil in which the fish were packed.

Linguine with Clams and Black Pepper

Serves 6

An exquisite dish, wonderful to look at and great for your health, this combines the big three—garlic, onions (shallots) and peppers. Plus, clams not only keep you away from other bad fat but help protect your heart by lowering cholesterol and especially triglycerides, according to research. My thanks to chef Kenneth Juran, Park Hyatt Hotel in Washington, D.C.

1lb (450g) fresh black peppercorn linguine or plain linguine with 2 teaspoons cracked black pepper

4 tablespoons olive oil

30 little neck clams

3 shallots, finely diced

4 garlic cloves, finely chopped

2 pak choi stalks, cut into $1/4$ inch (0.5cm) slices on the diagonal

$3/4$ pint (425ml) dry white wine

7fl oz (200ml) fish stock or clam juice

2 tablespoons chopped fresh basil

Salt and freshly ground pepper to taste

$1/2$ red pepper, diced

$1/2$ yellow pepper, diced

2 plum tomatoes, peeled and diced

Cook the pasta in boiling salted water with 2 tablespoons of the olive oil. Drain the pasta.

Heat a large, wide saucepan. Add the clams, shallots, garlic, and pak choi. Stir briefly, then add the white wine and fish stock. Cover immediately and cook for 2–3 minutes over a high heat, occasionally shaking the pan vigorously.

Remove the clams as they open, allowing the natural juices to remain in the pot.

Reduce the liquid by boiling for 1 minute, then add the basil, remaining 2 tablespoons olive oil, salt and pepper.

Arrange the pasta in the centre of individual bowls; place 5 clams in each bowl. Ladle the sauce over the pasta. Garnish with red and yellow peppers and diced tomato.

Per serving:

Calories	484
Total fat	9g
Saturated fat	1g
Cholesterol	25.5mg
Sodium	138mg

Rotelle with Judy's Fresh Tomato Sauce

Serves 6–8 (about 1¹/₂ pints/850ml sauce)

There is no better way to get your lycopene than by eating tomatoes. Lycopene? Yes, that's a red vegetable pigment that researchers suspect helps ward off cancer. In a Johns Hopkins study those with the highest levels of lycopene in their blood had the lowest risk of pancreatic cancer. And there's no better way to combine fresh, juicy tomatoes with fresh sweet basil than in this superlative pasta sauce passed down to my sister-in-law Judy by her Italian grandmother.

2–3 tablespoons olive oil
2 medium garlic cloves, finely chopped
1 medium onion, chopped
2lb (900g) ripe tomatoes, skinned and coarsely chopped
1oz (30g) parsley, chopped
3 tablespoons chopped fresh basil
1 teaspoon red wine vinegar
Salt to taste
1 teaspoon sugar (optional)
¹/₈ teaspoon freshly ground pepper or to taste
1lb (450g) rotelle (pasta wheels), spirals, or small shells, cooked
    until al dente
1oz (30g) freshly grated Parmesan cheese (optional)

Place the oil in a large saucepan and sauté the garlic and onion until translucent and soft. Add the remaining ingredients except the pasta and cheese, cover and simmer slowly for 15 minutes.

Remove from the heat and allow to sit in the tightly covered pan for 4–5 hours.

When ready to serve, return the sauce to the stove and bring to a simmer. Serve immediately over cooked pasta. Serve with Parmesan cheese to sprinkle if wished.

Per serving:

Calories	366
Total fat	7.1g
Saturated fat	1g
Cholesterol	0
Sodium	19mg

✔

COOK'S ADVICE
Calculating Pasta Portions

You can usually work on the basis that 4oz (115g) of dried pasta makes about 12oz (340g) of cooked pasta, or two servings:
Dried pasta should always be cooked in plenty of rapidly boiling water and only until it is *al dente*. It should never be soggy. A newer cooking method recommended by one of Italy's main pasta manufacturers is to cook in rapidly boiling water as usual but for two minutes only, then cover the pan with a very tightly-fitting lid, turn out the heat and leave for the remainder of the usual cooking time. The pasta is always perfectly cooked and maximum nutrients are retained.

Jean's Marco Polo Pasta

Serves 6

Parsley is one of the prime players in this salad and although most people think of parsley as just a pretty garnish, it actually is a top source of a compound called glutathione, which is a highly regarded anticancer agent. Long before I knew this, I often made this pasta, which was inspired by a famous Julia Child recipe. It's amazingly quick to assemble and guests are always generous with their praise. It's also terrific with ripe, juicy tomatoes in place of the red peppers.

8oz (225g) spaghetti, fettuccine or angel hair pasta
7oz (200g) jar roasted red peppers (or pimientos), drained and
    coarsely chopped
4oz (115g) parsley chopped
2oz (55g) chopped walnuts
2–3 tablespoons olive oil
1 garlic clove, crushed
Salt and freshly ground pepper to taste

Cook the pasta in boiling water until al dente.

While the pasta is cooking, lightly mix together the red peppers, parsley and walnuts.

When the pasta is done, toss with olive oil and crushed garlic. Add the pepper and parsley mixture, salt, and pepper and toss again. Serve immediately or at room temperature or chilled.

Per serving:

Calories	258
Total fat	11g
Saturated fat	1g
Cholesterol	0
Sodium	12mg

FOOD PHARMACY FACT
Parsley, Important at Last!

In a recent analysis parsley, along with broccoli and spinach, topped the list of 100 common foods analysed for their content of a disease-fighting compound called *glutathione*. According to Dr. Dean Jones, associate professor of biochemistry at Emory University School of Medicine, glutathione is a potent protector of bodily cells. At least thirty cancer-causing agents are deactivated when they encounter glutathione, he notes. Further, glutathione is an antioxidant (see page 3), which means it may help turn off numerous disease processes. For example, glutathione in Dr. Jones's lab tests has neutralized peroxidized fats that help clog arteries. "It's very exciting," he says.

Other foods rich in glutathione are many fruits and vegetables, especially broccoli and oranges. Fish has moderate amounts.

To get the most glutathione, eat foods raw. From 30–60 per cent is lost in cooking. Processed vegetables—as in canned green beans—have virtually no glutathione, says Dr. Jones.

Tabbouleh

Serves 4–6

Another excellent way to get your quota of parsley is to eat tabbouleh, a cracked wheat and parsley salad that is a staple in Middle Eastern countries, where they put in even more parsley than this recipe calls for.

4oz (115g) bulgar
8fl oz (225ml) water
4oz (115g) parsley, finely chopped
8 spring onions, thinly sliced
1½ teaspoons chopped fresh mint (more if desired)
1½ teaspoons finely chopped garlic
3 tablespoons lemon juice or to taste
1 small tomato, chopped
Salt and freshly ground pepper to taste
3 tablespoons chopped pecans (optional)
2 teaspoons olive oil

Cover the bulgar wheat with the water. Allow to soak for 30–60 minutes until tender. If necessary, add more water.

Put the bulgar in a strainer and squeeze out excess moisture.

Transfer the wheat to a bowl and add the parsley, spring onions, mint, garlic, lemon juice, tomato, salt and pepper and the pecans, if using. Toss, add the olive oil and toss again.

Per serving:

Calories	128
Total fat	2.8g
Saturated fat	.4g
Cholesterol	0
Sodium	23mg

Bulgar with Chickpeas

Serves 6

This is always a hit for picnics and buffets. While the wheat fibre works wonders on your intestinal tract, the chickpeas, pecans, garlic and spring onions provide your cells with shots of anticancer compounds of various sorts. It tastes great, too.

6oz (170g) bulgar, soaked in cold water and drained (see preceding recipe)
2 bunches spring onions, including some green, sliced
19oz (540g) can chickpeas, drained
2oz (55g) chopped pecans
2–3 tablespoons olive oil
2 tablespoons balsamic vinegar
1 teaspoon lemon juice
1 large garlic clove, crushed
Salt and freshly ground pepper to taste

Place the drained bulgar in a large bowl. Add the spring onions, chickpeas and nuts.

In a small bowl, mix the olive oil, vinegar, lemon juice, garlic, salt and pepper. Add to the bulgar mixture and toss.

Serve at room temperature or chilled.

Per serving:
Calories	298
Total fat	12g
Saturated fat	1.2g
Cholesterol	0
Sodium	274mg

DOCTOR'S ADVICE

Eat foods that are vitamin E powerhouses, advises Dr. James Duke, authority on medicinal plants at the U.S. Department of Agriculture. Vitamin E is a powerful, protective antioxidant. Unfortunately, information about the vitamin E content of food is scanty because analysis is tricky. But calculations by Dr. Duke from existing foreign data found that vitamin E is present in dark green vegetables, such as green peppers, parsley, spinach, broccoli and kale. It's even higher in almonds, peanuts, tomatoes, blackcurrants, blueberries and vegetable oils such as sunflower seed oil and notably wheat germ oil, which has the highest concentration of all foods.

Nutty Brown Rice

Serves 6

Rice has the distinction of being a prominent staple in the diet of the nation with the longest life span in the world—Japan. Although no one is sure what rice's secret longevity agent might be, rice, like other seed foods, does have protease inhibitors, which help combat cancer. Brown rice also has lots of fibre, which can lower blood cholesterol. The nuts in this recipe do add fat but it's not saturated cholesterol-raising and artery-destroying fat. And nuts have many therapeutic properties on their own. Besides, they provide a wonderful I-can't-stop-eating-this crunch that makes me devour this dish.

> 6oz (170g) brown rice
> 1 pint (570ml) water
> 2 teaspoons vegetable oil or butter
> 2 teaspoons seeded and finely chopped jalapeño pepper *or* $1/8$
>   teaspoon hot red pepper flakes
> 2 spring onions, thinly sliced
> 1oz (30g) walnuts, chopped
> 1oz (30g) pecans, chopped
> 1oz (30g) peanuts, chopped
> 3 tablespoons sesame seeds
> Salt and freshly ground pepper to taste

Put the rice and water in a saucepan and cook according to the package directions.

Put the oil or butter in a small frying pan and sauté the pepper and spring onions just until soft.

When the rice is cooked, combine all the ingredients.

Per serving:

Calories	225
Total fat	11g
Saturated fat	1.2g
Cholesterol	0
Sodium	23mg

Curried Apricot Rice

Serves 6

Apricots and onions both add cancer-inhibiting compounds to rice, which has its own anticancer agents, protease inhibitors. Here you get another infusion of cancer-fighting compounds in the curry spices. This is an exceptionally quick and easy dish to make—yet adds some exotic but healthy flavourings to plain rice.

2 teaspoons butter or margarine
3oz (85g) onion, chopped
1 pint (570ml) chicken stock
1oz (30g) dried apricots, chopped
1 teaspoon curry powder
6oz (170g) brown rice
2 tablespoons chopped parsley

Melt the butter in a medium saucepan. Add the onion and sauté until soft and translucent. Add the stock, apricots and curry powder and bring to the boil.

Add the rice. Cover, reduce the heat and simmer for 30 minutes or until the liquid is absorbed. Stir in the chopped parsley.

Per serving:
Calories	157
Total fat	2.9g
Saturated fat	1.1g
Cholesterol	3.5mg
Sodium	39mg

Greek Rice with Artichokes

Serves 4

Brown rice is high in bran, now known to help lower blood cholesterol. Artichokes have in some studies been found to do the same. In addition, onions are good for helping discourage blood clots. Altogether this is a satisfying, earthy dish, just what you'd expect from a country where grains are highly valued and heart disease is uncommon. It's adapted from a recipe given to me by Mary Koromvokis.

6oz (170g) brown rice
3/4 pint (425ml) chicken stock
1 tablespoon olive oil
1 medium onion, chopped
1lb (450g) fresh tomatoes, chopped or canned tomatoes, chopped with juice
14oz (400g) can artichoke hearts, drained
1 1/2 teaspoons dried rosemary, crushed
Salt and freshly ground pepper to taste

In a 3 pint (1.7 litre) saucepan, cook the rice according to package directions, using chicken stock instead of water.

While the rice is cooking, put the olive oil in a large frying pan and sauté the onion until soft and translucent. Add the tomatoes and bring to the boil. Add the artichokes, rosemary, salt and pepper, reduce the heat, and simmer for about 5 minutes or until the artichokes are really hot.

Add the tomato and artichoke mixture to the cooked rice, stir and serve.

Per serving:

Calories	266
Total fat	6g
Saturated fat	1g
Cholesterol	0
Sodium	68mg

Bulgar Pilaf with Fruit and Nuts

Serves 8–10

You can feel virtuous eating this very dense, fruity bulgar pilaf because it is packed with apricots, full of beta-carotene, as well as other dried fruits that are rich in a variety of disease-fighting compounds. Also, recent studies by U.S. Department of Agriculture scientists find that people who eat fruits and nuts are more apt to get their quota of boron, a mineral that helps keep the brain alert.

For a lighter, less dense version, add more cooked bulgar wheat. To cook the bulgar, put the quantity required in a measuring jug. Put double the volume of water in a pan and bring to the boil, pour in the bulgar slowly, return to the boil, then cover and reduce the heat to very low. Cook for 15 minutes or until all the water is absorbed.

    2 large onions, chopped
    1 teaspoon ground cumin
    1¼ teaspoons ground coriander
    2 teaspoons butter or margarine
    ¼ pint (140ml) chicken stock (more if needed)
    6oz (170g) mixed dried fruits, coarsely chopped
    2oz (55g) dried apricots, chopped
    6oz (170g) slivered almonds
    2oz (55g) currants
    1½lb (680g) cooked bulgar or more to taste
    2 teaspoons ground cinnamon
    ½ teaspoon ground cloves
    Salt and freshly ground pepper to taste

Sauté the onion, cumin and coriander in butter and chicken stock until the onion is translucent and soft.

Add the fruits, almonds and currants and cook until heated through. Add more chicken stock if needed.

Preheat the oven to 180°C/350°F/Gas 4. Place the cooked bulgar wheat in a large bowl. Add the cinnamon, cloves, salt and pepper and mix well.

Add the spicy fruit mixture to the bulgar mixture and toss until mixed thoroughly.

Put in a casserole dish and bake for about 30 minutes, until heated through or use as stuffing for a turkey.

Per serving:
Calories	348
Total fat	15g
Saturated fat	1.9g
Cholesterol	2.6mg
Sodium	28mg

FOOD PHARMACY FACT
Fruit and Nut Alert!

Not eating enough fruit and nuts high in the trace mineral boron can make your brain sluggish, according to research at the U.S. Department of Agriculture. In tests James G. Penland, Ph.D., put fifteen people over age forty-five alternately on a low-boron and a high-boron diet for about four months. In both cases he monitored the electrical activity of their brains. When they ate scant boron, their brain waves produced more beta and delta waves, signs of drowsiness and reduced mental activity. On high-boron diets their brain waves picked up.

"It's an exciting finding," he says, "because it confirms that a good diet enhances brain functioning." Foods high in boron are nuts, legumes, leafy vegetables like broccoli and fruits, especially apples, pears, peaches and grapes.

Shiitake Mushroom Sage Stuffing

Serves 8

A scientist at the University of Michigan first discovered in 1960 that the Oriental shiitake mushroom possessed a strong antiviral substance that stimulated immunity. But it is only recently that the wonderful meaty mushroom has become widely available in Britain. If you are lucky enough to get the fresh type, grab them but the dried variety when reconstituted in water is fine, too. Of three stuffings I made one Christmas, this was the favourite among most of the family. You can use any stale bread but for a very interesting flavour I once used half sourdough and half Italian bread. Oh yes, sage in the dressing helps relieve indigestion in case you overindulge.

12oz (340g) bread cubes
1 large onion, chopped
2 large stalks celery with leaves, thinly sliced
2oz (55g) chopped fresh or dried and rehydrated shiitake mushrooms
1oz (30g) butter or margarine
8fl oz (225ml) chicken stock
1oz (30g) parsley, chopped
3 tablespoons chopped fresh sage or 1 tablespoon dried
½ teaspoon dried thyme or 2 teaspoons fresh
Salt and freshly ground pepper to taste

Put the bread cubes on a large baking tray and toast in a 130°C/250°F/Gas 1/2 oven until crisp. Transfer to a large bowl.

Sauté the onion, celery and mushrooms in the butter and 4 tablespoons of the chicken stock until the vegetables are soft.

Preheat the oven to 180°C/350°F/Gas 4. Add herbs and onion mixture to the bread cubes. Add the remaining chicken stock and combine until the bread cubes are moistened. Add salt and freshly ground black pepper to taste.

Put the mixture in an ovenproof dish and bake for 30 minutes or until the top is brown and slightly crunchy.

Per serving:
Calories	102
Total fat	3.9g
Saturated fat	2g
Cholesterol	8.4mg
Sodium	247mg

Seafood, Poultry and Meat Main Dishes

Barbecued Salmon with Fruit Salsa

Serves 6

Nothing is quite as wonderful for health or taste as fresh salmon on the barbecue. Of course it's delectable with just a few squirts of lemon juice but for a spectacular presentation and taste treat you can accompany it with a mound of these fresh, diced tangy fruits. Need you be reminded that salmon is one of the highest of all fish in lifesaving omega-3-type oil?

1 ripe but firm mango, peeled and cut into ½ inch (1.5cm) cubes
6oz (170g) fresh pineapple, diced
6oz (170g) honeydew melon, diced
½ red pepper, diced
4fl oz (115ml) rice vinegar
½oz (15g) fresh coriander finely chopped
½ teaspoon hot red pepper flakes
2 kiwi fruit
6 salmon steaks or fillets (about 6oz/170g each)

In a bowl, mix the mango, pineapple, melon, pepper, vinegar, coriander and hot pepper. (Can be made up to 2 days ahead to this point and refrigerated.)

Just before serving, peel the kiwi fruit, cut into ¼ inch (0.5cm) cubes, and gently stir into the fruit mixture.

Grill or barbecue the salmon until firm and opaque, about 10 minutes. To serve, put the salmon on each plate and top with 2 tablespoons of the fruit salsa. Serve the remaining salsa in a bowl.

Note For variation, use other fish, including swordfish, shark, halibut, turbot and snapper.

Per serving:

Calories	307
Total fat	11g
Saturated fat	1.7g
Cholesterol	94mg
Sodium	84mg

✔

FOOD PHARMACY FACT
Fish Prolongs Life in Heart Attack Patients

A major British study found that eating oily fish like salmon, tuna, mackerel and sardines cut the death rate by one third in middle-aged men who had already suffered a heart attack.

In the study of 2,033 men under age seventy, researchers told one group of men to eat fish high in omega-3-type oil at least twice a week; another group was told to cut down on high-fat foods; another to eat more fibre; and a fourth was given no dietary advice. After two years the odds of dying of heart disease dropped by 29 per cent among the fish eaters compared with the other men in the study.

Peppered Tuna Steaks

Serves 4

This is the fisherman's steak au poivre—a quick, healthy way to get lots of omega-3s with little effort. How peppery the steaks are depends on the amount of pepper but the steak surface should be well covered.

Cracked black pepper to taste
1½lb (680g) tuna steaks (in 4 steaks)
1 teaspoon olive oil
Lemon wedges for serving

Sprinkle the black pepper over each piece of tuna and press down until the pepper is slightly embedded. Repeat with the other side of the tuna.

Coat a nonstick heavy frying pan with the olive oil and heat over medium-high heat.

Add the tuna steaks and sear until one side is nicely darkened and crusty. Turn the steaks and cook on the other side until the tuna is firm and opaque but still moist inside. Do not overcook or tuna will become dry and tough.

Serve with lemon wedges.

Per serving:

Calories	255
Total fat	9.5g
Saturated fat	1.3g
Cholesterol	65mg
Sodium	66mg

A THERAPEUTIC GUIDE TO SEAFOOD
OMEGA-3 IN GRAMS PER 3^1/$_2$OZ (100G)

NOTE: FIGURES ARE FOR RAW SEAFOOD UNLESS OTHERWISE NOTED

Finfish

Anchovy, European	2.1
Bass, freshwater	.3
Bass, striped	.8
Bloater, grilled	2.4
Bluefish	1.2
Catfish, Channel	.4
Cod, Atlantic, steamed	.3
Cod, Pacific	.2
Croaker, Atlantic	.2
Dogfish, Spiny	2.0
Eel	.3
Flounder	.2
Grouper	.3
Haddock, steamed	.3
Haddock, smoked, steamed	.3
Hake, Atlantic	trace
Hake, Pacific	.5
Halibut, steamed	.9
Herring, Atlantic, grilled	1.8
Herring, Pacific	1.9
Kipper, grilled	1.6
Lemon sole, steamed	.4
Mackerel, Atlantic	3.5
Mackerel, Horse	.7
Mackerel, King	2.4
Mullet, striped	.6
Ocean Perch	.2
Perch, white	.3
Pike, Northern	.2
Plaice, steamed	.3
Pollack	.5
Pilchards, canned	1.4
Rockfish, snapper	.5
Sablefish, black cod	1.5
Saithe, Coley, steamed	.2
Salmon, Atlantic, steamed	2.7
Salmon, Atlantic, smoked	.9
Salmon, Atlantic, canned	1.7
Salmon, Chinook	1.5

Salmon, Chum	1.1
Salmon, pink	1.0
Sardine	1.5
Seatrout, Sand	.4
Skate	.5
Snapper, Red	.3
Sole, Dover, European	.2
Spratt	.9
Swordfish	.2
Trout, Lake	1.7
Trout, Rainbow	.5
Tuna, Albacore	1.5
Tuna, Skipjack	.5
Tuna, Canned in oil	.3
Whitefish	1.4
Whiting	.4

Shellfish

Abalone	trace
Clam, Hardshell	trace
Clam, Softshell	.4
Crab, Alaska King	.3
Crab, Dungeness	.3
Crab, European, boiled	1.3
Crayfish	.2
Cuttlefish	trace
Lobster, European, boiled	.7
Mussel, European, boiled	.3
Mussel, Blue	.5
Oyster, European	.2
Oyster, Pacific	.6
Prawns, European, boiled	.5
Scallop, Atlantic, steamed	.2
Scallop, Callico	.2
Shrimp, Atlantic, boiled	.7
Shrimp, Japanese	.5
Shrimp, Northern	.5
Squid, Atlantic	.4
Squid, Short-finned	.6

Offals

Cod Roes	.5
Caviar	1.1

Source: The Fish Foundation

Three-Fish Teriyaki

Serves 4

Instead of grilling or barbecuing just one type of fish, try three different types, then cut them into chunks so diners can try all three. It's fun and festive and all three of these sea fish are high in the magical omega-3 fatty acids that appear to suppress various disease processes from inflammation to blood clots to cancer. If you're on a very strict low-sodium diet, skip the soy sauce marinade and simply brush the steaks with a little olive oil before grilling.

4 tablespoons light soy sauce
1 tablespoon olive or vegetable oil
2 tablespoons rice vinegar or lemon juice
1 tablespoon finely chopped garlic
1 tablespoon finely chopped fresh root ginger
12fl oz (340ml) pineapple or orange juice
About 8oz (225g) each of 1 inch (2.5cm) thick salmon steak, tuna
    steak and swordfish or shark steak.

In a small bowl, combine the soy sauce, oil, vinegar, garlic, ginger and pineapple juice.

Place the fish in a shallow baking dish and pour the marinade over. Cover and marinate in the refrigerator for 2 hours, turning the fish twice.

Remove the fish from the marinade, reserving the marinade. Grill the fish for about 5 minutes on each side.

In a small pan, bring the marinade to the boil, reduce the heat and simmer for 5 minutes. Serve with the fish.

Per serving:

Calories	278
Total fat	10.3g
Saturated fat	2g
Cholesterol	75mg
Sodium	400mg

Swordfish with Grapefruit and Brazil Nuts

Serves 4

Brimming with selenium and vitamins E and C, this dish fits the bill for lowering blood pressure, according to new research. Those three antioxidants have been linked to lower blood pressure. Swordfish and Brazil nuts are two of the most concentrated sources of selenium. If you can't get Brazil nuts, substitute walnuts, which are also high in omega-3 fatty acids, linked to lowering blood pressure. The spinach and grapefruit add a hefty shot of vitamin C and carotenoids both important to help protect lungs and arteries.

1lb 12oz (795g) swordfish steaks
Olive oil
6oz (170g) fresh spinach, washed, stems removed and leaves torn
    into bite-size pieces
1 grapefruit, peeled and divided into segments, cut in half
4fl oz (115ml) grapefruit juice
2 garlic cloves, finely chopped or crushed
2 teaspoons balsamic vinegar
½ teaspoon light soy sauce
⅛ teaspoon grated fresh root ginger (optional)
Freshly ground pepper to taste
2oz (55g) coarsely chopped Brazil nuts

Preheat the grill. Or prepare a barbecue for cooking.

Brush the fish steaks with a little olive oil. Grill until firm and opaque (about 10 minutes per 1 inch (2.5 cm) of thickness).

In the meantime, place the spinach in a bowl and add the grapefruit segments.

In a separate bowl, mix the grapefruit juice, garlic, vinegar, soy sauce and root ginger. Add to the spinach and grapefruit and toss lightly.

Place a bed of spinach on each dinner plate and top with a piece of cooked swordfish. Arrange grapefruit sections around the fish. Grind on fresh pepper and sprinkle with chopped Brazil nuts.

Per serving:

Calories	371
Total fat	18.9g
Saturated fat	4.8g
Cholesterol	69mg
Sodium	236mg

✔

FOOD PHARMACY FACT
Fish, Nuts and Greens May Keep
High Blood Pressure Away

A large-scale Finnish study of 722 men aged fifty-four at the University of Kuopio found that those with low amounts of vitamin C and selenium in their blood and a low intake of linolenic acid were most apt to have high blood pressure. Seafood, especially swordfish, is rich in selenium and linolenic acid, as are some nuts, notably Brazil nuts.

✔

FOOD PHARMACY FACT
Fish for Bad Genes

Here's another intriguing way that eating fish may help ward off heart disease. New research shows that many heart attack victims, especially younger men, have high blood levels of a peculiar type of cholesterol called *Lp(a)*. It's inherited, not very responsive to drugs or low-fat diets and it's dangerous. Too much Lp(a) doubles the risk of heart attack, even in those with low levels of total cholesterol and is estimated to trigger a quarter of all heart attacks in men under the age of sixty.

However, Dr. Jorn Dyerberg, a leading Danish scientist, found that fish oil lowered Lp(a) by a startling 15 per cent in a group of otherwise healthy men with high levels of this dangerous type of cholesterol. Every day for nine months the men took four grams of fish oil—equal to eating about 7oz (200g) of mackerel a day.

Note The fish oil does not seem to lower Lp(a) in those with normal levels.

Grilled Mackerel with Herbs and Spices

Mackerel is the king of fishes when it comes to omega-3—that wonderful type of oil that promises to save you from virtually everything. Mackerel, especially Atlantic mackerel, contains more omega-3 than any other species. Unfortunately this fish is not nearly as popular as it should be because it has a slightly stronger flavour than many fish. I must stress "slightly", for once you taste mackerel you may be surprised by how pleasant it is. It is best cooked with spices and herbs. Here are three quick ways with mackerel—simply grilled or barbecued with sage, garlic or cumin.

There is virtually no fat added to the mackerel in these recipes. The fat comes entirely from the fish and is mostly from healthy omega-3. For a special occasion you can substitute bluefish, which is also high in omega-3.

Mackerel with Sage   Serves 4

---

    4 mackerel fillets (about 2lb/900g)
    4 tablespoons lemon juice
    4 teaspoons dried sage
    Salt and freshly ground pepper to taste

Brush both sides of the fish with lemon juice and sage. Sprinkle with salt and black pepper. Grill or barbecue fillets for a total of 7–10 minutes or until opaque and firm.

    Per serving:

Calories	470
Total fat	32g
Saturated fat	7g
Cholesterol	160mg
Sodium	207mg

Mackerel with Garlic and Herbs   Serves 4

4 garlic cloves, crushed
3 tablespoons chopped fresh herbs or 1 tablespoon dried (thyme,
   rosemary, parsley, basil, etc.), crushed
Salt and freshly ground pepper to taste
4 mackerel fillets (about 2lb/900g)

Rub the garlic, herbs, salt and pepper on to both sides of the mackerel fillets. Grill or barbecue for a total of 7–10 minutes or until the fish is opaque and firm.

Per serving:
   Calories   471
   Total fat   31.5g
   Saturated fat   7g
   Cholesterol   159mg
   Sodium   206mg

Mackerel with Cumin   Serves 4

3 tablespoons lemon juice
3 garlic cloves, crushed
1 teaspoon ground cumin
1/8 teaspoon cayenne pepper
5 tablespoons natural very-low-fat yoghurt
Salt and freshly ground pepper to taste
4 mackerel fillets (about 2lb/900g)

In a small dish, combine the lemon juice, garlic, cumin, cayenne pepper, yoghurt, salt and pepper.

Place the fish in a dish. Cover with the yoghurt mixture and marinate for 30 minutes.

Grill or barbecue the fish for a total of 7–10 minutes or until opaque and firm.

Per serving:
    Calories   483
    Total fat   31.7g
    Saturated fat   7g
    Cholesterol   159mg
    Sodium   222mg

A BITE (OR TWO) OF FISH A DAY KEEPS HEART DISEASE AWAY

Dutch investigators found that eating 1oz (30g) of fish each day on the average cut the risk of deadly heart attack by 50 per cent.

British researchers found that telling men who had already had a heart attack to eat fatty fish twice a week cut their risk of death from a subsequent heart attack by 29 per cent.

U.S. researcher Therese Dolecek found that American men who eat an average of 600 milligrams of omega-3 type fish oil a day reduce their odds of heart attack by 36 per cent. That 600 milligrams translates into one or two servings a week of a fatty fish or a small daily "dose" of the following.

1oz (30g) fresh Atlantic mackerel
1oz (30g) canned anchovies (1/2 small can)
1 1/2oz (45g) fresh Atlantic salmon
1 1/2oz (45g) canned pink salmon
1 1/2oz (45g) canned Pacific sardines
1 1/2oz (45g) fresh herring
1 3/4oz (50g) sablefish
1 3/4oz (50g) canned pickled herring
2oz (55g) fresh tuna
2 1/2oz (70g) Greenland turbot
3oz (85g) bluefish
3oz (85g) bass
3oz (85g) shark
3 1/2oz (100g) swordfish
3 1/2oz (100g) canned white albacore tuna
4oz (115g) rainbow trout

Baked Bluefish with Herbs

Serves 4–6

A marvellous choice for getting lots of health-promoting omega-3 fatty acids in this unusual but quick-to-make flavourful bluefish. It's great for a fast family dinner but its slightly crunchy crust with herbs also gives it a dinner party touch and my guests have loved it. Each serving has a whopping 1,500 milligrams of omega-3s that can infuse your cells with protection. That's more than twice the daily amount found to put a 36 per cent dent in fatal heart attacks among American men.

2lb (900g) bluefish fillets
3 tablespoons reduced-calorie mayonnaise
3 tablespoons natural very-low-fat yoghurt
4oz (115g) dry breadcrumbs made from granary or wholemeal bread
$^1/_2$ teaspoon dried thyme, crumbled or to taste
$^1/_2$ teaspoon dried rosemary, crumbled or to taste
Salt and freshly ground pepper to taste
8 parsley sprigs

Preheat the oven to 180°C/350°F/Gas 4. Place the fish, skin side down, in a large, shallow roasting tin.

In a small bowl, combine the mayonnaise and yoghurt and spread over the top of the fish. Sprinkle with breadcrumbs, then thyme, rosemary, salt and pepper. Top with parsley sprigs.

Bake for 10–15 minutes or until fish is firm and opaque.

Per serving:

Calories	352
Total fat	13g
Saturated fat	3g
Cholesterol	138mg
Sodium	272mg

Shark Steaks with Orange

Serves 6

Surprisingly, shark is a very good fish choice because it is extremely well endowed with omega-3-type oil. You get a whopping 4,600 milligrams of omega-3s from each serving of this recipe. And it's quick and easy to make in a microwave.

2lb (900g) shark steaks
3 tablespoons orange juice
2 tablespoons light soy sauce
1 tablespoon tomato ketchup
2 teaspoons olive oil
1 tablespoon chopped parsley
2 teaspoons lemon juice
½ teaspoon dried oregano
1 garlic clove, finely chopped
1 large orange, peeled, seeded and segmented
1oz (30g) sliced water chestnuts

Place the shark steaks in a single layer in a shallow 3 pint (1.7 litre) baking dish. Combine the remaining ingredients except the orange and water chestnuts. Pour the sauce over the steaks and marinate in the refrigerator for 30 minutes, turning once.

Cover the dish leaving one corner to vent. Microwave on HIGH for 6–8 minutes, rotating the dish every 3 minutes.

Top the steaks with orange sections and water chestnuts. Return to the microwave and cook on HIGH for 1–2 minutes. Allow to stand, covered, for 2 minutes.

Per serving:
Calories	236
Total fat	8.4g
Saturated fat	1.6g
Cholesterol	22mg
Sodium	350mg

✔

COOK'S ADVICE

The only way to ruin fresh fish is to overcook it, drying it out. You're repeatedly told to cook fish until it flakes easily. But as Julia Child says, "If it flakes easily, it's overdone." It's done when it's opaque, she says. For a rule of thumb, cook fish for about ten minutes for every inch (2.5cm) of thickness at the thickest point. To check for doneness, break the flesh at the thickest point with a fork. It should appear slightly opaque, not flaky like canned fish. Microwaved fish, of course, takes less time—and depends on the quantity in the oven. A 6oz (170g) fish steak can take a couple of minutes or less to microwave, says Jane Morimoto, director of the test kitchen for the Alaska Seafood Marketing Institute.

Cajun Cod

Serves 4

"A spicy twist for a mild-mannered fish" is how well-known nutritionist Ann Louise Gittleman describes this fare in her book Beyond Pritikin. *Cod is a "lean" fish but about half its fat is made up of disease-fighting omega-3 fatty acids—more than any other popular fish, which makes it a favourite for the health-conscious. It is also very low in omega-6 fatty acids (3 per cent of total fat), which is desirable because omega-6 can help destroy the benefits of eating the omega-3s.*

1 medium onion, chopped
1 green pepper, chopped
1 garlic clove, finely chopped
1 teaspoon butter
2 tomatoes, seeded and chopped
4fl oz (115ml) dry red wine
1/4 teaspoon dried thyme
1/2 teaspoon cayenne pepper
4 × 5oz (140g) cod fillets
2 tablespoons lemon juice

Sauté the onion, green pepper and garlic in butter until tender. Add the tomatoes, wine, thyme and cayenne. Bring to the boil.

Add the cod, reduce the heat, cover and simmer for about 10 minutes or until the fish is firm and opaque.

Add the lemon juice before serving.

Per serving:

Calories	154
Total fat	2.2g
Saturated fat	.8g
Cholesterol	64mg
Sodium	94mg

Halibut with Tarragon and Sesame Seeds

Serves 4

Such a mild, lean and popular fish, halibut has an excellent balance of the wonderful omega-3 type fat and the less desirable omega-6-type fat. Also, there's evidence that all types of fish, even lean fish, help prevent cardiovascular disease. Another bonus is that low-fat, low-calorie fish gives you just as much protein as higher-fat meat.

1½lb (680g) halibut, cod, haddock or other white fish
1 teaspoon olive oil
1 tablespoon lemon juice
1 teaspoon dried tarragon
Salt and freshly ground pepper to taste
1 tablespoon sesame seeds
1 tablespoon chopped parsley

Preheat the grill. Brush the fish with oil. Mix the lemon juice, tarragon, salt and pepper. Pour it over the fish. Sprinkle sesame seeds evenly over the fish.

Grill the fish for 10 minutes, until the fish is opaque, firm and browned. Serve sprinkled with chopped parsley.

Per serving:
Calories	165
Total fat	3.4g
Saturated fat	.5g
Cholesterol	73mg
Sodium	94mg

Microwave Dilled Plaice

Serves 2

Nothing can be easier, quicker or more satisfying than a simple microwaved fish sprinkled with the herb most associated with fish—dill. With this recipe there's no excuse for not having fish more often. You can substitute numerous other fish, such as any type of white fish or salmon.

12 oz (340g) plaice fillets
3 tablespoons chopped fresh dill or 1 tablespoon dried
2 tablespoons lemon juice
Salt and freshly ground pepper to taste
1 lemon, cut into wedges

Arrange the fillets in a microwave dish in a single layer if possible. Sprinkle with dill, lemon juice, salt and pepper.

Cover tightly and microwave on HIGH for about 4–5 minutes, depending on the size and thickness of the fillets. Serve at once, garnished with lemon wedges.

Per serving:

Calories	162
Total fat	2g
Saturated fat	.5g
Cholesterol	81mg
Sodium	144mg

Plaice Stuffed with Vegetables

Serves 4

Fish fillets can be a hearty course when wrapped around rice and vegetables. Rice is one of those "seed" foods that contain lots of protease inhibitors, thought to help keep cancer at bay. You can make the rice and vegetable mixture the night before. Stuff the plaice fillets just before you put them into the oven to bake.

5oz (140g) cooked rice
2oz (55g) diced cooked carrots
1oz (30g) diced red and/or green peppers
2oz (55g) slivered almonds
1 tablespoon chopped parsley
Salt and freshly ground pepper to taste
1 teaspoon butter or margarine, melted
Vegetable oil
1½lb (680g) plaice fillets

Preheat the oven to 180°C/350°F/Gas 4. Combine the rice, carrots, peppers, almonds, parsley, salt, pepper and butter and mix well.

Spoon 3 tablespoons of the rice mixture on to each fillet. Roll and secure with cocktail sticks or skewers.

Brush a shallow roasting tin with vegetable oil. Place the fillets in the tin and bake, uncovered, for 20–25 minutes.

Per serving:
Calories	289
Total fat	9.2g
Saturated fat	1.6g
Cholesterol	84mg
Sodium	159mg

FISH, FAT AND CHOLESTEROL

Is it really good to eat fatty fish? After all, fat makes you fat and besides, we've been told to eat less fat, not more. And aren't some seafoods, especially shrimp, high in cholesterol, making them undesirable?

It's safe to say that very few people ever got fat eating fish. Compared with other sources of fat and protein—like red meat, poultry and cheese—even the highest-fat seafood is still relatively low in fat and calories. The fat in fish is mostly unsaturated and it's thought that saturated fat—as in meat and dairy products—is more likely than other fat to make you fat.

Further, the enormous benefit to the body in all kinds of ways from the omega-3 oils in fish outweighs any dangers from fat per se.

Seafood does have cholesterol but eating fish does not raise blood cholesterol. Shellfish does not have nearly as much cholesterol as previously thought, according to new techniques of analysis. Moreover, shellfish contains sterols that actually discourage absorption of cholesterol. All told, the cholesterol in seafood is not worrying, except in a few cases. Fish eggs are extremely high in cholesterol. 3¹/₂oz (100g) of roe from various species has 374 milligrams; the same amount of caviar has 588 milligrams. 3¹/₂oz (100g) of squid has 233 milligrams and shrimp 152. Fish generally has between 40 and 60 milligrams of cholesterol in 3¹/₂oz (100g).

The case for the benefits of fish, especially fatty fish, is overwhelming compared with any possible detrimental effects from fat and cholesterol.

Rainbow Trout with Orange Rice Stuffing

Serves 6

Rainbow trout are readily available and surprisingly high in omega-3 for freshwater fish. The rice stuffing turns this dish into a one-course meal and the fish are definitely dressed up and pretty enough for guests. I've served this platter of trout at dinner parties to much acclaim.

³/₄ pint (425ml) dry white wine
³/₄ pint (425ml) orange juice
2 tablespoons lemon juice
6 whole rainbow trout, cleaned
10oz (285g) rice
³/₄ pint (425ml) water
6oz (170g) watercress, chopped
3 spring onions, including the green parts, finely sliced
1 tablespoon grated orange zest
1oz (30g) flaked almonds, toasted
12 large parsley sprigs, plus additional for garnish
1 orange, sliced
Salt and freshly ground pepper to taste

To make a marinade, combine half of the wine, half of the orange juice and the lemon juice. Place the fish in a large, shallow baking dish and add the marinade. Marinate the fish in the refrigerator for 1 hour, turning twice to be sure all trout are exposed to the marinade.

In the meantime, cook the rice in the water and remaining orange juice according to the package directions. When the rice is about 10 minutes from being done, mix in the watercress, spring onions and orange zest. Continue cooking the rice until the liquid is absorbed. Stir in the toasted almonds.

Drain the fish and generously stuff the cavity of each trout with the rice mixture. You will have some rice left over

Preheat the oven to 180°C/350°F/Gas 4. Place the stuffed trout in a shallow baking dish. Cover each fish with 2 parsley sprigs and an orange slice. Sprinkle with salt and pepper. Add the remaining white wine and bake until the fish are opaque and firm, about 15–20 minutes.

Lift the fish out of the liquid and put them on a large serving plate surrounded by fresh parsley sprigs. Serve the remaining rice in a separate bowl. Reheat the rice in a microwave oven if necessary.

Per serving:
Calories	430
Total fat	8.4g
Saturated fat	1.3g
Cholesterol	90mg
Sodium	55mg

✔

FOOD PHARMACY FACT
Fish Eaters Have Less Breast Cancer

New evidence supports the theory that something in seafood—probably the oil—helps manipulate female hormones that in turn discourage breast cancer. Fish eaters around the world seem to have less breast cancer, according to investigators at the Ludwig Institute for Cancer Research in Toronto, who compared food consumption statistics with cancer rates in thirty-two countries. They noted that those countries where people ate the most calories from fish had the fewest new cases of and deaths from breast cancer. For example, in Japan, where fish consumption is high, breast cancer is low. Numerous animal studies find that omega-3 fatty acids in the fat of fish may block the development of various cancers, in particular breast cancer.

Sweet and Sour Fish Curry

Serves 3

An easy yoghurt-based curry, this recipe gives you an opportunity to use a variety of white fish in a piquant sauce full of health-preserving onions and spices. Serve it with brown rice, raisins that have been plumped in hot water and mango chutney.

2 medium onions, finely chopped
1 tablespoon olive oil
1 teaspoon finely chopped fresh root ginger
1 1/2 tablespoons good-quality curry powder
3 tablespoons lemon juice
2–3 teaspoons brown sugar or to taste
8oz (225g) natural very-low-fat yoghurt
Salt to taste
1lb (450g) fish fillets (rockfish, bass, cod, haddock, halibut), skin
    and bones removed, cut into serving pieces
3 tablespoons chopped parsley

In a large frying pan, cook the onion in the oil until golden. Add the ginger and curry powder and fry for 2–3 minutes, stirring several times.

Stir in the lemon juice, brown sugar, yoghurt and salt.

Pat the fish pieces dry and place them in the sauce. Simmer until done, stirring gently from time to time. Sprinkle the parsley over the fish and sauce and serve.

Per serving:

Calories	272
Total fat	7.6g
Saturated fat	1.2g
Cholesterol	54mg
Sodium	153mg

Judy's Old-Fashioned Salmon Loaf

Serves 4

Since my sister Judy became concerned about her blood cholesterol she has started serving and eating more fish. Here is one of her ways to use inexpensive canned salmon, which has so much heart-protective omega-3-type fat. The paprika deepens the pinkness of the pale fish. It's also a good way to use potassium-rich leftover mashed potatoes.

15^1/₂oz (440g) can pink or red salmon
1 tablespoon lemon juice
1 large egg
1 large egg white
2oz (55g) fresh breadcrumbs
8oz (225g) mashed potatoes made with skimmed milk
1 teaspoon celery seed
1^1/₄ teaspoons paprika
1 teaspoon yellow mustard
1 teaspoon crushed fennel seeds (optional)
^{1}/₂ teaspoon prepared horseradish or to taste (optional)
Salt and freshly ground pepper to taste
Vegetable oil

Remove as much skin from the salmon as possible. Mix together all ingredients except vegetable oil until well combined. Preheat the oven to 180°C/350°F/Gas 4.

Brush a small loaf tin with vegetable oil. Spoon the salmon mixture into the tin and bake, uncovered, for about 45 minutes.

Per serving:

Calories	226
Total fat	7g
Saturated fat	1.9g
Cholesterol	89mg
Sodium	554mg

✔

FOOD PHARMACY FACT
Fish Can Help Save Bones

Eating seafood may help protect older women from bone fractures. The reason is that seafood is one of the best sources of vitamin D and without enough vitamin D older women lose calcium from bones, rendering them more fragile and apt to break. So notes Dr Elizabeth A. Krall at the U.S. Department of Agriculture's research centre at Tufts University.

In her study of 333 postmenopausal women Dr. Krall found women need about twice as much vitamin D to prevent calcium loss as they typically get in their diet. Most women take in only 112 international units (IUs) of vitamin D, when they need at least 220 IUs, says Dr. Krall. Worse is that the ability to absorb vitamin D decreases with age. An excellent source of vitamin D is seafood. Eel has the most—3^1/$_2$oz (100g) of eel contains a whopping 6,400 IUs. The same amount of canned salmon has 500 IUs and canned sardines 300 IUs. 8fl oz (225ml) of milk fortified with vitamin D has 100 IUs.

Basque Tuna Stew

Serves 4

This seafood stew, a longtime tradition among fishermen, is a treasure of health-promoting ingredients and is a wonderful way to use fresh or frozen tuna with its high content of omega-3-type oil. It's brimming with vitamin C and vitamin A, both cancer fighters. And it contains a power-house of potassium, linked to preventing strokes.

1–2 tablespoons olive oil
1 medium onion, chopped
2 small green peppers, chopped
2 medium tomatoes, chopped, *or* 8oz (225g) drained canned
   tomatoes, chopped
1lb 12oz (795g) potatoes, peeled and cut into medium chunks
³/₄ pint (425ml) tomato juice
4 garlic cloves, chopped
¹/₂ teaspoon dried rosemary, crushed
¹/₂ teaspoon dried thyme
3 tablespoons chopped parsley
Pinch of hot red pepper flakes or to taste
Salt and freshly ground pepper to taste
1¹/₂lb (680g) fresh or frozen tuna, cut into large chunks
4 tablespoons Pernod or other anise-flavoured liqueur (optional)

In a large pan, heat the oil and sauté the onion and peppers until soft.

Add the tomatoes, potatoes, tomato juice, garlic, rosemary, thyme, parsley, red pepper flakes, salt, pepper and enough water to come about 1 inch (2.5cm) above the potatoes. Simmer gently until the potatoes are tender. Mash three or four potato chunks against the side of the pan to thicken the stew.

Add the tuna chunks and cook for about 10 minutes, until the fish is opaque and firm.

Add the Pernod if using and stir carefully. Or serve with a small jug of anise-flavoured liqueur and let diners add their own.

Per serving:

Calories	445
Total fat	12.2g
Saturated fat	2.7g
Cholesterol	65mg
Sodium	95mg

COOK'S ADVICE

Use potatoes as a low-fat thickener for soups, stews and sauces. When potatoes are already present in a stew, simply mash a few chunks of potato against the side of the pan and stir. Add mashed potatoes (made without butter or other fat) to soups or stews 5–10 minutes before other ingredients are cooked. To thicken soups, remove some liquid and purée it in the blender with a leftover baked or boiled potato. Mix the purée into the soup.

Caribbean-Style Mackerel by George!

Serves 6

Here's another way to prepare this marvellous fish with lots of vegetables, herbs and spices. It's the allspice that gives it a Caribbean flavour, says its creator, George Jacobs, who is also the creator of two cookbooks, including Light-Hearted Cooking by George! *I was fortunate enough to have George come to my own kitchen to make this dish. Its festive Spanish colours also make this dish a delight to present to a table of family or friends. It is worth noting that the fat in this recipe comes almost entirely from the fish itself and is what makes this fish so good for you—so high in omega-3 oils.*

1 large onion, thinly sliced
1 large green pepper, cut into spears
3 garlic cloves, chopped
Cooking oil
3lb (1.4kg) mackerel fillets
5oz (140g) fresh mushrooms, sliced
1 fresh tomato, cut into chunks
28oz (795g) can whole tomatoes, juice reserved
½ teaspoon ground allspice
¼ teaspoon dried thyme
⅛ teaspoon cayenne pepper or to taste
A handful of parsley sprigs
8fl oz (225ml) dry white wine

Put onion, green pepper and garlic in a microwave bowl, cover, and microwave on HIGH for 5 minutes to soften them.

Brush oil on the bottom of a large roasting tin. Lay the mackerel fillets, skin side down, in rows in the bottom of the tin.

Preheat the oven to 190°C/375°F/Gas 5. Over the top of the fish, sprinkle the mushrooms, fresh and canned tomatoes—arranging whole tomatoes over and around the fish—allspice, thyme, cayenne pepper and parsley. Add the reserved tomato juice and wine.

Bake for about 10 minutes or until the fish is opaque. Remove and place the pan under the grill for a couple of minutes, until the top vegetables are browned and the sauce is bubbling.

Put each fillet covered with vegetables and sauce on a plate or in a shallow soup bowl. Serve with crusty bread for mopping up the sauce.

Per serving:
Calories	523
Total fat	32g
Saturated fat	7.5g
Cholesterol	159mg
Sodium	429mg

FISH BEATS FISH OIL CAPSULES

If fish is good for you, why not simply take fish oil capsules, available at health food stores? Most experts discourage such use without medical supervision, warning that the supplements may be ineffective and even dangerous in some cases.

Experts' greatest fear is that people will overdose on fish oil capsules, perhaps causing excessive bleeding and other problems. Although the amount of fish oil in a capsule a day would "do wonders", as William Lands, University of Illinois, says, he advises eating fish instead of taking capsules because "there is much less chance of overdosing".

Fish oil capsules may also ironically deliver an unintended effect. They may raise cholesterol instead of lowering it. In studies they have actually promoted migraine headaches, impaired blood sugar metabolism and worsened psoriasis and blood pressure in certain individuals.

Also, fish oil supplements may not be as effective as eating the fish itself. Recently Dr. Paul Nestel, chief of Human Nutrition, Commonwealth Scientific & Industrial Research Organization in Australia, gave thirty-one men with moderately high cholesterol either fish oil capsules or a small fish serving a day (1½lb/680g a week), usually salmon or sardines. The capsules and the fish had equal amounts of protective omega-3 fatty acids.

But after five weeks blood tests showed that the "fish outperformed the fish oil capsules". The fish eaters had less bad-type LDL blood cholesterol, less of a blood-clotting factor (fibrinogen), "thinner blood" and depressed production of a hormonelike agent (thromboxane) that promotes blood clotting.

"Is there something else beneficial in the fish?" asks Dr. Nestel. Possibly, he speculates, it's because the fish was richer in a type of omega-3 called *DHA* and the fish oil supplements were made up of omega-3 EPA, with different effects on blood.

Additionally, other factors in seafood, such as the trace mineral selenium, may help protect against cardiovascular and other diseases. Dutch researchers raised this possibility when they noted that eaters of lean fish (low in omega-3) as well as fatty fish (high in omega-3) had lower rates of fatal heart attack.

Garlic Smoked Mussels with Tomatoes

Serves 4

Those mighty molluscs, including mussels, do very good things for your cardiovascular system, according to research. They lower your blood cholesterol, improve the ratio of your good cholesterol to bad cholesterol and even promote absorption and metabolism of damaging cholesterol molecules so they do not get a chance to clog your arteries. I like this recipe also because it includes lots of therapeutic garlic and is an imaginative way to do mussels on the barbecue. This recipe comes from Chef Frank Terranova, one of the winners in a competition for seafood chefs sponsored by the American National Fish and Seafood Promotional Council on behalf of the seafood industry.

    8 large elephant garlic cloves, peeled
    3 dozen mussels, well scrubbed
    Fresh Tomato Concasse (recipe follows)

Prepare a barbecue and when the coals are ready to cook, place the garlic on a grid, 4–5 inches (10–13cm) above the hot coals.

Quickly place the mussels in a single layer on the grid and cover with the lid or foil to seal in the smoke. Cook until the shells open, 8–10 minutes for large and 4 minutes for small mussels. Break off and discard the top shells, discarding any mussels that haven't opened.

Arrange the mussels on a hot tray or serving platter. Spoon a little Fresh Tomato Concasse on each mussel and serve immediately.

    Per serving:
        Calories   98
        Total fat   1.7g
        Saturated fat   .3g
        Cholesterol   20mg
        Sodium   210mg

Fresh Tomato Concasse   About 12fl oz (340ml)

   1lb (450g) tomatoes, preferably plum
   2 tablespoons olive oil
   4 teaspoons white wine vinegar or balsamic vinegar
   1 tablespoon chopped fresh basil or 1 teaspoon dried
   1 tablespoon chopped fresh oregano or 1 teaspoon dried
   $1/4$ teaspoon freshly ground pepper

Place the tomatoes on the barbecue grid, 4–5 inches (10–13cm) above the hot coals. Cook, turning frequently, until the skins pop and the tomatoes are slightly charred, about 10 minutes.

Skin, cut in half and scoop out the seeds. Coarsely chop the tomatoes and place them in a bowl with the oil, vinegar, herbs and pepper. Serve at room temperature.

Note You can put the tomatoes under the grill instead.

Per 1-tablespoon serving:
Calories	14
Total fat	1g
Saturated fat	.2g
Cholesterol	0
Sodium	1mg

Stir-Fried Scallops with Walnuts and Mangetout

Serves 4

Scallops are extraordinarily low in fat but what fat they do have is virtually all from omega-3—which makes them particularly attractive for health. Walnuts are one of my favourite nuts because they too have omega-3 as well as other identified disease-fighting compounds. Combined, they also taste terrific as this quick stir-fry illustrates. Most of the fat in this stir-fry comes from the walnuts and is unsaturated.

1 tablespoon cornflour
4fl oz (115ml) chicken stock
2 tablespoons dry sherry
2 tablespoons light soy sauce
1 teaspoon grated fresh root ginger
$^1/_4$ teaspoon hot red pepper flakes or to taste
4oz (115g) walnut halves
1$^1/_2$ tablespoons vegetable oil
1 tablespoon finely chopped garlic
8 spring onions, including some of the green, sliced into 1 inch
    (2.5cm) lengths on a diagonal
5oz (140g) mangetout
1lb 4oz (565g) sea scallops, halved or quartered and dried with paper
    towels

In a small bowl, combine the cornflour and chicken stock. Whisk in the sherry, soy sauce, root ginger and red pepper flakes. Set aside.

Spread the walnut halves on a baking tray and toast in a 180°C/350°F/Gas 4 oven—about 10 minutes.

Put half the oil in a wok or large frying pan over high heat. When the oil is hot, add the garlic, spring onions and mangetout and stir-fry for 2 minutes, until they are tender-crisp. Remove from wok.

Add the remaining oil and the scallops and stir-fry for 1 minute. Stir in the stock mixture and cook until slightly thickened, about 1 minute. Add the spring onions, mangetout and toasted walnuts. Cook for 1 more minute (do not overcook scallops). Serve at once.

Per serving:

Calories	385
Total fat	21.9g
Saturated fat	2.2g
Cholesterol	46.8mg
Sodium	542mg

Chef Kenneth's Crab Cakes

Serves 6

Chef Kenneth Juran, executive chef at the Washington, D.C., Park Hyatt Hotel is famous for these crab cakes, full of luscious Chesapeake Bay crabmeat. Eating crab instead of high-saturated-fat foods like meat can lower your cholesterol and triglycerides, according to studies. Although crab has some cholesterol, it's not enough to cause concern. Crab also contains cell-protecting omega-3 fatty acids. Two crab cakes contain about 500 milligrams of omega-3s, nearly the daily dose needed to cut fatal heart attack risk by 30–40 per cent, according to studies. Chef Kenneth often serves the crab cakes with a red pepper sauce but I find them delectable plain or sprinkled lightly with fresh lemon juice.

2lb (900g) fresh crabmeat
2 eggs
1 tablespoon Dijon mustard
2 drops Tabasco sauce
2½ tablespoons chopped parsley
1 teaspoon Worcestershire sauce
Salt and freshly ground pepper to taste
1oz (30g) fresh white breadcrumbs
½oz (15g) butter
1 teaspoon olive or rapeseed oil

Pick over the crab, removing all bits of shell and foreign material.

In a small bowl, combine the eggs, mustard, Tabasco, parsley, Worcestershire sauce, salt and pepper and mix well.

Add the egg mixture to the crabmeat. Mix well. Them fold in the breadcrumbs to bind.

Form 12 crab cakes. Preheat the oven to 190°C/375°F/Gas 5.

Put half the butter and half the oil in a large nonstick frying pan. Cook half the crab cakes over medium heat until lightly browned on both sides. Transfer the crab cakes to a shallow ovenproof dish and repeat the process with the remaining six crab cakes. Bake the crab cakes for 8–10 minutes.

Per serving:
Calories	217
Total fat	7.3g
Saturated fat	2.2g
Cholesterol	227mg
Sodium	566mg

Seafood Chilli with Red Beans

Serves 10

Chilli has never been like this—a remarkable blending of the Mexican tradition of beans and hot peppers with, yes, the most popular food pharmacy lifesaver—seafood—substituting for the traditional beef. This does take a little time to make but it is worth it—and beautiful with its burnt sienna base flecked with green and red. The chilli is wonderfully flavourful even without the seafood. More thanks to my friend Chef Kenneth Juran for this remarkable health-promoting recipe.

3½ pints (2 litres) chicken stock, preferably homemade
1lb (450g) red kidney beans, soaked
2 tablespoons olive oil
2 tablespoons chopped garlic
4 small onions, finely diced
2 red peppers, finely diced
2 poblano peppers, finely diced, *or* 2 green peppers, finely diced,
    plus 1 teaspoon Tabasco sauce
4fl oz (115ml) tomato purée
10 very ripe plum tomatoes, finely chopped, *or* 10 canned plum
    tomatoes, drained and chopped
1 teaspoon ground cumin
5 tablespoons mild chilli powder or to taste
1 tablespoon chopped fresh oregano
1 tablespoon chopped fresh thyme
1 tablespoon chopped fresh coriander
¾ pint (425ml) dry white wine
1½lb (680g) fresh seafood (shrimp, lobster, swordfish, scallops), cut
    into bite-size pieces.

Bring the chicken stock and beans to the boil. Boil rapidly for 10 minutes, then reduce the heat and simmer for about 20 minutes.

In a separate pan, heat the oil and sauté the garlic over medium heat for 1 minute (do not let garlic brown). Add the onions and continue cooking, stirring constantly, for 3 minutes more. Now add all the chopped peppers, tomato purée and tomatoes. Cook for 10 minutes over medium heat, continuing to stir so it does not scorch on the bottom. Add the cumin and chilli powder.

When the beans are done, remove half the beans and chicken stock and purée in a blender or food processor. Return the purée to the whole beans and stock. Then add the bean mixture to the pepper mixture. Add all the fresh herbs.

Put the wine and seafood in a pan and cook slowly over medium heat until cooked all the way through; cooking time will vary with type of seafood. Shrimp and scallops take only a couple of minutes; swordfish, about 10 minutes. With a slotted spoon, remove the seafood and add to the pan of chilli. Bring the mixture just to a simmer. Turn off the heat and serve immediately.

Per serving:
Calories	327
Total fat	6.9g
Saturated fat	1.1g
Cholesterol	51mg
Sodium	283mg

✔

FOOD PHARMACY FACT
Want Good Cholesterol? Eat Vitamin C Foods

At least that's what government research suggests after studying 238 elderly Chinese-Americans, who eat more high-vitamin-C foods than most Americans. Researchers at Department of Agriculture's Human Nutrition Research Center on Aging at Tufts found that among the Chinese-Americans those with the highest blood levels of vitamin C also had the highest levels of good-type HDL cholesterol, which whisks the bad-type LDL cholesterol out of the system. Previously scientists had discovered the same thing among a group of 700 mostly Caucasian men and women over sixty. But it does not hold true for smokers, who consistently had lower levels of C in their blood. The presumption is that eating more vitamin C somehow drives up the HDLs, thus lessening the danger of cardiovascular disease.

Puerto Rican Sardine Pie

Serves 6

For sardine lovers, here is a dish literally to please your heart, plus your bones, joints, skin and cells in general. The recipe also calls for that too infrequently used Swiss chard, a dark green vegetable also chockful of cell-protecting compounds. In addition, this pie tastes terrific, like a deep-pan pizza. It's one of my favourites. However, if you're on a low-sodium diet, you may want to give this recipe a miss. Many thanks to Phyllis Richman, The Washington Post, *for this hearty taste sensation.*

1 bunch Swiss chard (or spinach), cut into 1 inch (2.5cm) pieces
1 beefsteak tomato (8oz/225g), chopped
8oz (225g) onions, chopped
1 small green pepper, chopped
Salt to taste
1 tablespoon olive oil
8–10 canned sardines (about 2 × 4³/₄oz/135g tins)
2 pimientos or canned red peppers, cut into strips

Base

1 teaspoon sugar
4fl oz (115ml) lukewarm water
1 scant tablespoon active dry yeast
¹/₂ teaspoon salt
1¹/₂oz (45g) butter or margarine, melted
1 egg, beaten
8oz (225g) plain flour

Add 1 teaspoon sugar to the lukewarm water, then add the yeast slowly and allow to stand for 10 minutes. If using easy-blend yeast do not add to the water, add to the flour following package directions.

Add the salt, butter, and egg and mix well. Add the flour slowly to form a smooth dough. Knead lightly and place in a greased bowl. Allow to rise in a warm place until double in bulk, about an hour.

Sauté all the vegetables in the olive oil until softened, about 10 minutes. Preheat the oven to 180°C/350°F/Gas 4.

Roll half of the dough into a circle about 10 inches (25cm) in diameter and 1/4 inch (0.5cm) thick. Place the dough in a 9 inch (23cm) pie tin and build up the 1 inch (2.5cm) overhang to form a ridge. Reserve the remaining dough for another use or double the filling and make 2 pies.

Drain excess liquid and spread the vegetables over the pie base. Arrange the sardines in spokes over the vegetables and decorate with pimiento strips. Bake for 25 minutes. Serve hot or at room temperature.

Per serving:

Calories	357
Total fat	13.8g
Saturated fat	4.6g
Cholesterol	101mg
Sodium	602mg

HOW TO CHOOSE THE SAFEST FISH

Some fish can be contaminated by environmental pollutants, like PCBs and pesticides, which tend to concentrate in fatty fish so could eating fish do more harm than good? "Generally no", say even the most dedicated environmental experts. However, the government should definitely tighten regulations to ensure safe fish; although the hazard is slight it makes good sense to be cautious. Here are some facts and advice.

- Open-ocean fish are less likely to be contaminated than fresh-water fish.
- The greatest threat of contamination is in sport fish caught by recreational fishermen.
- Most endangered by pollutants in fish are nursing mothers, pregnant women and children.
- Always heed local warnings from health authorities about contamination dangers in special waters.
- It's best to shop for fish in large commercial markets.
- Eat a variety of fish to protect against possible contamination from one source.
- According to Dr. David Rall, former director of the American National Institute of Environmental and Health Sciences, "The nasty stuff is mainly in the skin and liver of the fish. If you avoid that—as most people do—there does not seem to be any problem. We think the danger of eating the flesh of fish is about zero."

Carol Mason's White Chilli

Serves 6

Fans of Carol Mason, a chef and cooking instructor in Washington D.C., have been raving about her white chilli made with white beans and chunks of chicken for as long as I can remember. After trying it, you'll undoubtedly agree it's one of the best chillies you've ever had. I like it especially because the low-fat chicken is a welcome change from traditional beef. I've reduced the amount of oil to make it even lower in fat.

1lb (450g) dried cannellini beans, soaked and drained, *or* 2¹/₂–3lb
    (1.1–1.4kg) canned beans with liquid
2¹/₂–3 pints (1.4–1.7 litres) homemade chicken stock
    (¹/₂–³/₄ pint/285–425ml if using canned beans)
1 tablespoon garlic, finely chopped
12oz (340g) onions, chopped
1 tablespoon olive oil
4oz (115g) can chopped green chillies *or* 4oz (115g) fresh Anaheim
    chillies, seeded and chopped
1 poblano chilli, seeded and chopped
2 teaspoons ground cumin
2 teaspoons dried oregano
¹/₄ teaspoon ground cloves
¹/₄ teaspoon cayenne pepper
Dash of Tabasco sauce (more if desired)
1¹/₂lb (680g) skinless chicken breast poached and cubed
Coarsely grated cheese, chopped spring onions, chopped tomatoes,
    chopped fresh coriander or Salsa Cruda (page 385) for garnish
    (optional)

In a large casserole combine the drained dried beans with 2¹/₂ pints (1.4 litres) of the chicken stock. Add the garlic and half the onions.

Bring the beans to the boil, reduce the heat, partially cover and simmer until the beans are tender but not mushy—about 2–3 hours. Add more chicken stock if necessary.

In a small saucepan sauté the remaining onions in the oil until translucent and soft. If using canned beans sauté all the garlic and onion at this point. Add the chillies and seasonings and mix thoroughly. Add the onion and chillies mixture to the cooked or canned beans in a large pan.

Add the chicken cubes and cook over low heat for about 5 minutes or until the chicken is heated through. Add more chicken stock if needed and heat through.

Serve with a compatible mixture of some of the suggested garnishes.

Note If you use canned beans, you will need only ½–¾ pint (285–425ml) chicken stock, which you can add as needed to maintain the desired amount of liquid in the chilli.

Per serving:

Calories	485
Total fat	7.7g
Saturated fat	1.7g
Cholesterol	80mg
Sodium	231mg

✔

FOOD PHARMACY FACT
Chicken Surprise

When you eat poultry, you take in some omega-3 fatty acids of the type found in fish that is so beneficial to health. The reason for this is that since 1960 some farmers have included fish meal in chicken feed. The fish meal helps create omega-3s in the flesh of the chickens. It's estimated that we may be getting up to 20 per cent of all our omega-3s from poultry. "Since Americans eat so little fish, this may be what's saving us from even more heart disease," quipped one expert on fish oil.

Ellen Brown's Jambalaya

Serves 8

For a gourmet party dish that's really good for your health, you can't beat this jambalaya created by Ellen Brown, a food writer and recipe origina- tor par excellence. Just putting those colourful heaps of chopped onions, celery, peppers and garlic into the pot makes you feel healthier already. Although the recipe calls for chicken, I've also made it with chunks of uncooked turkey breast and found it equally delicious. The recipe is reprinted from Brown's The Gourmet Gazelle Cookbook, *which contains many other low-fat health-promoting recipes.*

2 tablespoons vegetable oil

3oz (85g) salt-reduced ham

2 large onions, peeled and coarsely chopped

2 celery stalks, washed and coarsely chopped

1 green pepper, coarsely chopped

6 spring onions, including 3 inches (7.5cm) of the green, chopped

3 garlic cloves, finely chopped

7oz (200g) brown rice

1lb (450g) boneless, skinless chicken breasts, trimmed and cut into
    2 inch (5cm) cubes

2 bay leaves

$1/2$–1 teaspoon cayenne pepper (to taste)

1 tablespoon chopped fresh oregano or 2 teaspoon dried

2 teaspoon chopped fresh thyme or $1/2$ teaspoon dried

Salt to taste

2 tablespoons tomato purée

20oz (565g) canned tomatoes, drained and chopped

8fl oz (225ml) fish stock

8oz (225g) medium prawns, peeled and deveined

Preheat the oven to 180°C/350°/Gas 4. Heat the vegetable oil over medium-high heat in a large flameproof casserole. Add the ham and sauté for 1 minute. Add the fresh vegetables and garlic. Sauté for 5 minutes, stirring often, until the onion is translucent. Add the brown rice and sauté for 3 more minutes, stirring constantly.

Add the chicken, bay leaves, cayenne pepper, oregano, thyme and salt. Cook for 2 minutes.

Add the tomato purée, tomatoes and fish stock. Bring to the boil, cover the casserole and place in the centre of the oven. Cook for 20 minutes. Stir the casserole, add the prawns and return to the oven for 10–15 minutes or until the liquid has been absorbed and the rice is tender. Serve immediately.

Note You can make this dish up to two days in advance; however, remove it from the oven after the initial 20 minutes. It will still be slightly liquid. Before serving, place it in a 180°C/350°F/Gas 4 oven for 30 minutes, then add the prawns and continue to bake for 10 minutes.

Per serving:

Calories	261
Total fat	6g
Saturated fat	.1g
Cholesterol	73mg
Sodium	440mg

Navajo Stew with Sweet Potatoes and Black Beans

Serves 6–8

Sweet potatoes, chilli spices and beans ... this is an inspired combination, from both the health and taste standpoints. The sweet potatoes give you a huge shot of beta-carotene and vitamin A—about 38,000 international units—enough to last you for a week and one-and-a-half times the daily dose of beta-carotene being used in the government's human studies to test the compound's powers to prevent cancer. The beans are full of anticancer compound also. And combined with the chilli spices, they taste so great that my friend Jim ate two huge servings—an unusual event. I thank Gourmet magazine for the inspiration, although I have modified many of the ingredients.

    2 medium or 4 small onions, chopped
    4 teaspoons chilli powder
    4fl oz (115ml) orange juice
    2lb (900g) boneless turkey breast, cut into 1 inch (2.5cm) cubes
    4fl oz (115ml) water
    2 teaspoons honey
    Salt to taste
    3 large sweet potatoes (about 3lb/1.4kg), peeled and cut into 1 inch
        (2.5cm) cubes
    2 teaspoons butter or margarine, softened
    2 teaspoons flour
    2 × 10oz (285g) cans black beans, drained and rinsed

Put the onions, chilli powder and half the orange juice in a large bowl. Cover and microwave on HIGH for 3 minutes. Stir and microwave on HIGH for 3 minutes more or until the onions are limp.

Add the turkey cubes, remaining orange juice, water, honey, salt and sweet potatoes. Stir to combine all ingredients. Cover and microwave on HIGH for about 30 minutes or until the sweet potatoes are done but still hold their shape and are not mushy. Test and stir after 15–20 minutes.

Blend the butter and flour.

Add the beans along with the butter and flour mixture and microwave on HIGH for 4 minutes, until the stew has thickened slightly.

Per serving:
Calories	475
Total fat	4.7g
Saturated fat	1.7g
Cholesterol	97mg
Sodium	56mg

Pineapple Ginger Chicken

Serves 6

Search no further for an excellent ginger chicken recipe, high in flavour and low in fat and calories. I especially like the combination of ginger and chicken because in tests ginger actually destroys the salmonella bacteria that frequently contaminate chickens. It's as if the Oriental creators of this combination long ago were privy to some modern scientific wisdom. The pineapple juice is also a powerhouse of manganese, needed to protect bones. This recipe was created by Tracy Ritter, chef at the Golden Door Spa in California.

3/4 pint (425ml) unsweetened pineapple juice
1/2 pint (285ml) dry white wine
2 tablespoons finely chopped fresh root ginger
5 tablespoons whole-grain mustard
2 tablespoons light soy sauce
2 teaspoons dark sesame oil
2 spring onions, chopped
1 garlic clove, finely chopped
6 whole boneless, skinless chicken breasts, cut in half

Combine the pineapple juice, wine, ginger, mustard, soy sauce, sesame oil, spring onions and garlic in blender. Blend until creamy.

Reserve half the marinade for the sauce. Arrange the chicken pieces in a shallow dish large enough to hold them in a single layer. Pour the marinade over them and cover. Refrigerate for 2–3 hours or overnight.

Preheat the grill. Remove the chicken from the marinade and arrange on grill rack. Cook on lowest level of grill, 6–8 minutes total, or until the chicken is tender and brown. Baste once after turning.

To make the sauce, bring the reserved marinade to the boil and cook over high heat for about 10 minutes, until the sauce thickens slightly. Spoon the sauce over the chicken.

Per serving:

Calories	345
Total fat	8g
Saturated fat	1.9g
Cholesterol	146mg
Sodium	380mg

Barbecued Turkey with Garlic and Chilli Sauce

Serves 4

This low-fat, spicy marinated turkey with its zingy barbecue sauce was the big winner at the great garlic cook-off held during the 1989 annual Garlic Festival in Gilroy, California. And small wonder. It combines all the best taste of health-promoting garlic and chilli peppers with the lowest-fat animal protein around. Its originator, Chuck Dell'Ario of Oakland, was crowned with a garland of garlic.

4 dried ancho or pasilla chillies
8fl oz (225ml) water
1 tablespoon olive oil
1 onion, chopped
8 garlic cloves, finely chopped
2 tamarillos, chopped
2 tablespoons Worcestershire sauce
1 tablespoon sugar
1 tablespoon chocolate chips
1 teaspoon ground cinnamon
1 teaspoon ground cumin
Salt and freshly ground pepper to taste
4–8 turkey breast fillets (1½–2lb/680–900g total)
2oz (55g) fresh coriander, chopped for garnish

Stem and seed the chillies. Heat the water, pour it over the chillies, and leave to stand for at least 30 minutes. Drain, reserving the water.

Heat the oil in a large saucepan. Sauté the onion and garlic until soft and translucent but not browned, about 5 minutes. Add the tamarillos, chillies, half the chilli soaking water, Worcestershire sauce, sugar, chocolate chips, cinnamon and cumin. Simmer for 20 minutes. Add salt and pepper to taste.

Transfer the mixture to a food processor or a food mill and purée, then strain through a medium sieve. The sauce should be thick.

Put the turkey in a bowl. Cover with the sauce, then cover the bowl tightly and marinate in the refrigerator for at least 2 hours.

Drain the turkey, reserving the sauce.

Barbecue over hot coals or cook under a preheated grill until just done, 4–5 minutes per side, basting with 4fl oz (115ml) sauce.

Heat the remaining sauce and serve with the cooked turkey. Garnish the turkey with the chopped coriander.

Note The sauce may be made up to 2 days ahead.

Per serving:

Calories	354
Total fat	9.6g
Saturated fat	1.8g
Cholesterol	123mg
Sodium	224mg

✔

FOOD PHARMACY FACT
It's Not the Meat; It's the Fat

You don't have to give up red meat, poultry and eggs to lower your blood cholesterol and blood pressure. That's what Rita Dougherty of USDA's Western Human Nutrition Research Center in San Francisco found in a study of twelve men on low-fat diets. The men had an average blood cholesterol of 5.7 and average blood pressure of 135/85. They ordinarily ate 40–44 per cent of their calories in fat, 21 per cent from saturated fat.

During the test, for forty days they ate the same number of calories, but 25 per cent of the calories came from fat, with 6 per cent of those from saturated fat. They ate beef and pork from which the fat had been trimmed, poultry without skin, margarine instead of butter, skimmed milk instead of whole, vegetable oil instead of animal cooking fats.

In fact they ate as much meat, poultry and dairy products as before and more total food. Still their cholesterol dropped on average over 15 per cent to 4.8 and their blood pressure around 10 per cent to 124/79. As Dougherty points out, the men ate red meat and eggs several times a week and milk and margarine daily, as much as they had previously. Obviously, she says, it's not these foods per se that are the villains but the fat they carry as baggage. Get rid of that, and they are cholesterol-safe to eat.

Barley and Turkey Skillet Dinner

Serves 6

Here's a simple country-style way to eat barley, that often neglected grain that is high in both soluble and insoluble fibre, both known to be excellent for health. Barley, it's been shown, is just as effective as oats in lowering blood cholesterol. Using minced turkey also keeps down the fat content. Thanks to barley researcher Dr. Rosemary Newman, University of Montana, for this recipe.

1lb (450g) minced turkey, chicken or lean beef
3oz (85g) onion, chopped
2oz (55g) celery, chopped
1oz (30g) green pepper, diced
1 garlic clove, finely chopped
2 tablespoons vegetable oil
5oz (140g) pearl barley
16oz (450g) can tomatoes, chopped, with juice
12fl oz (340ml) water
4fl oz (115ml) chilli sauce
1 teaspoon Worcestershire sauce
1/2 teaspoon dried marjoram
Salt and freshly ground pepper to taste

In a heavy frying pan, sauté the turkey, onion, celery, green pepper and garlic in the oil for 3–4 minutes.

Add the remaining ingredients, bring to the boil, reduce the heat to simmer, cover and cook for about 1 hour or until the barley is tender and most of the liquid is absorbed. Adjust the seasonings.

Note You may substitute diced uncooked turkey or chicken in place of minced poultry.

Per serving:
Calories	283
Total fat	10.8g
Saturated fat	2g
Cholesterol	55mg
Sodium	519mg

Chinese Pepper Steak

Serves 3–4

Not only does this stir-fry have the typical peppers; it has the added appeal of Chinese black mushrooms known as tree-ear or wood-ear and mo-er. These are known in ancient Chinese medicine as "blood thinners" and "good for the heart". Indeed recent studies show the mushroom contains anticoagulant-like chemicals that do impede blood clotting; their effect is somewhat the same as that of aspirin, a well-proven "blood thinner" thought to help prevent heart attacks and strokes. Thus eating the small doses of mushrooms in this recipe will probably produce a "blood-thinning" effect.

1lb (450g) lean sirloin steak, trimmed of fat and cut into ¼ inch
   (0.5cm) strips
6 dried Chinese black tree-ear mushrooms
2–3 tablespoons olive oil
1 inch (2.5cm) piece of fresh root ginger, finely chopped
2 garlic cloves, finely chopped
2 spring onions, finely chopped
1 green pepper, cut into 1 inch (2.5cm) pieces
1 red pepper, cut into 1 inch (2.5cm) pieces
1 yellow pepper (or another red one), cut into 1 inch (2.5cm) pieces

---

Marinade

---

2 tablespoons light soy sauce
2 tablespoons rice wine or dry sherry
1 tablespoon dark sesame oil
½ teaspoon hot chilli oil or Tabasco sauce
1 teaspoon sugar
2 teaspoons cornflour

Combine the ingredients for the marinade and marinate the beef in it for 20 minutes.

Pour boiling water over the mushrooms and soak for 15 minutes. Remove the stems and cut the mushrooms into thin strips.

Just before serving, drain the meat, reserving the marinade. Heat 2 tablespoons of the oil almost to smoking in a wok or large frying pan. Add the ginger, garlic and spring onions and stir-fry for 30 seconds or until fragrant. Add the beef and stir-fry for 1–2 minutes or until cooked to taste. Transfer the beef to a bowl and keep warm.

Add 1 tablespoon oil to the wok if necessary. Add the mushrooms and peppers and stir-fry for 1 minute. Return the meat to the wok and add the marinade. Stir-fry for 30 seconds or until all the ingredients are heated and the sauce is lightly thickened.

Per serving:
    Calories   411
    Total fat   23g
    Saturated fat   4.5g
    Cholesterol   92mg
    Sodium   501mg

✔

DOCTOR'S ADVICE
Eat Like the Chinese Do

"We're basically a vegetarian species and should be eating a wide variety of plant foods and minimizing our intake of animal foods." So says Dr. T. Colin Campbell, nutritional biochemist at Cornell University, after receiving preliminary data from China of the largest, most comprehensive study ever done of the relationship between diet and chronic disease.

Dr. Campbell's study of 6,500 Chinese, done in cooperation with Chinese doctors, clearly shows, he says, that the Chinese plantfood-oriented diet is healthier than our animal-dependent diet.

For example, the average Chinese eats but 64g of protein a day, 93 per cent of it from plants. The average American eats one-third more protein (91g) and a whopping 70 per cent comes from animal products. Chinese who eat the most protein, particularly animal protein, also have the most heart disease, cancer and diabetes.

The average Chinese eats a mere 15 per cent of calories from fat compared with about 37 per cent of calories from fat by the average American.

A typical Chinese, due to a high plant diet, eats about three times as much dietary fibre as the typical American. Though most Chinese eat virtually no dairy calcium, they rarely suffer from osteoporosis. They eat only half as much calcium as Americans and nearly all their calcium comes from plants.

Chinese women have extremely low rates of breast and reproductive-system cancers.

The average blood cholesterol among Chinese is 3.3 compared with 5.5 among those on a Western diet.

Nor is the iron in meat necessary to prevent anaemia, says Dr. Campbell. Anaemia is very rare among Chinese. They eat twice as much iron as Americans but by far most of it comes from plants.

Dr. Campbell advises eating primarily a plant-based diet, with 80 per cent of calories or more coming from plant foods, such as fresh or frozen fruits and vegetables and whole-grain foods.

Pork and Apple Stir-Fry

Serves 4

Many experts say we should eat more like Asians, as this recipe exemplifies, with small amounts of meat mixed with lots of vegetables and, in this case, apples. The apples not only add an interesting taste but, as Japanese studies show, may help reduce the risk of strokes. You can substitute chicken breast for the pork.

1 tablespoon vegetable oil
3 garlic cloves, crushed
8oz (225g) lean boneless pork, thinly sliced (about 1/4 inch/0.5cm thick)
8oz (225g) broccoli florets and sliced stalks
1 large red pepper, thinly sliced
1lb (450g) Chinese leaves, sliced
1 apple, such as Golden Delicious, cored and cut into 16 slices

Sauce

2 tablespoons water
1 tablespoon light soy sauce
1 teaspoon cornflour
1 teaspoon sugar
1 1/2 teaspoons grated fresh root ginger
1/8 teaspoon hot red pepper flakes

Heat the oil in a large nonstick frying pan or wok over medium heat. Add the garlic and stir-fry until golden, then discard.

Add the sliced pork and stir-fry over medium-high heat until lightly browned. Transfer to a large serving bowl.

Add the broccoli and red pepper and stir-fry for about 2 minutes. Add the pork, Chinese leaves and apple slices and stir-fry for about 2 minutes.

Combine the sauce ingredients, add them to the pan and stir-fry for about 3 minutes. Transfer to a serving bowl and serve immediately with rice or soft noodles.

Per serving:

Calories	199
Total fat	8g
Saturated fat	1.9g
Cholesterol	36mg
Sodium	214mg

Oriental Hot Pot

Serves 6–8

The fondue parties of the Sixties are being resurrected for the Nineties—with one big change. Instead of high-fat cheese as the dipping sauce, it's now stocks simmering with lean meat, seafood and vegetables of all types. It's no longer high-calorie Swiss fondue; it's the Oriental hot pot. In this traditional Japanese recipe the cooking liquid is a delicate stock flavoured with ginger and anise. Such one-pot dinners are fun, the diners do the cooking and can pick and choose what they want—and certainly it's low in fat and a treasure of health-promoting vitamins, minerals and other compounds.

2–2¹/₂ pints (1.1–1.7 litres) chicken stock, preferably homemade
1 inch (2.5cm) piece of fresh root ginger, thinly sliced
2 spring onions
2 star anise, if available*
4oz (115g) cellophane or bean thread noodles
1 small Chinese leaves, broken into leaves
12oz (340g) boneless lamb loin
12oz (340g) sea scallops
Sesame Dipping Sauce (recipe follows)
1 bunch watercress, washed and long stems removed
8oz (225g) fresh spinach, washed and stemmed
8oz (225g) mushrooms, cleaned and cut in half
12oz (340g) boneless, skinless chicken breasts, trimmed of fat and
   sinew and cut into bite-size pieces
12oz (340g) prawns, peeled and deveined
11lb (450g) firm tofu, cut into 1 inch (2.5cm) cubes

Combine the chicken stock with the ginger, spring onions and star anise. Simmer for 10 minutes and strain.

Soak the noodles in cold water to cover for 15 minutes, then drain.

Cut the Chinese leaves crosswise into 1-inch (2.5cm) strips. Slice the lamb as thinly as possible (partial freezing ahead of time makes slicing easier). Remove the small half-moon-shaped membrane on the sides of the scallops.

Put the sesame dipping sauce in a small bowl. Arrange the noodles, water-cress, spinach, mushrooms, chicken, lamb, seafood and tofu on a large platter (ideally one with a rotating base).

Fill a hot pot or fondue pot most of the way up with stock.

Let each person dip vegetables, noodles, tofu, meats and seafoods into the simmering broth, cooking to taste, then into the dipping sauce. Add stock as necessary.

Per serving:
Calories	457
Total fat	13.5g
Saturated fat	2.9g
Cholesterol	148mg
Sodium	325mg

Sesame Dipping Sauce   8fl oz (225ml)

4oz (115g) tahini (sesame seed paste)
2 tablespoons light soy sauce
5–6 tablespoons skimmed milk or yoghurt

Mix all the ingredients until well blended.

Per tablespoon:
Calories	48
Total fat	4.1g
Saturated fat	.6g
Cholesterol	.4mg
Sodium	139mg

Note For other dipping sauces, see page 391–392.

---

*Star anise is a star-shaped spice available in Oriental grocers. If it is unavailable, you can use a teaspoon of aniseeds, fennel seeds or a splash or anisette liqueur but the flavour will not be as pungent or distinct as from the spice.

Moroccan Lamb Stew with Fruit

Serves 6

The oranges and dried fruit are what attract me to this North African lamb dish. Even orange peel has been shown to have antioxidant cell-protecting properties. And the concentration of compounds in dried fruits undoubtedly helps account for their excellent showing in helping lower the risk of certain cancers. And prunes, it is true, are one of the highest-fibre foods.

3lb (1.4kg) leg of lamb, cubed and trimmed of fat and gristle
2oz (55g) flour
Salt and freshly ground pepper to taste
1 tablespoon olive oil plus extra for browning
6oz (170g) onions, chopped
4 garlic cloves, finely chopped
Grated zest of 2 oranges
2 teaspoons dried thyme, crushed
1 teaspoon cumin seeds
2 teaspoons dried rosemary, crushed
2 bay leaves
3/4 pint (425ml) chicken stock
Juice of 2 oranges
12 stoned prunes, halved
8 dried figs, halved
2oz (55g) slivered almonds, toasted
Chopped parsley for garnish

Pat the meat dry. Mix the flour with salt and pepper in a shallow bowl and dredge the lamb cubes. Barely coat the bottom of a large flameproof casserole with olive oil and heat over medium-high heat. Brown a single layer of lamb on all sides, remove and set aside; repeat until all the meat is browned. Wipe out the pan.

In the same pan, heat 1 tablespoon olive oil, add the onions and cook until soft and lightly browned. Add the garlic, orange zest, thyme, cumin, rosemary and bay leaves. Heat for about 1 minute, until fragrant, stirring constantly. Preheat the oven to 170°C/325°F/Gas 3.

Return the lamb to the casserole, add the stock and orange juice, stir together, and bring to the boil. Cover, transfer to the oven for 1 hour. Stir in the prunes, figs and almonds and cook for another 30 minutes. Remove the bay leaves. Garnish with parsley and serve with bulgar wheat or brown rice.

Per serving:
Calories	602
Total fat	24g
Saturated fat	5g
Cholesterol	145mg
Sodium	166mg

Desserts

Date-Wrapped Nuts

20 pieces

These simple titbits are a delectable way to end a meal and to get the rich amounts of selenium and other health-protecting antioxidants and compounds in nuts, notably Brazil nuts. Dried fruits like dates are often found in the diets of those with lower rates of certain cancers.

20 stoned dates
20 Brazil nuts or almonds
2oz (55g) granulated sugar

Insert a nut into the pocket of each date. Roll in granulated sugar and arrange on a plate.

Per piece:
Calories	56
Total fat	2.4g
Saturated fat	.6g
Cholesterol	0
Sodium	.3mg

DON'T POP A PILL—EAT A BRAZIL NUT

Brazil nuts are so high in the trace mineral selenium that eating but one nut a day is as protective as popping a selenium pill from a health food store, according to Dr. Donald J. Lisk, director of Cornell University's Toxic Chemical Laboratory. The Brazil nut (which is actually a seed inside a hard brown crescent) is highest of all nuts in selenium, a powerful antioxidant that scientists believe helps protect against toxins and a number of chronic diseases, including cancer and cardiovascular disease.

It's well known, for example, that people with low levels of selenium in their blood are more apt to have heart attacks, strokes and, in particular, cancer. Lab studies also show that selenium at fairly low levels can block the development of cancer in animals.

Selenium has another amazing protective ability, particularly intriguing in an age of high environmental pollution. Selenium "dramatically protects against toxicity from heavy metals, such as mercury, lead and cadmium," says Dr. Lisk. When animals are fed these dangerous heavy metals and also given selenium, they do not experience the expected symptoms of poisoning. The selenium somehow has the ability to wipe out or detoxify the metals' awful consequences to a large extent. This means that selenium may be a partial antidote to some of our modern environmental hazards by helping neutralize the danger of mercury contamination from certain fish, for example or high lead levels in water or in lead paint, which may damage brain cells.

When Dr. Lisk and colleagues recently measured Brazil nuts for selenium content, they were amazed to find that on average Brazil nuts contain up to 2,500 more units of selenium than any other nut. In fact, says Dr. Lisk, eating a single Brazil nut daily would easily correct or ward off any fears of selenium deficiency. Eating only half a dozen nuts rapidly boosts blood selenium levels by 100–350 per cent. The reason is that the nuts come from trees growing in a section of Brazil where the soil is extremely high in selenium.

There is a warning however. In excess, selenium can become poisonous so don't go overboard, cautions Dr. Lisk. Though the studies are not conclusive, you probably would not want to eat more than half a dozen nuts a day as an average consumption.

Other foods high in selenium are seafood, notably swordfish, salmon, tuna, lobster, prawns, oysters and haddock. Cereals, grains, sunflower seeds, pasta and calves and ox liver are also high.

Strawberries with a Meringue Cloud

Serves 8

So quick and simple to make but so luscious is this baked strawberry dessert. It also makes a stunning presentation, resembling baked Alaska, with heaps of fluffy white surrounded by a moat of deep red. Strawberries, like other red berries and vegetables, are full of lycopene and ellagic acid, both anticancer agents.

2¹/₂lb (1.1kg) strawberries, sliced
5 tablespoons Grand Marnier
6oz (170g) granulated or caster sugar or to taste
4 egg whites
Pinch of salt
Pinch of cream of tartar
1oz (30g) slivered almonds, toasted
1 tablespoon icing sugar or to taste

Preheat the oven to 230°C/450°F/Gas 8.

Mix the strawberries with the Grand Marnier and sugar, reserving 4 tablespoons of sugar. Pour into a shallow, heatproof serving dish. The dessert can be prepared ahead to this point.

Beat the egg whites slowly with the salt and cream of tartar until frothy. Increase the speed to high and, when the whites form soft peaks, beat in the reserved 4 tablespoons sugar. Continue to beat the whites until stiff peaks are formed.

Mound the mixture over the centre of the strawberries, leaving 1–2 inches (2.5–5cm) of the outer edge of strawberries uncovered. Sprinkle with the nuts and then dust with the icing sugar.

Bake for about 5 minutes in the hot oven or until the top is just golden. Serve immediately.

Per serving:

Calories	174
Total fat	2g
Saturated fat	.2g
Cholesterol	0
Sodium	46mg

✔

FOOD PHARMACY FACT
The Seeds of Berry Power

Strawberries, blackberries, raspberries and to a lesser extent blue-berries, cranberries, grapes, apples, Brazil nuts, walnuts and cashews all contain the anticancer compound ellagic acid, says Dr. Gary D. Stoner, a pathologist at the Medical College of Ohio.

Ellagic acid is an antioxidant that helps detoxify cancer-causing agents in several different ways. It may block the activation of carcinogens, inhibit the carcinogen itself, or keep the DNA in cells from undergoing mutation.

For example, in one test, ellagic acid blocked damage in human and mouse lung cells dosed with cancer-causing agents. This detox-ifying acid stopped from 45–70 per cent of the genetic damage to the cells. Strawberries are particularly rich in ellagic acid. It's high in both the pulp and the seeds. So if you sieve the berries, discarding the seeds, you also throw away some of the berry's anticancer capabilities.

Ginger Baked Apples with Vanilla Topping

Serves 4

Speaking of rich-tasting desserts, you would never guess this is virtually lacking in fat, it is so satisfying. Many baked apples are made with cinnamon but these use crystallized ginger, which provides a flavour surprise. You can also blend a tablespoon or two of amaretto liqueur (if using almonds) or orange-flavoured liqueur (if using walnuts) into the yoghurt topping. Sit back and enjoy what the apples are doing for your heart.

4 cooking apples, cored, a 1 inch (2.5cm) circle of peel
    removed at top
2 tablespoons chopped almonds or walnuts
1 tablespoon currants
3 teaspoons chopped crystallized ginger
1¹/₂ tablespoons lemon juice
7oz (200g) maple syrup
8oz (225g) vanilla very low-fat-yoghurt, strained for at least 4 hours

Arrange the apples in a microwave dish large enough so they do not touch. In each cavity place equal amounts of nuts, currants and crystallized ginger. Mix the lemon juice and maple syrup and pour into the cavities and around the apples.

Microwave, covered, on HIGH for about 10 minutes or until the apples are soft when pierced with a knife. Allow to stand for 5 minutes.

Place each apple in a separate bowl, pour the maple sauce over the apples and top with 2 tablespoons vanilla yoghurt.

Per serving:
Calories	323
Total fat	2.7g
Saturated fat	.3g
Cholesterol	1.7mg
Sodium	35mg

Summer Berry Pudding

Serves 10–12

Once a peasant dish made with leftover bread, this makes a virtually nonfat dessert for those of elegant taste. There's never sufficient praise for the health benefits of berries and the beta-carotene-rich peach or mango. All of them contain various cell-protecting antioxidants as well as antiviral properties; berries are also rich in fibre. This lovely dessert is often made by Chef Kenneth Juran, Park Hyatt Hotel in Washington, D.C., who gave us this recipe.

> 18–20 slices bread (remove crusts if too thick)
> 10oz (285g) strawberries, washed, hulled and quartered
> 10oz (285g) raspberries, washed, *or* 2 × 10oz (285g) packs frozen
>   berries, thawed and drained
> 2oz (55g) sugar
> 5oz (140g) blueberries, washed and picked over
> 1lb (450g) ripe peaches or mangoes, peeled and sliced

Lay the bread slices out on baking sheets to dry overnight at room temperature.

Purée half of the strawberries and half of the raspberries in a food processor or a blender with the sugar. Mix the purée with the remaining strawberries, raspberries and blueberries.

Line the bottom and sides of a 3 pint (1.7 litre) soufflé dish or pudding basin with some of the bread slices, cut to fit the dish. Cover the bread with about 1 cup berry mixture and some of the peach slices.

Layer the remaining bread and fruit, ending with bread. Cover the dish with a plate just large enough to fit inside. Stand on a tray, then place a weight, such as heavy cans (about 5lb/2.2kg), on top of the plate to make the pudding firm. Refrigerate overnight.

Unmould the pudding on to a round serving platter and slice in wedges to serve.

Per serving:

Calories	155
Total fat	1.5g
Saturated fat	.3g
Cholesterol	1mg
Sodium	193mg

FOOD PHARMACY FACT
Blueberry Power

Add blueberries to the list of foods that might help your heart by lowering blood cholesterol. A study at Ohio State University found that blueberries have about the same amount of pectin as apples, pears and peaches (but not as much as citrus fruits). Several studies find that pectin—a soluble fibre—in foods significantly lowers blood cholesterol.

New research also shows that blueberries, like cranberries, may help prevent urinary tract infections. Israeli scientists noted that blueberries contain unknown compounds that combat bacteria known to cause such infections. Blueberries work the same way cranberries do, said the scientists.

Coffee Crème Caramel

Serves 6

When cravings for this classic French dessert take over, it's nice to know there's a way to make it without all those egg yolks and fat. And I can vouch for the fact it still tastes good; some individuals I have served it to have eaten three portions at one sitting. That's not recommended if you are counting calories, because although this dessert is low in fat, it still has sugar to boost the calorie count.

3 tablespoons instant coffee
3 tablespoons boiling water
1¼ pints (710ml) skimmed milk
5 egg whites
4oz (115g) sugar

Caramel

5oz (140g) sugar
4 tablespoons water

Preheat the oven to 180°C/350°F/Gas 4.

For the caramel, combine the sugar and water in a heavy saucepan. Cook, covered, over high heat for 2 minutes. Uncover the pan and continue cooking over moderate heat until the sugar caramelizes—turns golden brown. Pour the caramel into 6 individual ramekins or an 8-inch (20cm) cake tin and tilt to coat bottoms and sides. (Since molten sugar is extremely hot, you may wish to wear gloves to protect your hands.)

Meanwhile, in a small bowl dissolve the coffee in the boiling water. Scald the milk by heating it just until it is ready to boil.

In a large bowl, whisk together the egg whites and sugar. Whisk the hot milk, little by little, into the egg mixture. Whisk in the dissolved coffee.

Pour the coffee mixture into the ramekins or cake tin, filling to within ¼ inch (0.5cm) of the top.

Set the ramekins or cake tin in a roasting tin and pour boiling water into the roasting tin up to ½ inch (1.5cm) deep. Bake the crème caramel for 40–60 minutes or until just set. (An inserted knife will come out clean when the crème caramel is done.) Add more boiling water to the tin if needed.

Let the crème caramel cool to room temperature, then refrigerate for at least 6 hours, preferably overnight. Just before serving, run the tip of a sharp knife around the inside rim of each ramekin or the cake tin. Place a dessert plate over the ramekin or cake tin, invert, and give a firm shake. Lift the ramekin or tin; the crème caramel should slide out easily.

Per serving:
Calories	219
Total fat	1.3g
Saturated fat	.8g
Cholesterol	4.9mg
Sodium	108mg

DOCTOR'S ADVICE
Sweet Tooth Better than Fat Tooth

If you have a sweet tooth and fruit doesn't satisfy, eat a sugary food without the fat, advises Dr. George Blackburn, associate professor of surgery at Harvard Medical School. That means low-fat cake made with egg whites instead of cheesecake and ginger snaps instead of doughnuts. You'll still satisfy the sweet cravings without the added calories and hazards of fat. Plain old sugar, he says, is not as likely to put on weight or cause obesity or other medical problems as foods with a high fat content.

Barley Cream Pudding

Serves 8

*In parts of the Middle East barley is known as "good heart medicine".
That's what Dr. Rosemary Newman, Montana State University, also found
when she tested barley on volunteers. Their cholesterol went down, so she
developed new recipes using barley and published them in a booklet,* New
Ways with Barley. *Her low-calorie barley pudding also contains apples,
another known cholesterol lowerer.*

3½oz (100g) pearl barley
8fl oz (225ml) water
1 pint (570ml) skimmed milk
1oz (30g) raisins
1oz (30g) apples, chopped
2oz (55g) brown sugar
¼ teaspoon salt
3 tablespoons flour
1 teaspoon margarine or butter
1 teaspoon vanilla essence

Put the barley and water in a saucepan. Bring to the boil, cover and
simmer for 30 minutes. Add more water if necessary. Add the milk,
raisins and apples and bring to the boil again. Cover and reduce the heat
to simmer for 15 minutes.

Stir in the sugar and the salt.

Remove a mugful of the mixture and blend with the flour. Return to the
pan and simmer for 5 minutes, stirring constantly. If the flour forms
lumps, beat with a rotary beater for 1 minute. Cool slightly. Stir in the
margarine and vanilla and serve warm or cold.

Per serving:
Calories	134
Total fat	1.5g
Saturated fat	.6g
Cholesterol	3mg
Sodium	115mg

Joan's Banana Bread Pudding

Serves 8

For a quick, easy, luscious low-fat dessert, here is my sister Joan's recommendation. It's ideal for guests because it looks gorgeous when it puffs up and browns. Yet you can put it together in a few minutes. And it's easy on the stomach. Bananas have been found to soothe the stomach, fighting dyspepsia and possibly helping ward off ulcers.

2 ripe bananas, sliced
10 slices French stick with crust, about 1 inch (2.5cm) thick
$^3/_4$ pint (425ml) skimmed milk
2 eggs
4oz (115g) maple syrup
1 tablespoon icing sugar (optional)
$^1/_4$ teaspoon ground cinnamon (optional)

Preheat the oven to 190°C/375°F/Gas 5. Distribute the banana slices in the bottom of a 10 inch (25cm) deep pie dish. Cover the bananas with the bread slices.

Whisk together the milk, eggs and maple syrup. Pour over the bread and bananas, pushing the bread down to soak up the liquid.

Bake for about 30 minutes or until slightly browned and puffy and the liquid has been absorbed. For additional browning, put the pudding under the grill for a couple of minutes.

Sprinkle the top with icing sugar and cinnamon if desired.

Per serving:
Calories	243
Total fat	2.8g
Saturated fat	.8g
Cholesterol	56mg
Sodium	304mg

Egg White Chocolate Cake

Serves 8

For those who love chocolate but want to escape saturated fat and cholesterol, this cake is truly the answer. It is moist and dense with chocolate and as decadently satisfying as any cake I've ever had. The nuts, with their predominately monounsaturated fat, vegetable protein, fibre and other compounds have a variety of pharmacological benefits.

8 egg whites
¹/₂ teaspoon salt
2oz (55g) unsweetened cocoa powder
8oz (225g) sugar
3 tablespoons vegetable oil, preferably rapeseed
4oz (115g) coarsely chopped nuts (almonds, hazelnuts, walnuts or a combination)
1¹/₂oz (45g) icing sugar (optional)

Preheat the oven to 180°C/350°F/Gas 4.

Beat 6 of the egg whites with the salt until they hold firm peaks. Set aside.

Combine the cocoa with the sugar, oil and remaining 2 egg whites in a large bowl. Add the nuts and mix well. Add one quarter of the beaten egg whites and mix to lighten. Fold in the remaining egg whites.

Oil a 9 inch (23cm) cake tin. Cover the bottom of the tin with greaseproof paper cut to fit. Lightly oil the top of the paper. Pour the mixture into the cake tin. Bake for approximately 30 minutes or until a knife inserted in the centre comes out clean. Transfer to a wire rack to cool.

Turn out on to a cake plate. Remove greaseproof paper. Put right side up and sprinkle the top with icing sugar. Serve with fruit if desired.

Per serving:

Calories	282
Total fat	14.6g
Saturated fat	2.1g
Cholesterol	0
Sodium	194mg

DOCTOR'S ADVICE

Don't deny sugar cravings if you suffer premenstrual syndrome (PMS), says Judith Wurtman, Ph.D., a brain chemistry researcher at the Massachusetts Institute of Technology and a noted authority on carbohydrates and mood.

In recent tests she discovered that carbohydrates, including sugar, can dramatically relieve the symptoms of PMS. Women who were depressed, angry, hostile, fatigued and weepy returned to normal moods within one hour after eating 2oz (55g) of carbohydrate-rich cornflakes sweetened with glucose. "It was an amazing effect from a food," Wurtman says, "just like taking a Valium."

The theory is that eating carbohydrates leads to increased levels of a brain chemical called *serotonin*, which acts like a tranquillizer.

So, women with PMS mood swings should not deny a craving for carbohydrates, such as sweets, bread, potatoes, rice, pasta and beans, says Dr. Wurtman. "That craving represents a cure for your PMS, not a cause."

Ginger Snaps

3 dozen biscuits

Great-tasting and packed with high-fibre rice bran, these special ginger snaps were used experimentally as part of a diet to lower blood cholesterol by researcher Maren Hegsted and colleagues at Louisiana State University. They apparently worked. Average blood cholesterol dropped about 8 per cent when a group of subjects ate these biscuits as well as other rice bran foods. Each ginger snap contains 5 grams of bran and 1.2 grams of dietary fibre.

8oz (225g) brown sugar
6fl oz (170ml) vegetable oil
3oz (85g) molasses
1 egg
6oz (170g) plain flour
5oz (140g) rice bran
2 teaspoons bicarbonate of soda
1 teaspoon ground cinnamon
1 teaspoon ground ginger
½ teaspoon ground cloves
3 tablespoons granulated sugar

Preheat the oven to 190°C/375°F/Gas 5. Combine the brown sugar, oil, molasses and egg in a large mixing bowl. Beat until well mixed.

Combine the flour, bran, bicarbonate of soda, cinnamon, ginger and cloves. Add to the molasses mixture and mix until thoroughly blended.

Form into 1 inch (2.5cm) balls, roll in granulated sugar and place on a greased baking tray. Bake for 6–8 minutes.

Per biscuit:

Calories	105
Total fat	5.4g
Saturated fat	.7g
Cholesterol	6mg
Sodium	50mg

Lemony Chickpea Cake

Serves 8

Instead of traditional flour or grains, this cake uses chickpeas, one of the wealthiest beans in known health-protecting compounds. Yet it is moist and light-textured and it comes from Mexico, according to the authors of The Brilliant Bean, *who gave us this brilliant recipe for what is truly a rich and wonderful-tasting cake.*

12oz (340g) canned chickpeas, drained and rinsed, any loose skins discarded
4 eggs
8oz (225g) sugar
1/2 teaspoon baking powder
Grated rind of 1 lemon
Juice of 1 lemon
Icing sugar

Place the drained beans in a food processor and purée. Add the eggs, sugar, baking powder and lemon rind to the purée and pulse a few times just to combine the ingredients well.

Preheat the oven to 180°C/350°F/Gas 4. Grease a 9 inch (23cm) cake tin. Cut a circle of greaseproof paper to fit the bottom of the tin, set it in place and grease the paper. Pour in the mixture.

Bake on the centre shelf for 45 minutes or until a knife inserted in the centre comes out clean.

Cool on a wire rack for 15 minutes, then remove the cake from the tin and allow to cool to room temperature.

Before serving, squeeze lemon juice over the cake and sprinkle generously with icing sugar.

Per serving:
Calories	206
Total fat	3.2g
Saturated fat	1g
Cholesterol	106mg
Sodium	238mg

✔

FOOD PHARMACY FACT
Sugar—the Bone-Builder

U.S. Department of Agriculture scientists swear it's true. A little sugar helps you absorb calcium that leads to strong bones needed to forestall bone fractures and the crippling disease osteoporosis. Researchers found that ten grams of glucose sugar taken with calcium increased the body's uptake of calcium by nearly 25 per cent. It worked in postmenopausal women who ordinarily do not absorb calcium very efficiently.

Frozen Yoghurts

The great advantage in making your own frozen yoghurt is that you know for sure it has live, active cultures responsible for yoghurt's multiple health benefits. Freezing does not destroy the cultures. However, some commercial frozen yoghurts do not contain live cultures. You can also control the fat content when you make your own. It's easy to create frozen yoghurt flavours; just use your imagination. Here are a couple of ideas to get you started.

Peach Frozen Yoghurt   Serves 6

    3 large fresh peaches
    1lb (450g) natural very-low-fat yoghurt
    2 tablespoons brown sugar
    2 tablespoons Grand Marnier (optional)
    ½ teaspoon vanilla essence or to taste

Peel, stone and slice the peaches and purée them in a blender or food processor.

Transfer the peach purée to a bowl and add the yoghurt, brown sugar and liqueur.

Blend thoroughly and freeze in an ice cream maker or freeze until slushy, then beat again and freeze until firm.

    Per serving:
        Calories   96
        Total fat   .2g
        Saturated fat   .1g
        Cholesterol   1.5mg
        Sodium   59mg

Jill's Favourite Pumpkin Frozen Yoghurt   Serves 6

This, of course, tastes a little like pumpkin pie and gives you an extra shot of pumpkin, which is chockful of beta-carotene, nature's antioxidant. This is the creation of my niece Jill. Sometimes pumpkin purée is available canned in quality grocers but if not, steam, boil or microwave pumpkin until tender, drain and purée in a food processor or blender.

1lb (450g) natural very-low-fat yoghurt
8oz (225g) pumpkin purée
2 tablespoons sugar
6 tablespoons maple syrup
1 teaspoon ground cinnamon
$1/2$ teaspoon ground ginger
$1/4$ teaspoon ground cloves
Pinch of salt

Mix together all ingredients and freeze in an ice cream maker or freeze until slushy, beat and freeze again until firm.

Per serving:
Calories	124
Total fat	.3g
Saturated fat	.2g
Cholesterol	1.5mg
Sodium	84mg

Lemon Mousse

Serves 4

There's no better way to end a meal than with a cool, refreshing lemon mousse and for years I have collected recipes for the same. Alas, I have given up the high-fat variety and this very low fat recipe, made from thick, luscious yoghurt, has become my new favourite. You can forgo the chocolate shavings if you wish but chocolate and lemon do go together and this little bit is not likely to hurt you. This is a tart mousse; to make it sweeter, add more icing sugar.

> 2lb (900g) lemon very-low-fat yoghurt, strained overnight to make about 1lb (450g)
> 2oz (55g) icing sugar
> ½ teaspoon grated lemon zest
> 1 tablespoon unflavoured gelatine
> 2½ tablespoons lemon juice
> 3 tablespoons plain chocolate shavings

Gently mix together the lemon yoghurt, sugar and lemon zest. Dissolve the gelatine in the lemon juice and add to the yoghurt mixture. Chill and serve topped by chocolate shavings.

Note If gelatine or other setting agent has been added to the yoghurt, it will not drain and become thick. Consult the label.

Per serving:

Calories	318
Total fat	5g
Saturated fat	3g
Cholesterol	9mg
Sodium	135mg

Phyllis's Strawberry Sorbet

Serves 4

You can whip up this sorbet in a jiffy to end a dinner party, as my friend Phyllis Bonanno often does; it looks beautiful when mounded into a large glass bowl. The vanilla yoghurt is already sweetened. If you want more sweetness, you can simply add a little sugar or a tablespoon or two of frozen orange juice concentrate, says Phyllis. You can buy the strawberries already frozen or simply put fresh ones and the banana slices in separate plastic bags and pop them in the freezer.

1lb (450g) frozen strawberries
1 banana, sliced and frozen
3 tablespoons vanilla very-low-fat yoghurt

Put all the ingredients in a food processor or blender and process until smooth. Serve immediately.

Per serving:
Calories	75
Total fat	.2g
Saturated fat	.1g
Cholesterol	.3mg
Sodium	10mg

FOOD PHARMACY FACT
Pain-Killing Sugar

Scientists have long suspected that eating sugar and other carbohydrates affects brain chemistry through a complicated mechanism, that boosts levels of a brain neurotransmitter called serotonin. Serotonin is known as a "calming" chemical.

Some researchers also think that sugar may have a more direct effect on the brain by activating natural painkillers. One bit of evidence to support this was found recently by researchers at Cornell University. A few drops of sugar water virtually eliminated crying among a small group of newborn infants in a hospital nursery. Using a syringe, the researchers gave the crying infants a drop of either plain water or a water solution of 14 per cent sugar once every minute for five minutes.

The babies who got the sugar water immediately stopped crying and remained quiet for about 5 minutes. The babies who got the unsweetened water cried on.

In another test the researchers found that a sugar solution was three to five times more effective at stopping the infant's crying than a dummy.

Psychologist Elliott Blass, who directed the study, suspects the sugar may activate natural "opioid" chemicals in the brain that reduce pain and distress.

FOOD PHARMACY FACT
Apples Suppress Blood Pressure and Strokes

For twenty years Japanese researcher Naosuke Sasaki, professor emeritus at the Hirosaki University School of Medicine in Hirosaki, Japan, has tracked the blood pressure in more than 2,400 villagers in two adjoining prefectures in northeast Japan. In the prefecture of Aomori farmers eat lots of apples. In Akita prefecture they do not, preferring rice instead. Dr. Sasaki has found that those eating less than one apple a day tend to develop typical high blood pressure as they age. But villagers eating one to two apples a day had only modest increases in blood pressure. And those eating three or more apples a day did not have the expected high blood pressure. Furthermore, apple eaters of Aomori had a much lower stroke rate. Dr. Sasaki suggests that something in the apples—perhaps potassium—helped counteract the blood-pressure-raising effects of a high-sodium diet resulting from a liberal use of soy sauce.

Breads, Muffins, Scones and Crackers

Squash Bread

1 loaf (16 slices)

This is a welcome and health-promoting change from carrot bread. Yellow summer squash, like carrot, has antioxidants, including beta-carotene and newly studied quercetin, linked to helping block numerous disease processes. This bread is also low-fat since the liquid used in the mixture comes from yoghurt and egg whites.

4oz (115g) wholemeal flour
1 1/2 teaspoons baking powder
1 teaspoon bicarbonate of soda
10oz (285g) yellow (crookneck) squash, coarsely grated
4oz (115g) natural low-fat yoghurt
2 teaspoons lemon juice
1 1/2 teaspoons ground cinnamon
1/2 teaspoon ground nutmeg
1/2 teaspoon ground cardamom
1/2 teaspoon salt (optional)
2 tablespoons molasses
3 egg whites

Preheat the oven to 180°C/350°F/Gas 4. In a large bowl, stir together the flour, baking powder and bicarbonate of soda. Stir in the grated squash, yoghurt, lemon juice, spices, salt and molasses.

Beat the egg whites in a small bowl until foaming and stir them into the squash mixture. Pour the mixture into a nonstick 9 × 4 inch (23 × 10cm) loaf tin.

Bake for 40 minutes. Cool for 15 minutes before removing from the tin, then cool completely on a wire rack.

Per slice:

Calories	44
Total fat	.3g
Saturated fat	1.7g
Cholesterol	.4mg
Sodium	107mg

Corn Bread

Serves 8

I'm always looking for the perfect corn bread recipe and this may be it. It has come along just in time, considering that scientists are finding that the fibre in corn lowers blood cholesterol just about as well as other grain fibres, such as those in oat and rice bran. It was an unexpected finding because the fibre in corn is largely insoluble, which scientists did not think could lower cholesterol. This recipe makes an old-fashioned-type grainy corn bread that crumbles—just the way I like it.

8fl oz (225g) skimmed milk
1 egg
1oz (30g) butter or margarine, melted
2 tablespoons maple syrup *or* 1 teaspoon sugar
4oz (115g) yellow cornmeal
4oz (115g) flour
1 tablespoon baking powder
1 teaspoon salt (less if desired)

Preheat the oven to 220°C/425°F/Gas 7.

In a large bowl, whisk together the milk, egg, melted butter and maple syrup or sugar.

In another bowl, mix together the cornmeal, flour, baking powder and salt. Stir the wet ingredients into the dry ingredients just until the ingredients are combined.

Pour the mixture into a greased 8 inch (20cm) square cake tin and bake for about 25 minutes or until the top of the corn bread is lightly browned and a knife inserted in the centre comes out clean.

Per serving:
Calories	179
Total fat	4g
Saturated fat	2g
Cholesterol	35mg
Sodium	489mg

✔

FOOD PHARMACY FACT
I Say Bananas, You Say Potatoes

When men with normal blood pressure were put on low-potassium diets for nine days, their blood pressure went up, according to Dr. G. Gopal Krishna and colleagues at Temple University in Philadelphia. Their blood pressure returned to normal when they ate normal amounts of potassium for another nine days. Interestingly, when the men got little potassium, they retained sodium. That may be why their blood pressure went up, says Dr Krishna. Thus he theorizes that potassium can help offset the risk of table salt. Both bananas and white potatoes are super sources of potassium. For other examples, see page 21.

Banana and Ginger Muffins

12 muffins

These muffins taste really good (especially warm). In case you need other reasons to make them, bananas are high in fibre and potassium. Ginger, according to new tests, may help soothe the pain of arthritis and potassium seems to control high blood pressure.

4oz (115g) wholemeal flour
1½ teaspoons baking powder
1 teaspoon bicarbonate of soda
2–3 ripe bananas, mashed or puréed
2 tablespoons frozen unsweetened orange juice concentrate
4oz (115g) natural low-fat yoghurt
1 teaspoon ground ginger
1 teaspoon ground nutmeg
1 tablespoon honey
3 egg whites, beaten until foamy and thick

Preheat the oven to 180°C/350°F/Gas 4.

Sift the flour, baking powder and bicarbonate of soda into a large bowl. Add the bananas, orange juice concentrate, yoghurt, ginger, nutmeg and honey. Mix well. Stir the beaten egg whites into the mixture.

Pour the mixture into nonstick or greased deep bun tins. Bake for about 25 minutes.

Per muffin:
Calories	73
Total fat	.5g
Saturated fat	2.5g
Cholesterol	.6mg
Sodium	143mg

Barbara Bush's Bran Muffins

4¹/₂ dozen muffins

Yes, this is what George and Barbara often eat for breakfast, according to The Washington Post *and a good choice it is. The unprocessed wheat bran is the best natural laxative in existence. Additionally, there's compelling evidence the bran helps combat the early stages of colon cancer. The raisins also have anticancer properties. Just as the White House chef does for the Bushes, you can freeze these muffins and use as wanted.*

1¹/₄lb (565g) wholemeal flour
14oz (400g) wheat bran
2 tablespoons baking powder
1¹/₂ teaspoons salt
10oz (285g) raisins
10 eggs, beaten
18oz (510g) honey
1¹/₂ pints (850ml) skimmed milk
¹/₄ pint (140ml) vegetable oil
1¹/₂ teaspoons vanilla essence

Preheat the oven to 190°C/375°F/Gas 5.

In a bowl, mix the flour, bran, baking powder, salt and raisins. Add the remaining ingredients and stir until blended.

Spoon the mixture into lightly greased deep bun tins and bake for 20–25 minutes.

Per muffin:
Calories	159
Total fat	4.8g
Saturated fat	.8g
Cholesterol	39.7mg
Sodium	132mg

FOOD PHARMACY FACT
New Cancer Fighters in Bran

Scientists have discovered a couple of specific agents in wheat bran that may help explain why it seems to protect against cancer, notably colon cancer. University of Maryland School of Medicine investigators found that phytic acid, a compound concentrated in wheat bran, reduced cancers in animals by 35 per cent.

Norwegian scientists, in conditions simulating the human stomach, found that wheat bran (the amount found in two slices of wholemeal bread) reduced the concentrations of nitrite, which reacts in the stomach with other substances to form cancer-causing nitrosamines. One wheat component that reduced nitrite was ferulic acid, shown in other studies to be anticancer.

Three-Grain Super-Fibre Muffins

12 muffins

Dr. Rosemary Newman, a barley researcher at Montana State University, came up with this super muffin to give you fibre from three different grains all in one muffin—soluble gum fibre or beta-glucans in barley and oat bran to fight cholesterol and heart disease and insoluble wheat fibre in wholemeal flour and All-Bran cereal to keep you regular and ward off colon cancer.

3oz (85g) barley flour
2oz (55g) wholemeal flour
1/2 teaspoon baking powder
1 teaspoon bicarbonate of soda
1/4 teaspoon salt
2oz (55g) sugar
1oz (30g) All-Bran cereal
2oz (55g) oat bran cereal
8fl oz (225ml) buttermilk
1 egg
3oz (85g) molasses
2oz (55g) butter or margarine
3oz (85g) raisins

Preheat the oven to 200°C/400°F/Gas 6.

Combine the barley flour, wholemeal flour, baking powder, bicarbonate of soda, salt and sugar. Set aside.

Combine the All-Bran, oat bran and buttermilk. Allow to stand for 2 minutes or until the cereal is moistened.

Add the egg, molasses and butter or margarine to the moistened cereal. Beat until combined.

Stir the raisins into the cereal mixture. Then add the flour mixture. Beat just until moistened.

Put the mixture into greased deep bun tins and bake for 15–20 minutes or until lightly browned.

Per muffin:

Calories	146
Total fat	5g
Saturated fat	2.7g
Cholesterol	29mg
Sodium	232mg

FOOD PHARMACY FACT
All-Bran vs. Colon Cancer

In an important first, researchers found that eating a high-fibre diet, including two bowls of Kellogg's All-Bran cereal a day, suppressed precancerous growths in the colon that can erupt into full-blown colon and rectal cancer. So discovered Dr. Jerome J. De Cosse, a surgeon at the New York Hospital–Cornell Medical Center in 1989. In his four-year study of fifty-eight patients at high risk for colon cancer because they were prone to developing precancerous growths or polyps, one group ate about 22g of fibre daily (most of it in All-Bran) and another, 12g—typical among Americans.

Within six months Dr. De Cosse observed that those on the high-fibre diet had fewer and smaller polyps. Within three years polyps had shrunk even more. Medical belief is that if you can keep polyps away, the bowel cancer cannot grow. Several surveys of dietary practices have found links between higher intakes of cereal fibre and lower rates of colon cancer. This is the first substantial proof that the cereal is indeed the active preventive agent.

Maxine's Apple Bran Muffins

14 muffins

These muffins are made from the stuff that was found effective in shrink-ing the precancerous signs of colon cancer in a recent study. That's right—All-Bran. More than twenty studies done around the world show that people who eat more high-fibre wheat bran, like All-Bran and unpro-cessed wheat bran, are less likely to develop colon cancer. Here's a won-derful-tasting high-fibre wheat bran muffin that includes spices and heart-protecting apples.

4oz (115g) plain flour
2oz (55g) wholemeal flour
2¹/₂ oz (70g) wheat bran cereal (such as All-Bran)
¹/₄ teaspoon salt
1 teaspoon ground cinnamon
¹/₄ teaspoon ground cloves
1 teaspoon bicarbonate of soda
6oz (170g) Golden Delicious apple (or other sweet apple), coarsely
    chopped
1 egg, lightly beaten
6fl oz (170ml) low-fat buttermilk
1 tablespoon molasses
1oz sultanas, plumped in 8 tablespoons concentrated apple
    juice for 15 minutes

Preheat the oven to 180°C/350°F/Gas 4. In a large bowl, stir together the flours, wheat bran cereal, salt, spices, bicarbonate of soda and chopped apple.

Beat the egg in a small bowl and add the buttermilk, molasses, plumped sultanas and apple juice.

Stir the egg mixture into the dry ingredients.

Spoon the mixture into nonstick or greased deep bun tins. Fill the spaces about three-quarters full.

Bake for 20 minutes. Remove the muffins from the tin and cool on a wire rack.

Per muffin:

Calories	106
Total fat	.9g
Saturated fat	.2g
Cholesterol	16mg
Sodium	175mg

COOK'S ADVICE
Apples Are Good for You Cooked or Raw

It matters little whether you eat the apple raw or cooked as far as getting its fibre is concerned, says Ruth Matthews, an expert on food fibre at the U.S. Department of Agriculture. "Cooked apples should be as effective as raw apples in lowering cholesterol," she says. "If you eat the whole apple, either raw or cooked, baked or as apple sauce or whatever, you still get the same amount of fibre."

Dr. Rosenthal's Blues-Fighting Muffins

1 dozen muffins

These muffins may put you in a good mood, literally, according to Dr. Norman Rosenthal, a depression expert at the National Institute of Mental Health and author of Seasons of the Mind: Why You Get the Winter Blues and What You Can Do About It. *One thing, he says, that may help if you are subject to light-deprivation-type winter depressions is to snack on high-carbohydrate foods. In Rosenthal's tests depressed patients who did that seemed to pep up, have more energy and feel less fatigued and depressed. High in oat bran, which makes them dense and grainy like corn bread, these muffins are also likely to put a dent in your cholesterol.*

6oz (170g) uncooked oat bran cereal
1oz (30g) raisins
2 teaspoons baking powder
$^1/_2$ teaspoon salt (optional)
6fl oz (170ml) skimmed milk
4oz (115g) honey
2 eggs, beaten
1 tablespoon vegetable oil, preferably rapeseed oil

Preheat the oven to 220°C/425°F/Gas 7.

In a large bowl, combine the oat cereal, raisins, baking powder and salt. Add the remaining ingredients and mix just until the dry ingredients are moistened.

Grease a deep bun tin or line with paper cases. Fill the prepared bun spaces almost full. Bake for 15–17 minutes or until golden brown.

Per muffin:

Calories	127
Total fat	3g
Saturated fat	.5g
Cholesterol	36mg
Sodium	91mg

✔

FOOD PHARMACY FACT
Sweet Cure for the Winter Blues

Eating carbohydrates—sweets and starches—can help relieve a type of depression known as *seasonal affective disorder (SAD)*, according to Dr. Norman Rosenthal, a psychiatrist at the National Institute of Mental Health.

Such depression, also called "the winter blues", strikes during dark winter days when sunlight is scarce and it affects about thirty-five million Americans. In tests Dr. Rosenthal found that such depressed patients pepped up—had more energy and less fatigue and tension—within two hours of eating six biscuits containing a hefty 105g of carbohydrate. In contrast, normal people eating the biscuits felt more lethargic and drowsy.

Theory holds that victims of such depression have changes in brain chemistry that are somewhat reversed by eating foods high in carbohydrates. Dr. Rosenthal's advice is that if you crave carbohydrates in winter, eat them; you'll feel better. And never go on a low-carbohydrate diet in the winter. Depression-alleviating high-carbohydrate foods include not only the sugary sweet treats but also more nutritious starchy foods, like dried beans, pasta, cereal, bread and crackers.

OAT BRAN DOES WORK!

If you're worried about high cholesterol, oat bran may make a dent. Fully eight out of nine studies on humans—and countless studies on animals—have documented that.

A much-quoted Northwestern University study found that oat bran lowered cholesterol about 3 per cent over and above a low-fat diet. Other studies found much greater results. A study at the College of Medicine at the University of California in Irvine compared the effect of muffins made from oat bran, wheat bran, or mixed wheat and oat. In the double-blind study seventy-two medical student volunteers ate two muffins per day for twenty-eight days. Each oat bran muffin had 5g of dietary fibre, the amount in one rounded tablespoon of oat bran. Oat bran eaters saw their total cholesterol drop 5 per cent, their bad-type LDL cholesterol sink 9 per cent and their triglycerides go down by 8 per cent. Their good-type HDL cholesterol did not change. On the other hand the cholesterol of the wheat and wheat-oat muffin eaters stayed the same and their triglycerides rose 6 per cent.

Dr. James Anderson, University of Kentucky pioneer in oat bran studies, found that 1½oz (45g) of oat bran daily depressed cholesterol by an average of 20 per cent.

Then, in early 1990, along came a Harvard study claiming that oat bran was no better than a wheat cereal like cream of wheat in reducing cholesterol. Both reduced cholesterol about 7 per cent, but researchers insisted it was because the oat bran and the cream of wheat both replaced fat in the diet that would ordinarily drive up cholesterol. However, a peculiarity of the study was that the subjects all had fairly low cholesterol—an average of 4.8—and there were only twenty-one subjects. What the study may prove is that oat bran does not further lower cholesterol when it is already that low—or, as one expert said, in people who don't really need to have it lowered.

Yet a subsequent study at the University of Syracuse did bring up another critical point: oat bran does not work equally well on everyone. In that study by Dr. Wendy Demark-Wahnefried of seventy-one men and women with high cholesterol, oat bran worked as well as a low-fat diet. Eating 1.7oz (48g) of ordinary oat bran or 1.5oz (42g) of Quaker's high-fibre oat bran cold cereal daily reduced cholesterol an average of 10–17 per cent—about the same as cutting down on fatty foods. Still, for some oat bran was a health bonanza, driving down their cholesterol by 2–2.6 mmol/litre.

The bottom line is that oat bran, especially in small amounts, is not a universal cholesterol cure-all but it does work to varying degrees in many people. If it works for you, use it.

Oatmeal Scones

About 16 scones

In the Midwest of America where I grew up, scones were made more healthy and crunchier by adding oats. Although we call them by the traditional American name of biscuits and eat them with savoury foods they are always a treat. Here is the recipe my sister Judy uses.

6oz (170g) plain flour
1 tablespoon baking powder
1 teaspoon salt (less if desired)
2¹/₂oz (70g) vegetable cooking fat
2oz (55g) uncooked quick or rolled oats
¹/₄ pint (140ml) skimmed milk

Preheat the oven to 230°C/450°F/Gas 8.

Sift the flour, baking powder and salt together into a large bowl. Cut in the cooking fat until the mixture looks like large crumbs. Stir in the oats. Add the milk and combine with a fork to make a soft dough.

Put the dough on a lightly floured surface and knead lightly with your fingertips. With a rolling pin, roll the dough to a ¹/₂-inch (1.5cm) thickness or pat out with your hand. Using a floured 2 inch (5cm) round cutter, cut scones. Place them on an ungreased baking sheet and bake for 8–10 minutes or until lightly browned.

Per scone:

Calories	90
Total fat	4.5g
Saturated fat	1g
Cholesterol	.2mg
Sodium	223mg

Oat Crackers

About 40 crackers

Here's a quick, pleasant, unusual way to get your quota of oat bran and oatmeal, both of which are good for your heart. These crackers are surprisingly easy to make, even if you've never thought of making crackers before. They have received acclaim from friends who are not even worried about high cholesterol. For flavour you can use the seeds of your choice. In an informal test a group of friends preferred the caraway seeds. I like the flavour from the aniseeds best. You can serve them with soup, with dips, or just as a super savoury snack.

3oz (85g) oat bran
6oz (170g) rolled oats
2 teaspoons aniseeds or caraway, dill or fennel seeds
1 tablespoon vegetable oil
4fl oz (115ml) water
Coarse salt to taste

Preheat the oven to 170°C/325°F/Gas 3.

In a bowl, mix the oat bran and 4oz (115g) of the rolled oats. Add the aniseeds, oil and water and stir into a dough.

Sprinkle half of the remaining oats on a work surface. Place the dough on top of the oats. Pat the dough out slightly and top with the remaining oats. Roll out the dough until 1/8 inch (0.3cm) thick. Sprinkle with coarse salt to taste. (**Note** The oats on the bottom and top of the dough make it easier to roll out and are especially important on top because when baked they turn a nice golden brown.)

Using a 2 inch (5cm) cutter, cut out rounds. Put the rounds on an ungreased baking sheet and bake in the middle of the oven for about 35 minutes. Remove the crackers from the baking sheet and cool on a wire rack.

Per cracker:

Calories	21
Total fat	.7g
Saturated fat	.1g
Cholesterol	0
Sodium	.2mg

✔

FOOD PHARMACY FACT
Oatmeal Equals Oat Bran

An amazing, often overlooked fact is that in a prominent study pro-claiming the cholesterol-lowering powers of oat bran plain oatmeal actually worked as well. The study was done by Linda V. Van Horn and colleagues at the Northwestern University Medical School with 200 middle-aged subjects averaging blood cholesterol of 5.4. All were on a low-fat diet; additionally, some ate oat bran or oatmeal.

In both cases cholesterol dropped an additional 3 per cent. Yet the amount of fibre in the oat bran was more than double that of the oatmeal. The researchers were at a loss to explain the mystery of why oat bran then did not pack twice the cholesterol-lowering punch. Perhaps it's not all in the fibre.

✔

FOOD PHARMACY FACT
Here Comes Rice Bran!

Rice bran—the stuff that is removed from the kernel when brown rice is converted to white rice—can reduce blood cholesterol about as well as oat bran, according to animal and human studies. That also helps confirm that brown rice does more for your heart than white rice.

First researchers at the U.S. Department of Agriculture in California discovered that rice bran depressed blood cholesterol in hamsters. Then tests at the University of California at Davis found that cholesterol fell an average of 8 per cent in a group of men and women with high cholesterol (6–8) who ate 3oz (85g) of rice bran daily for six weeks. Most important, the reduction was due entirely to a drop in harmful-type LDL cholesterol. Rice bran also pushed down another blood component, apolipoprotein-B, which has been linked to heart disease. In the study rice bran rivalled oat bran in effectiveness; however, rice bran, unlike oat bran, raised triglyc-erides, another blood fat linked to heart disease, especially in older women.

Rice Bran Rolls

6 rolls

The outer coating of a grain of brown rice is the rice bran. That's what these rolls are made with. Rice bran, like oat bran and barley, is rich in soluble fibre and has been shown to help lower blood cholesterol. Each roll in this recipe contains 10g of bran and 5.1g of dietary fibre. Thanks to researchers at Louisiana State University for the recipe used in cholesterol-lowering studies.

1 tablespoon active dry yeast
½ pint (285ml) warm water (about 43°C/110°F)
1 tablespoon sugar
3 tablespoons skimmed milk powder
1 teaspoon salt (less if desired)
1 tablespoon vegetable cooking fat
2½oz (70g) rice bran
10–14oz (285–400g) strong plain flour

Dissolve the yeast in the warm water and allow to stand for 10 minutes.

Combine the sugar, milk powder, salt and vegetable fat. Add the softened yeast and mix until blended. Add the bran and then enough flour to make a soft but not sticky dough. Mix until the dough is smooth and elastic.

Let the dough rise in a warm place for approximately 1 hour or until double in bulk. Punch the dough down and shape it into 6 rolls. Place on greased baking sheets. Allow to rise again for approximately 1½ hours or until double in bulk.

Preheat the oven to 200°C/400°F/Gas 6 and bake the rolls for 30–40 minutes or until the rolls are golden brown and sound hollow when tapped on the bottom.

Note If using easy-blend yeast do not mix with water. Add to the flour, following package directions.

Per roll:
Calories	276
Total fat	5.2g
Saturated fat	1g
Cholesterol	.4mg
Sodium	381mg

Beverages

Orange and Banana Frappé

This shake—morning, noon or night—gives your body a jolt of potassium to help ward off high blood pressure and strokes.

8fl oz (225ml) orange juice
1 banana, peeled and cut into chunks
4 dried apricots (8 halves)
4oz (115g) natural very-low-fat yoghurt

Put all the ingredients in a blender and whirl until smooth.

Per serving:
Calories	173
Total fat	.5g
Saturated fat	.2g
Cholesterol	1mg
Sodium	46mg

Cool Yoghurt Drinks

In India they call it lassi, in Turkey ayran (eyé-ran). In any language it is delicious and so good for you—yoghurt whipped together with water or juices into a cool drink. After returning from Turkey, where ayran is a popular drink, I continued to drink it. Here are some of my favourite yoghurt drink combinations.

Plain Ayran   Serves 1

4oz (115g) natural very-low-fat yoghurt
4fl oz (115ml) cold water

Whip the yoghurt and water together in a blender.

Per serving:

Calories	64
Total fat	.2g
Saturated fat	.2g
Cholesterol	2.3mg
Sodium	86mg

Fruit Yoghurt Drink   Serves 1

4oz (115g) natural very-low-fat yoghurt
½ banana *or* 2–3oz (55–85g) of any of the following fruit *or* 4fl oz (115ml) of any juice:

- fresh or frozen strawberries, raspberries, blueberries, or peaches
- fresh papaya or cantaloupe melon
- fresh or canned pineapple chunks
- orange juice

- pineapple juice
- guava juice
- prune juice
- any other juice or fruit that strikes your fancy alone or in combination

Whip the yoghurt and fruit or juice together in a blender.

Per serving:

Calories	115
Total fat	.5g
Saturated fat	.3g
Cholesterol	2.3mg
Sodium	87mg

Fruit Fizzes

Real carbonated juices—what a treat and what a difference from the fruit-deficient soft drinks. When mixing fruit and fruit juices to make healthy drinks, there is no end to what you can create. To launch your experimentation, here are five samples that my guests have liked. You can serve them with or without ice. For celebratory occasions you can also mix them with champagne or sparkling wine instead of soda water.

Melon and Citrus Fizz   Serves 4

1 medium honeydew melon, very ripe
8fl oz (225ml) orange juice
2 tablespoons lime juice
2 teaspoons honey
Soda water

Halve the melon, discard the seeds and scoop the flesh into a food processor or blender. Purée until smooth.

Add the orange juice, lime juice and honey and blend. Pour into a container and chill.

To serve, mix 2 parts juice with 1 part soda water.

Per serving:

Calories	100
Total fat	.2g
Saturated fat	0
Cholesterol	0
Sodium	18mg

✔

FOOD PHARMACY FACT
Fruit Zaps Appetite

Dieters, you may be better off drinking a 100-calorie fruit juice than a zero-calorie diet soft drink. That's because the sugar in fruit—fructose—stifles appetite. In a test Dr. Judith Rodin, Yale University, had two dozen men and women drink a lemonade-flavoured drink with different sweeteners, including fructose and aspartame, used in diet drinks. About forty minutes later the subjects were offered a buffet and told to eat until "comfortably full".

The fructose drinkers generally ate 20–40 per cent fewer calories than those who consumed aspartame. And that more than compensated for the 200 calories in the fructose drink itself, said Dr. Rodin. Most important, after drinking fruit fructose the subjects chose fewer ultra-fattening foods like ham, cheese and biscuits.

Pineapple and Grapefruit Fizz   Serves 3

1lb (450g) can pineapple pieces in natural juice, drained and juice
   reserved
8fl oz (225ml) grapefruit juice
1/4 teaspoon ground allspice (more if desired)
4fl oz (115ml) pineapple juice
Soda water

Finely chop the pineapple in a food processor. Add half of the grapefruit juice and the allspice and purée.

Add the remaining grapefruit juice and the pineapple juice, blend and
chill.

To serve, mix 2 parts juice with 1 part soda water.

Per serving:
Calories	122
Total fat	.2g
Saturated fat	0
Cholesterol	0
Sodium	2.4mg

Spiced Peach Fizz   Serves 4

8fl oz (225ml) water
2 tablespoons sugar
6 peppercorns
6 cloves
6 allspice berries
1lb (450g) very ripe peaches, peeled and sliced
Soda water

Bring the water, sugar and spices to the boil in a small saucepan.
Reduce the heat and simmer for 20 minutes. Strain the syrup and cool.

Put the peaches and cooled syrup in a food processor or blender and blend until smooth. Chill.

To serve, mix equal parts juice and soda water.

Per serving:
Calories   80
Total fat   .1g
Saturated fat   0
Cholesterol   0
Sodium   .5mg

Cranberry and Cherry Fizz   Serves 5

    1lb (450g) stoned cherries
    8fl oz (225ml) cranberry juice cocktail
    $1/2$ tablespoon honey or sugar
    $1/4$ teaspoon ground cinnamon
    $1/4$ teaspoon ground allspice
    Soda water

Put the cherries in a food processor or blender and blend until smooth. Add half of the cranberry juice, the honey, cinnamon and allspice and blend again. Add the remaining cranberry juice, blend and chill.

To serve, mix equal parts of juice and soda water.

    Per serving:
        Calories   100
        Total fat   .9g
        Saturated fat   .2g
        Cholesterol   0
        Sodium   1.2mg

Cantaloupe and Orange Fizz   Serves 6

---

    1 very ripe medium cantaloupe melon
    2 tablespoons frozen orange or other citrus juice concentrate
    1 tablespoon honey
    $1/2$ teaspoon ground cinnamon
    $1/4$ teaspoon ground cardamom
    Soda water

Halve the cantaloupe melon, discard the seeds and scoop the flesh into a food processor or blender. Blend until smooth. Add the orange juice concentrate, honey, cinnamon and cardamom and blend. Pour into a container and chill.

To serve, mix equal parts juice and soda water.

Per serving:

Calories	52
Total fat	.3g
Saturated fat	0
Cholesterol	0
Sodium	8.4mg

Fruit Slushes

Here are two other ways that you can use fruit and fruit juices to make healthy beverages.

Strawberry and Pineapple Slush   Serves 4

    8oz (225g) strawberries, sliced
    Juice of 1 lemon
    2 tablespoons sugar
    8fl oz (225ml) pineapple juice

Banana and Orange Slush   Serves 4

    1 ripe banana, sliced
    Juice of 1 lemon
    2oz (55g) sugar
    8fl oz (225ml) orange juice
    Orange slices, fresh mint leaves, pineapple wedges or strawberries
       for garnish (optional)

Using a blender or a food processor, combine the fruit, lemon juice and sugar. Blend well. Slowly add the fruit juice, blending until smooth.

Pour the mixture into a bowl or large measuring cup, cover, and freeze for about 1 hour.

Just before serving, stir to break up the chunks and spoon into glasses or small cups. Garnish with orange slices, mint leaves, pineapple wedges or strawberries.

Per serving (strawberry and pineapple):
    Calories   75
    Total fat   .2g
    Saturated fat   0
    Cholesterol   0
    Sodium   1mg

Per serving (banana and orange):
    Calories   104
    Total fat   .2g
    Saturated fat   0
    Cholesterol   0
    Sodium   1mg

Creamy Fruit Cooler

Serves 2

5oz (140g) fruit (raspberries, peaches, strawberries, etc.)
2oz (55g) sugar
$^{1}/_{2}$ teaspoon vanilla essence
8fl oz (225ml) skimmed milk
4fl oz (115ml) water
6 ice cubes
Ground nutmeg (preferably freshly grated) or ground cinnamon plus
   2 slices of fruit for garnish (optional)

Place all the ingredients except ice cubes and garnishes in a blender or food processor and blend until smooth. Add the ice cubes, one at a time and blend until smooth.

Sprinkle with nutmeg or cinnamon and garnish with a slice of fruit. Serve immediately.

Per serving:
Calories	204
Total fat	4.4g
Saturated fat	2.5g
Cholesterol	17mg
Sodium	60mg

Festive Punch

3 pints (1.7 litres)

8fl oz (225ml) fresh orange juice
Juice of 2 lemons
³/₄ pint (425ml) cranberry juice cocktail
8oz (225g) caster sugar
1¹/₂ pints (850ml) lemonade or soda water
Lemon and orange slices or other fresh fruit for garnish (optional)

In a large jug, combine the juices and the sugar. Stir to dissolve the sugar. Add ice and pour in the lemonade or soda. Garnish with fresh fruit.

Per 4fl oz (115ml) serving:

Calories	74
Total fat	.06g
Saturated fat	0
Cholesterol	0
Sodium	13mg

Sauces and Dressings

Fresh Cocktail Sauce

Serves 16

Dipping seafood into this cocktail sauce can help clear your sinuses and may help relieve the stuffed-up symptoms of a cold. The more horseradish you use, the better it works. Horseradish is a well-known cold remedy in the Soviet Union and Middle European countries.

2 medium onions, finely chopped
1 large green pepper, finely chopped
1 tablespoon vegetable oil
3 large tomatoes, peeled, seeded and chopped
2 teaspoons sugar
Salt and freshly ground pepper to taste *or* 1 teaspoon each
2 tablespoons red wine vinegar
6oz (170g) can tomato purée
8 tablespoons prepared horseradish

In a saucepan, sauté the onions and pepper in the oil for 5 minutes or until the onions are translucent and the pepper is soft. Add the tomatoes and cover. Simmer for 5–10 minutes, until tender.

Uncover and add the sugar, salt, pepper, vinegar and tomato purée. Boil, uncovered, stirring until the mixture has thickened, about 4 minutes.

Allow to cool in a non-metallic bowl. If you're going to serve it immediately, stir in the horseradish. (It's best to add it at the last minute so it doesn't lose any of its oomph!)

In a blender or a food processor, blend the mixture until it is the consistency you like, either chunky or smooth.

Per serving:
Calories	32
Total fat	1g
Saturated fat	.1g
Cholesterol	0
Sodium	94mg

A HOT PEPPER PRIMER

Anaheim: Also called California green or chilles verdes and, when ripe, chilli Colorado. Mildly hot. About 7 inches (18cm) × 1½ inches (4cm). Known as a stuffing pepper, often used for chilles rellenos.

Ancho: Moderately hot, from 3–4 inches (7.5–10cm) long and 2–3 inches (5–7.5cm) wide. Dark red to almost black. Made by drying poblano chillies.

Arbol: Very hot. Dried bright red chilli, small and slender like a green bean.

Cayenne: Also called finger chilli, bird pepper and ginnie pepper. Fiery, bright red and slender. Can be used fresh or dried; it is the pepper ground into cayenne pepper, commonly used.

Cherry pepper: Also called Hungarian cherry pepper, bird cherry and Creole cherry. Medium to very hot. Cherry-shaped, about 2 inches (5cm) in diameter. It is used both green and red-ripe.

Chipotle: Fiery, dried, smoked jalapeño, commonly canned in tomato sauce.

Guajillo: Moderately hot. Slender, about 4–6 inches (10–15cm) long, dried reddish-brown chilli.

Habanero: Also called Scotch bonnets. The hottest chilli pepper in the world. It's walnut-size, yellow to light green, lantern-shaped and is found in the Yucatan Peninsula of Mexico, where it is used in sauces. Also common cooked or raw in the cuisine of Cuba, Jamaica, Puerto Rico and Haiti. When still green the habanero is up to five times more tongue-blistering than a jalapeño pepper; when ripe and red, the habanero's fire-power is magnified ten times.

Jalapeño: Fairly hot. An American favourite, about 2 inches (5cm) long, dark green, used raw or cooked.

Mulato: Spicy, earthy flavour resembling chocolate. Triangle-shaped, 3–4 inches (7.5–10cm) long, heavily wrinkled, dark brown to black skin. Used in Mexican mole poblano.

New Mexico red: Also known as wreath chillies because they are often tied in wreaths.

Poblano: Large—about 5 inches (13cm) long—dark green, mildly hot, the pepper of choice for chilles rellenos.

Serrano: Also called chilli verde. Slightly hotter than jalapeño, with a delayed action bite. Bright green, smaller than a jalapeño. Can be substituted for jalapeños.

Spices from Chilli Peppers: **Ancho**, dark maroon, used in most commercial chilli powders; **cayenne**, red, extra hot; **paprika**, usually mild; **chipotle**, smoked dried jalapeño, brick red, very hot.

Salsa Cruda (Mexican Hot Sauce)

Serves 4

This simple sauce is a staple of Mexico and is served in Mexican restaurants everywhere. It's great as a dip for crisps or served with fajitas, tacos or burritos. You can make it as hot as you wish.

2 tomatoes, peeled, seeded and diced
1 small red onion, finely chopped
1 or 2 jalapeño peppers, finely chopped, seeds removed
1oz (30g) coriander, coarsely chopped
Juice of 1–2 limes
Salt and freshly ground pepper to taste

In a bowl, gently mix together all the ingredients. For the freshest taste, serve within 20 minutes.

Note If you like a really hot salsa, leave the seeds in the jalapeño peppers. Otherwise, remove them.

Per serving:

Calories	20
Total fat	.2g
Saturated fat	0
Cholesterol	0
Sodium	6.2mg

Berber Sauce
(For Barbecued Meat, Poultry or Fish

About 7fl oz (200ml)

Umm, luscious is this unusual spicy barbecue sauce or marinade that originated with the Berbers, a nomad people in North Africa. The toasted spices promise to help clear out your sinuses and help bring your lungs up to peak performance. It is wonderful on lamb chump chops or lamb neck fillet or lean steak and I have also used it on grilled swordfish with great success.

1 small onion, finely chopped
1 garlic clove, finely chopped
1 jalapeño pepper or other hot chilli, finely chopped
1 inch (2.5cm) piece of fresh root ginger, finely chopped
2 teaspoons cracked black peppercorns
1 teaspoon coriander seeds
1 teaspoon cardamom grains
1/8 teaspoon ground cinnamon
1/8 teaspoon ground allspice
1 clove
1 1/2 teaspoons salt or to taste
5 tablespoons paprika
4fl oz (115ml) olive oil
Juice of 1 lemon

Place the onions, garlic, chilli, ginger and all spices in a dry frying pan and cook over medium heat for 1–2 minutes or until the spices are fragrant and lightly toasted.

Combine the toasted spices and seasonings with the olive oil and lemon juice in a blender or food processor and blend to a smooth paste.

Spread the paste on meat, poultry or seafood. Let it marinate in the refrigerator for 6–8 hours for red meat, 2–3 hours for poultry and 1 hour for seafood. Barbecue, grill or roast the marinated food.

Per tablespoon:

Calories	80
Total fat	8g
Saturated fat	1g
Cholesterol	0
Sodium	237mg

COOK'S ADVICE

Generally, the smaller the pepper, the hotter. The fieriest parts are the veins and seeds. To reduce the heat, remove the veins and seeds. When handling hot chilli peppers, wear protective plastic or rubber gloves. And don't touch your eyes or face after handling chillies with bare hands; the residue can last for several hours and sting.

Quick Marinara Sauce (For Pasta or Pizza)

Serves 8

When juicy fresh summer tomatoes are not available or when you just don't have time to bother, you can still get loads of health protection in tomatoes by cooking up this Italian tomato sauce in a jiffy.

1 medium white onion, finely chopped
1 garlic glove, finely chopped
2 tablespoons olive oil
28oz (795g) can plum tomatoes, chopped
1 tablespoon parsley, finely chopped
1 tablespoon fresh basil, finely chopped *or* ¼ teaspoon dried
Salt and freshly ground pepper to taste

In a large saucepan, sauté the onion and garlic in the oil until translucent and soft. Add the tomatoes, herbs, salt and pepper. Cover partially and simmer, for 30 minutes.

Note If the sauce becomes too thick, add 4–8 tablespoons boiling water to desired consistency.

Per serving:
Calories	54
Total fat	3.6g
Saturated fat	.5g
Cholesterol	0
Sodium	162mg

Yoghurt Dressings

Yoghurt is an excellent substitute for soured cream, oils and mayonnaise in salad dressings and at only a fraction of the fat and calories. Additionally, yoghurt contains natural antibiotics that help fight infections. Here are some ways to make yoghurt dressings interesting.

Mango Yoghurt Salad Dressing   About ¼ pint (140ml)

3oz (85g) mango, peeled and chopped
1½ tablespoons reduced-calorie mayonnaise
4 tablespoons very-low-fat vanilla yoghurt

Place all the ingredients in a blender or food processor and purée.

Per tablespoon:

Calories	13
Total fat	.5g
Saturated fat	.1g
Cholesterol	.7mg
Sodium	14mg

Orange Yoghurt Salad Dressing   About ¼ pint (140ml)

4oz (115g) natural very-low-fat yoghurt
¼ teaspoon vanilla essence
1 teaspoon honey
2 tablespoons frozen orange juice concentrate

Place all ingredients in a small bowl and stir until combined.

Per tablespoon:
Calories	14
Total fat	0
Saturated fat	0
Cholesterol	.2mg
Sodium	9mg

Mustard Yoghurt Sauce   About ¼ pint (140ml)

5oz (140g) natural low-fat yoghurt
1 teaspoon Dijon mustard
Salt and freshly ground pepper to taste

Combine all the ingredients and chill until ready to use.

Per tablespoon:
Calories	10
Total fat	.3g
Saturated fat	.1g
Cholesterol	.8mg
Sodium	29mg

Mock Soured Cream   About ¾ pint (425ml)

8oz (225g) low-fat cottage cheese
8oz (225g) natural very-low-fat yoghurt
2 teaspoons cider vinegar

Place all the ingredients in a blender or food processor and process on high until the mixture is smooth and thick. Refrigerate.

Per tablespoon:
Calories	9
Total fat	.1g
Saturated fat	0
Cholesterol	.4mg
Sodium	34mg

Dipping Sauces

Here are some sauces for dipping seafood or cooked meats.

Horseradish Sauce   About ¼ pint (140ml)

  4oz (115g) natural low-fat yoghurt
  1 tablespoon Dijon mustard
  1–2 tablespoons prepared horseradish
  1 tablespoon fresh lemon or orange juice
  Salt and freshly ground pepper to taste

Combine all the ingredients in a bowl and whisk to blend.

  Per tablespoon:
     Calories   8
     Total fat   .2g
     Saturated fat   .1g
     Cholesterol   .6mg
     Sodium   46mg

Chilli Sauce   About ¼ pint (140ml)

  5oz (140g) natural low-fat yoghurt
  2–3 teaspoons chilli powder
  1 pickled jalapeño pepper, finely chopped
  Salt and freshly ground pepper to taste

Combine the ingredients in a bowl and whisk until smooth.

  Per tablespoon:
     Calories   12
     Total fat   .4g
     Saturated fat   .1g
     Cholesterol   .8mg
     Sodium   45mg

Ginger Sauce   About ¼ pint (140ml)

2 tablespoons fresh root ginger, finely chopped
2 garlic cloves, finely chopped
2 spring onions, finely chopped
1 serrano or other hot chilli, finely chopped
3 tablespoons light soy sauce
3 tablespoons water or chicken stock
2 tablespoons rice wine or mirin (sweet rice wine)
1 tablespoon dark sesame oil
1 teaspoon sugar or maple syrup

Combine the ingredients in a bowl and whisk to mix.

Per tablespoon:
Calories	20
Total fat	1g
Saturated fat	.2g
Cholesterol	0
Sodium	150mg

Recipe Credits

Appetizers, Starters and Snacks

Quick Mexican Bean Dip: Jean Carper
Guacamole: Jean Carper
Tzatziki: Mary Koromvokis and Lee Koromvokis
Chickpea Dip (Hummus): adapted from a recipe by Howard Solganik
Rena's Syrian Baba Ghanouj (Aubergine Dip): Rena Dweck
Radicchio with Garlic: Jean Carper
Bruschetta: Kathleen Drew
I Matti's Beans and Onions: I Matti Restaurant, Washington, D.C.,
    Roberto Donna, owner
Dr. David's Caponata (Aubergine Appetizer): Dr. David Rall
Gazpacho Vegetable Pâté: reprinted from *Enjoy! Make-Ahead Dinner
    Party Menus* by Nina Graybill and Maxine Rapoport, Farragut
    Publishing Company, Washington, D.C.
Yoghurt Cheese: Jean Carper
Yoghurt Cheese and Lox: Jean Carper
Herbed Yoghurt Cheese: Jean Carper
Yoghurt Roquefort Walnut Dip: Jean Carper
Steamed Clams Portuguese: Steven Raichlen
Cucumber Rounds with Anchovy Topping (Tapenade): Steven Raichlen
Mackerel Salad Spread: adapted from a recipe by Howard Solganik
Molly's Chopped Herring: Molly Schuchat
Salmon Pâté: adapted from *Beyond Pritikin* by Ann Louise Gittleman,
    Bantam Books, New York
Oriental Tuna-Stuffed Mushrooms: adapted from a recipe by Howard
    Solganik
Sardine and Avocado Sandwich: Lynn Fischer

Soups

Easy Pumpkin and Apple Soup: adapted from *Cold Soups* by Maxine
Rapoport and Nina Graybill, Farragut Publishing Company,
Washington, D.C.

Spiced Carrot Soup: adapted from a recipe provided by Gravetye Manor
Restaurant, Sharpthorne, West Sussex

Curried Broccoli Soup: Jean Carper

Potato and Kale Soup: Steven Raichlen

Minted Pea Soup: Jean Carper

Tomato and Basil Soup: adapted from a recipe by Howard Solganik

My Favourite Lentil Soup: Jean Carper

Mariana's Salmon and Corn Soup: Mariana Gosnell

Oyster Chowder: Steven Raichlen

Seafood Minestrone: reprinted from *The Gourmet Gazelle Cookbook* by
Ellen Brown, Bantam Books, New York

Dr. Ziment's Garlic Chicken Soup for Colds and Coughs: Dr. Irwin
Ziment, adapted from *The Food Pharmacy* by Jean Carper, Bantam
Books, New York

Dr. Weil's Miso Soup: reprinted from *Natural Health, Natural Medicine*
by Andrew Weil, M.D., Houghton-Mifflin Company, New York

Chicken or Turkey Stock: Patricia Krause, adapted from *The
Revolutionary Seven-Unit Low Fat Diet* by Audrey Eyton and Jean
Carper, Bantam Books, New York

Vegetable Stock: Patricia Krause, adapted from *The Revolutionary Seven-
Unit Low Fat Diet* by Audrey Eyton and Jean Carper, Bantam Books,
New York

Grapefruit and Vegetable Gazpacho: reprinted from *Cold Soups* by Nina
Graybill and Maxine Rapoport, Farragut Publishing Company,
Washington, D.C.

Grape Gazpacho (Ajo Branco): Steven Raichlen

Avocado Ceviche: adapted from a recipe by Pascal Vignau, executive
chef, Four Seasons Hotel, Beverly Hills, California

Peachy Ginger Soup: adapted from a recipe by Howard Solganik

Chilled Cantaloupe Soup: adapted from *Cold Soups* by Nina Graybill and
Maxine Rapoport, Farragut Publishing Company, Washington, D.C.

Cranberry Soup: Patricia Krause, adapted from *The Revolutionary Seven-
Unit Low Fat Diet* by Audrey Eyton and Jean Carper, Bantam Books,
New York

Salads, Relishes and Chutneys

Cabbage and Pepper Coleslaw: Jean Carper

Apple Coleslaw with Peanuts: Jean Carper

Dr. Duke's Anticancer Slaw: Dr. James Duke and Sara Benum, adapted from *Medical Nutrition*, Summer 1990

Turnip Slaw with Banana Dressing: Patricia Krause, adapted from *The Revolutionary Seven-Unit Low Fat Diet* by Audrey Eyton and Jean Carper, Bantam Books, New York

Carrots with Pineapple, Raisins and Walnuts: Jean Carper

Carrots with a Touch of Cumin: Jean Carper

Minted Carrots with Lime Juice: Jean Carper, with thanks to Molly O'Neill, *The New York Times*

Tomatoes and Onions with Fresh Basil: Jean Carper

Red and Yellow Onion Rings: Jean Carper

Peach, Onion and Pepper Salsa: Carol Mason

Cantaloupe and Pear Salsa: Carol Mason

Tomato and Onion Salsa: Carol Mason

Confetti Jicama Salsa: Carol Mason

Onion and Rhubarb Salsa: Carol Mason

Chopped Broccoli and Pepper Salad: Maxine Rapoport

Broccoli and Cauliflower Garlic Salad: Jean Carper

Lynn's Caesar Salad: Lynn Fischer

Spinach with Strawberries and Honey Dressing: Jean Carper

Mixed Leaves with Tangy Avocado Dressing: Jean Carper

Green Salad with Apples and Blue Cheese Dressing: Jean Carper

Shredded Brussels Sprouts with Dates: Maxine Rapoport

Dilled Potato Salad: adapted from *Hearty Salads* by Nine Graybill and Maxine Rapoport, Farragut Publishing Company, Washington, D.C.

Black Bean Salad with Feta Cheese and Mint: Steven Raichlen

Three-Bean Salad with Poppy Seed Dressing: Jean Carper

Waldorf Salad with Sardines: Jean Carper

Herring Salad with Potatoes and Beetroot: Joan Nathan

Orange and Sangria Salad: adapted from a recipe by Elaine Halgarten, *Daily Mail*

Mango, Banana and Blueberry Salad: Jean Carper

Joanna's Cranberry Fantasy: Joanna Simon

Spicy Indian-Style Fruit Salad: adapted from a recipe by Howard Solganik

Banana Raita: Jean Carper

Mint Raita: Carol Mason
Green Pepper and Watercress Raita: Carol Mason

Vegetables and Legumes

Whole Roasted Garlic: adapted from a recipe by Howard Solganik
Italian Baked Onions: adapted from a recipe by Howard Solganik
Carrot Purée: Maxine Rapoport
Honey Lemon Carrots and Apples: Maxine Rapoport, adapted from a
    recipe by Phyllis Richman
Squash Purée with Apricot: adapted from a recipe by Howard Solganik
Spinach with Soy and Sesame Seeds: Jean Carper
Greens with Garlic and Walnuts: inspired by Annemarie Colbin
Spring Greens with Smoked Chicken: adapted from a recipe by Steven
    Raichlen
Stir-Fried Kale: Jean Carper
Chinese Mustard Cabbage: adapted from a recipe by Jean Carper
Gingered Green Beans: Carol Mason
Sweet and Sour Cabbage: Jean Carper
Cabbage and Beans with Ham: adapted from a recipe by Carol Mason
Mapled Brussels Sprouts: Jane Stevens
Spicy Curried Cauliflower: Jean Carper
Roasted Potatoes with Garlic and Rosemary: Jean Carper
Phyllis Richman's Garlic-Stuffed Potatoes: Phyllis Richman
Genevieve's Italian Potatoes and Peppers: Genevieve Trezza Hill
Shepherd's Pie with Curried Aubergine: Jean Carper
Sweet Potatoes Amandine: Jean Carper
Slow-Baked Plantains: Jean Carper
Scalloped Corn with Peppers: Jean Carper
Turnips with Nutmeg: Joan Claybrook
Mexican "Refried" Beans: Patricia Krause, adapted from *The
    Revolutionary Seven-Unit Low Fat Diet* by Audrey Eyton and Jean
    Carper, Bantam Books, New York
Microwave Bean Burritos: Jean Carper
Boston Baked Soya Beans: Maxine Rapoport
Dr. Jenkins's Greek Bean Stew: Dr. David Jenkins and Alexandra Jenkins
David Taylor's Hoppin' John: David Taylor
Butter Beans with Apple and Cinnamon: Jean Carper

L & N's Bean Casserole: Lisa Berger and Nina Graybill
Cuban Black Beans and Rice: adapted from *The Brilliant Bean* by Sally
   and Martin Stone, Bantam Books, New York
Spicy Tofu Stir-Fry with Vegetables: Steven Raichlen

Pizza, Pasta and Grains

Pissaladière (Onion Pizza): reprinted from *Mediterranean Light* by
   Martha Rose Shulman, Bantam Books, New York
Pasta Salad with Tuna and Grapes: U.S. Department of Agriculture
Vegetable Confetti Pasta Salad: reprinted from *The Pasta Salad Book* by
   Nina Graybill and Maxine Rapoport, Farragut Publishing Company,
   Washington, D.C.
Spaghetti with Broccoli, Pine Nuts and Parmesan: reprinted from
   Mediterranean Light by Martha Rose Shulman, Bantam Books, New
   York
Pasta with Asparagus and Salmon: Jean Carper
Pasta with Tuna and Tomato Sauce: Patricia Krause, adapted from *The
   Revolutionary Seven-Unit Low Fat Diet* by Audrey Eyton and Jean
   Carper, Bantam Books, New York
Linguine with Clams and Black Pepper: Kenneth Juran, executive chef,
   Park Hyatt Hotel, Washington, D.C.
Rotelle with Judy's Fresh Tomato Sauce: Judy Carper
Jean's Marco Polo Pasta: Jean Carper
Tabbouleh: Jean Carper
Bulgar with Chickpeas: Jean Carper
Nutty Brown Rice: adapted from a recipe by Howard Solganik
Curried Apricot Rice: adapted from a recipe by Howard Solganik
Greek Rice with Artichokes: adapted from a recipe by Mary Koromvokis
Bulgar Pilaf with Fruit and Nuts: Jean Carper
Shiitake Mushroom Sage Stuffing: Jean Carper

Seafood, Poultry and Meat Main Dishes

Barbecued Salmon with Fruit Salsa: Carol Mason
Peppered Tuna Steaks: Jean Carper
Three-Fish Teryaki: Jean Carper

Swordfish with Grapefruit and Brazil Nuts: Jean Carper
Mackerel with Sage: Jean Carper
Mackerel with Garlic and Herbs: Jean Carper
Mackerel with Cumin: Jean Carper
Baked Bluefish with Herbs: Jean Carper
Shark Steaks with Orange: U.S. Department of Commerce
Cajun Cod: reprinted from *Beyond Pritikin* by Ann Louise Gittleman, Bantam Books, New York
Halibut with Tarragon and Sesame Seeds: U.S. Department of Commerce
Microwave Dilled Plaice: Jean Carper
Plaice Stuffed with Vegetables: adapted from a recipe by Howard Solganik
Rainbow Trout with Orange Rice Stuffing: Jean Carper
Sweet and Sour Fish Curry: adapted from a recipe by Carol Mason
Judy's Old-Fashioned Salmon Loaf: Judy Stevens
Basque Tuna Stew: Jean Carper
Caribbean-style Mackerel by George!: George Jacobs
Garlic Smoked Mussels with Tomatoes: Chef Frank Terranova for the National Fisheries Association
Stir-Fried Scallops with Walnuts and Mangetout: Jean Carper
Chef Kenneth's Crab Cakes: Kenneth Juran, executive chef, Park Hyatt Hotel, Washington, D.C.
Seafood Chilli with Red Beans: Kenneth Juran, executive chef, Park Hyatt Hotel, Washington, D.C.
Puerto Rican Sardine Pie: Phyllis Richman
Carol Mason's White Chilli: Carol Mason
Ellen Brown's Jambalaya: reprinted from *The Gourmet Gazelle Cookbook* by Ellen Brown, Bantam Books, New York
Navajo Stew with Sweet Potatoes and Black Beans: Jean Carper
Pineapple Ginger Chicken: Tracy Ritter, chef, Golden Door Spa, California
Barbecued Turkey with Garlic and Chilli Sauce: Chuck Dell'Ario for the Gilroy Garlic Festival
Barley and Turkey Skillet Dinner: Dr. Rosemary Newman
Chinese Pepper Steak: Steven Raichlen
Pork and Apple Stir-Fry: Maxine Rapoport, adapted from a recipe by the International Apple Institute
Oriental Hot Pot: Steven Raichlen
Moroccan Lamb Stew with Fruit: adapted from *Enjoy!* by Nina Graybill and Maxine Rapoport, Farragut Publishing Company, Washington, D.C.

Desserts

Date-Wrapped Nuts: Jean Carper
Strawberries with a Meringue Cloud: Carol Mason
Ginger Baked Apples with Vanilla Topping: Jean Carper
Summer Berry Pudding: Kenneth Juran, executive chef, Park Hyatt Hotel, Washington, D.C.
Coffee Crème Caramel: Steven Raichlen
Barley Cream Pudding: reprinted from *New Ways with Barley* by Dr. Rosemary Newman, Montana State University
Joan's Banana Bread Pudding: Joan Hickson
Egg White Chocolate Cake: Carol Mason
Ginger Snaps: Louisiana State University
Lemony Chickpea Cake: reprinted from *The Brilliant Bean* by Sally and Martin Stone, Bantam Books, New York
Peach Frozen Yoghurt: Jean Carper
Jill's Favourite Pumpkin Frozen Yoghurt: Jill Hickson
Lemon Mousse: Jean Carper
Phyllis's Strawberry Sorbet: Phyllis Bonanno

Breads, Muffins, Scones and Crackers

Squash Bread: Maxine Rapoport
Corn Bread: Jean Carper
Banana and Ginger Muffins: Patricia Krause, adapted from *The Revolutionary Seven-Unit Low Fat Diet* by Audrey Eyton and Jean Carper, Bantam Books, New York
Barbara Bush's Bran Muffins: Phyllis Richman
Three-Grain Super-Fibre Muffins: Dr. Rosemary Newman
Maxine's Apple Bran Muffins: Maxine Rapoport
Dr. Rosenthal's Blues-Fighting Muffins: reprinted from *Seasons of the Mind* by Dr. Norman Rosenthal, Bantam Books, New York
Oatmeal Scones: Judy Stevens
Oat Crackers: Jean Carper
Rice Bran Rolls: Louisiana State University

Beverages

Orange and Banana Frappé: adapted from a recipe by Howard Solganik
Plain Ayran: Jean Carper
Fruit Yoghurt Drink: Jean Carper
Melon and Citrus Fizz: Maxine Rapoport
Pineapple and Grapefruit Fizz: Maxine Rapoport
Spiced Peach Fizz: Maxine Rapoport
Cranberry and Cherry Fizz: Maxine Rapoport
Cantaloupe and Orange Fizz: Maxine Rapoport
Fruit Slushes: adapted from a recipe by Howard Solganik
Creamy Fruit Cooler: adapted from a recipe by Howard Solganik
Festive Punch: adapted from a recipe by Howard Solganik

Sauces and Dressings

Fresh Cocktail Sauce: adapted from a recipe by Howard Solganik
Salsa Cruda (Mexican Hot Sauce): Steven Raichlen
Berber Sauce (for Barbecued Meat, Poultry or Fish): Steven Raichlen
Quick Marinara Sauce: Judy Carper
Mango Yoghurt Salad Dressing: Jean Carper
Orange Yoghurt Salad Dressing: Jean Carper
Mustard Yoghurt Sauce: Patricia Krause, reprinted from *The Revolutionary Seven-Unit Low Fat Diet* by Audrey Eyton and Jean Carper, Bantam Books, New York
Mock Soured Cream: Patricia Krause, reprinted from *The Revolutionary Seven-Unit Low Fat Diet* by Audrey Eyton and Jean Carper, Bantam Books, New York
Horseradish Sauce: Steven Raichlen
Chilli Sauce: Steven Raichlen
Ginger Sauce: Steven Raichlen

Index

404   THE FOOD PHARMACY COOKBOOK

Blueberry *(continued)*
  Summer Berry Pudding, 332
Blue cheese dressing, 154
Bluefish, Baked, with Herbs, 278
Bonanno, Phyllis, 346
Bones
  boron and, 123
  fruit and, xxii
  nuts and, xxii
  pineapple and, 128
  strong bone foods, 124
Book on Light-Hearted Cooking, The
    (Jacobs), 293
Bordia, Arun, 179
Boron
  brain activity and, 123, 262
  foods high in, 262
  in grapes, 116, 262
  osteoporosis and, 124
  in peanuts, 123, 124
  studies, 124, 262
Boston Baked Soyabeans, 223
Bowen, Phyllis, 131
Bradlow, H. Leon, 202
Brain
  boron and, 123, 262
  fruit and, xxii
  nuts and, xxii
Brazil nuts, 7, 20, 271, 272, 328
  Date-wrapped Nuts, 327
  Swordfish with Grapefruit and, 271
Bread
  corn, 351
  squash, 349
Breast cancer
  Asian women and, 161, 287, 320
  cruciferous vegetables and, 202
  fish and, 287
  fish oil (Omega-3) and, xxii, 29, 287
  green beans and, 199
  soyabeans and, 162
  vitamin C and, 155
Brilliant Bean, The (Stone & Stone), 221, 232,
    341
Broccoli, xxii, 7, 92, 143, 145, 192, 242
  and Cauliflower Garlic Salad, 145
  Chopped, and Pepper Salad, 143
  Curried, Soup, 91
  microwaving, 178
  Pork and Apple Stir-Fry, 321
  Spaghetti with, Pine Nuts and Parmesan,
    243
Bronchial Asthma
  capsaicin and, 45
  omega-3 and, 29
  onions and, 137

Brown, Ellen, 103, 309
Brown rice. *See* Rice
Bruschetta, 66
  al fagioli e cipolla, 68
Brussels Sprouts, 157, 192
  Mapled, 203
  Shredded, with Dates, 156
BSN Groupe, Paris, 39
Bulgar
  with Chickpeas, 256
  Pilaf with Fruit and Nuts, 261
  Tabbouleh, 255
Burkitt, Denis, 14–15
Burr, Dr. Michael, 28
Butter beans, 18
  -with Apple and cinnamon, 229
Butterhead lettuce, 152
Butyric acid, 209

Cabbage, 202, 213
  Apple Coleslaw with Peanuts, 123
  and Beans with Ham, 201
  Dr. Duke's Anticancer Slaw, 125
  Oriental Hot Pot, 323
  -and Pepper Coleslaw, 122
  Pork and Apple Stir-Fry, 321
  raw, 122
  Sweet and Sour, 200
Cabbage lettuce, 152
Caesar Salad, Lynn's, 146
Caffeic acid, 6, 116
Caffeine, 51
Cajun Cod, 281
Cajuns, pancreatic cancer among, 12
Calcium
  boron and, 124
  broccoli and, 92
  salt and, 51
  seafood and, 290
  sugar and, 342
Calcium pectate, 144
Californian, life expectancy, male, 11
Calories
  from fruit/vegetables vs. meat, 320
  life expectancy and, 109
Cambridge University, 19, 209
Campbell, T. Colin, 320
Canada
  life expectancy, 109
  National Cancer Institute, 155
Cancer
  anticancer agents, 7, 24, 36, 44–45, 62, 71,
      89, 92, 97, 99, 101, 113, 122, 125, 134,
      141, 162, 191, 204, 209, 216, 219, 223,
      224, 229, 238, 253, 258, 329, 355
  apples and, 229